Blood in the Streets

Racism, Riots and Murders
in the Heartland of America

DANIEL L. BAKER and GWEN NALLS

Forensic Publications, LLC
an American Company
2014

Forensic Publications, LLC
P.O. Box 14443 Cincinnati, Ohio 45250
www.forensicpublications.com

Library of Congress Cataloging-in-Publication Data
ISBN 978-0-9898450-0-7
LCCN 2013952758
Includes bibliographic references

Cover photo courtesy of *Dayton Daily News* Archive, Special Collections and Archives, University Libraries, Wright State University, Dayton, Ohio

Design and layout by Vancouver Desktop Publishing Centre
Printed in the United States of America

"A great story...amazing detail...pictures and scenes painted with attention to every sensory and emotional aspect."

—Dr. T. Rueth, PhD Psychologist
University of Dayton, Professor Emeriti

"Enjoyed candid description of lack of coordination during riots; not written in an offensive way, but truthful...Learned a lot from those experiences making policing a profession; thanks to people like Dan Baker."

—R. Labatzky, Major
Dayton Police Department (Ret.)

"I enjoyed reading about homicide detectives in the days before DNA and highly trained CSI's. Characters came to life...unexpected emotion drew me in...eager to turn the pages."

—Nathan Lefebvre
Director Forensic Training Source, Cumming, GA

"Blood in the Streets"...Is a valuable addition to our collection—not only for our Criminal Justice Majors, but for our students who are studying history, urban development, political science and racism.

—S. Purtee, Librarian
Academic Information Technology and Libraries,
University of Cincinnati

"I had a front row seat to history...held my interest all the way...impressive research...reminded me of crime stories by James Patterson and Joseph Wambaugh."

—Timothy 'Bets' Wegner, Dayton, Ohio

"I was spellbound...terrific descriptions of the hard life in the hills of Eastern Kentucky and the move north by thousands to find work...held my interest throughout...as if I looked over the shoulders of cops on the job."

—D. Sizemore, history buff
Cincinnati, Ohio

Blood In The Streets is dedicated to the nearly twenty thousand (20,000) law enforcement personnel who died in the line of duty in the United States since 1791.

During research for this book, the authors examined fatality statistics maintained by the National Law Enforcement Officers Memorial Fund in Washington, D.C. For the period covered in this story, from January 1965 through December 1975, two thousand two hundred sixteen (2,216) individuals lost their lives in performance of their duties. This was one of the most explosive and violent periods in our law enforcement history in America.

"...and when we lay down our night sticks, enroll us
in your heavenly force, where we will be as proud to
guard the throne of God as we have been to guard the
city of all the people. Amen."

—*Closing paragraph*
Police Officer's Prayer to St. Michael.

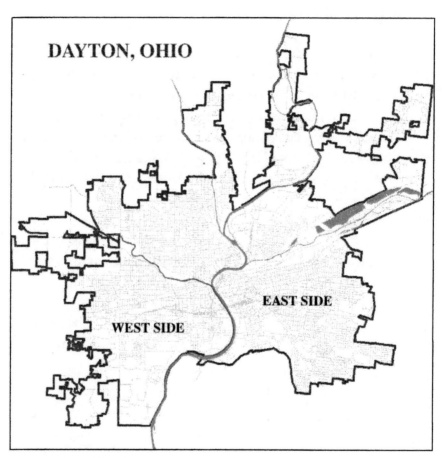

DAYTON, OHIO

EAST SIDE

WEST SIDE

Map of City of Dayton. West Side-East Side

Authors' Note

THE STORY

Blood in the Streets is a story based on actual events covering a period of unprecedented racism, riots and murders in the United States from 1965 through 1975. The story is set in Dayton, Ohio, in the heartland of America.

The genre is true crime novel and is written in a predominately journalistic style that captures the backbone of the story. The authors maintained the integrity of known facts and retold them to the best of their ability. Since the key events are over forty years old, some gaps naturally exist due to the unavailability of records and some individuals. Therefore, the authors took literary liberties to use a modest amount of fiction to flesh out background and character development in some cases. Merging of the two styles did not change the arc, core, or truth regarding racism, riots and murders depicted in the story.

Firsthand knowledge and experience of one of the main characters, Police Officer/Detective Dan Baker leads the reader through the novel strewn with violence and conflict. The story also draws on life experiences of co-author Gwen Nalls. While she is not a character in the story, she contributed personal knowledge and perspective of life as she grew up on Dayton's West Side, dubbed by The *Dayton Daily News* in 1966 as, "The major Negro ghetto."

The authors researched public records, media reports, publications and conducted personal interviews and conversations. A few secondary events were compressed, modified or moved in time to facilitate flow of the story. While many quotes by specific characters are sourced, some dialogue was constructed by the authors based on actual historical events, personal knowledge and background information. Generally, the story unfolds chronologically, laced with vernacular, facts and quotes of the day.

USE OF WORDS AND TERMS

To reflect violent events accurately in a racially charged America, some phrases, words and occasional profanity is used to factually represent events that transpired and in keeping with the times. Racial terms such as "Negro," "colored" and "black" evolve in the story, as they did in time. A few negative racial terms were used sparingly in context. While some words and terms are derogatory and inappropriate by today's standards, those terms were commonly used in the era and are not intended to offend the reader. We ask your indulgence in our efforts to depict the era accurately.

THE CHARACTERS

Due to the violent nature of this story, we used a mixture of real names and pseudonyms. Generally, the real names are people directly sourced in public material. Other names were changed or created to protect the privacy of individuals not directly sourced. Any similarity to fictitious names is purely coincidental.

During the mid 1960s, only a few women were members of the Dayton Police force and had not yet served in uniform or on senior level detective squads. Hence, only a few women are mentioned in this story. Fortunately, today women are members of the profession and occupy senior command positions and specialized units.

Dayton Police Officers handled unprecedented challenges with limited technology, resources and training during the 1960s and early 1970s. On a few occasions, police may have stepped 'over the line' to protect the public, their fellow officers and themselves. No justification is offered for their actions. That is just the way it was.

THE PLACES

Every effort was made to accurately identify places, streets, buildings and geography. Due to the passage of time and events, some have been demolished, moved or renamed, and the authors used the best information available.

Prologue

The Watts Riot in Los Angeles, California in 1965 was the largest and most devastating urban riot in the United States. It lasted six days and resulted in the loss of thirty-four lives. Damage to property exceeded $200 million dollars (the equivalent of $1.5 billion in 2013). The decade that followed Watts from 1965 through 1975, was the most violent period in the history of urban America.

Black Americans were plagued by high unemployment, poor housing, segregated public schools and grinding poverty. Demands for an end to segregation went unanswered and black ghettos erupted in riots. Relentless waves of violent crime flooded through the streets.

No urban city was immune and many required assistance of National Guard troops to quell the violence. Most police departments were ill-prepared for full-scale riots and mass demonstrations. Their response was often disorganized and dangerous.

The Civil Rights Act of 1964 did not bring about immediate change for blacks. In cities all over America, blacks were restless and many engaged in the non-violent struggle for justice. Some militant groups like the Black Panthers rose up. "Black Power" became the clarion call for millions of black people. "Burn Baby, Burn!" was shouted in the streets. Black people were beyond the boiling point, cooked over the hot stove of racism.

Against this backdrop, a Ku Klux Klan-sympathizing white serial killer prowled the streets of Dayton, Ohio in the heartland of America. A classic and sulking loner, he was driven by his hatred of "colored" people. He launched a series of vigilante-style targeted shootings of black men and believed his acts would stop the tide of change and efforts to integrate society. He had a bizarre fascination with the paranormal and he sought revenge for failures in his miserable life as he slipped deeper into Paranoid Schizophrenia.

Research for this story disclosed that the Federal Bureau of Investigation, (FBI), and the Dayton, Ohio Police Department failed to connect the dots on several occasions during unrelated investigations, and the killer was never considered as a possible suspect. A true 'lone wolf', the vigilante was unchecked as he expanded his attacks and his victims piled up on city streets.

———◄○►———

The story is about racial hatred, violence, reconciliation and healing of a riot-torn city. Put your riot helmet on and hold tight. The authors will take you back to policing the way it was done 'back in the day': low tech, gritty, rough and raw. It ain't pretty.

ONE

Racist Roots Run Deep

1860, in the hills of Eastern Kentucky

The menfolk gathered around the Wolfe County Courthouse in the small dirt road town of Campton, Kentucky. It was the month of March 1860. An auctioneer climbed atop a hastily built rough-hewn wooden platform and initiated activities that repeated every few months in Eastern Kentucky. About forty white farmers and merchants drew close. The auctioneer leafed through notes in a well-worn journal. He peered over the top of his glasses and saw the County Recorder who sat at a small crudely made desk. His quill pen and ink well were poised to document the auction and sales. At 9:00 a.m., it was time to proceed.

Smoke curled up from the long-stem smoking pipes used by a dozen men. The cool damp morning air hung low and blanketed the valley. The crowd perked up. They pointed and talked among themselves as two white men unloaded the valuable property that was for sale.

Seventeen men, women and children ranged in age from forty-two to one year. They were herded together and lined up near the auctioneer's platform. Their faces showed dread. The crowd studied the dark-skinned humans as if they looked to buy a cow or a goat. To the buyers, it was the same decision making process. To the Negroes that stood together in fearful submission, it was sheer terror.

One by one, Negro men were ordered to stand on the platform in their ragged clothes while the auctioneer described each one. The auctioneer never used a name. Slaves had no names in the white man's world.

The women and children came next. The women were examined one by one. A few were paired with children, if a buyer chose to bid that way.

The very young children remained with their mother but the older children were sold separately.

After the brief showing, buyers had a few minutes to formulate their bids. As the bidding began, slaves realized their lives were no better than that of a mule or an ox. Even though some slaves did not speak any English and others only spoke the Gullah tongue, they knew that their fate following the auction was a horrifying uncertainty.

The auction was completed within an hour. The Negroes were tied-up and hauled away by their new owners. Some of the Negroes cried and attempted to resist, only to be brought to their knees by a rain of switches or a buggy whip that was unleashed on the offender.

Finally, the County Recorder documented the sale of the chattel and necessary entries were made in the Official Journal of Wolfe County. The heading on each printed page of the journal left room for handwritten entries to document new ownership of the Negroes.

One buyer, Mr. Mullins, purchased a 25-year-old female and two children ages six and five. The slaves, to be known henceforth as "Mullins' slaves," were logged under Mullins' name as follows:

In the County of *Wolfe*, 16 *March* 1860
- Name of Slave Owners: Mullins
- Number of Slaves: 1 and 2 children
- Description: Age: 25; Sex: F; Color: dark
- Fugitive from the State: No
- Number Manumitted,
  Deaf & Dumb,
  blind, insane or idiotic: None

Mr. Mullins joked and said, "A slave woman is happier if she has her children with her. I can raise them young'ens to be good slaves, too. What a bargain!"

Generations of white folks who hailed from the hills of Wolfe County were inbred with the belief that Negroes were less than human. They had no inherent rights or personhood. They were just "niggers."

The County Recorder finalized the auction and completed documentation of the slave sale on Schedule 2 of the U.S. Census 1860 Slave Schedule.

This was done to account for slaves in the general population as part of the second U.S. Federal Census of Slaves completed in 1860.

———◄○►———

In 1927, sixty-seven years after the sale of slaves in 1860, the population of Wolfe County was about 3,500 people, ninety-nine percent were white. The remaining one percent was American Indian and Hispanic. The town of Campton had fewer than 450 people. Many of the men worked in coal mines. Campton had a few dirt streets that turned to ankle deep mud when it rained. Campton, Kentucky, was 190 miles south of Dayton, Ohio and it rested about fifty miles north of Hazard, Kentucky.

———◄○►———

September 11, 1927, the first screams of life from a white newborn baby boy were heard when he forced his way out of his mother's womb onto a blanketed floor.

The child began life in a dingy main room of a run-down house in Campton, Kentucky. He was born into poverty and a very dim future. Nevertheless, the family momentarily marveled at the blessing. Reality soon set in; having one more mouth to feed tinged the happiness. The small boy was named Carma Long.

Carma Long had a hard start in life. His parents divorced when he was two years old. He never knew his natural mother, Bessie Peck, and it became a source of emotional pain for him. His father, Samuel, married Alma Collinsworth and they bore nine other children in the coming years. Carma Long was the eldest of the ten children. Carma always questioned why his momma left him. Mistrust and fear of abandonment took root. He retreated behind an emotional wall to shield himself from hurt again.

TWO

Two Men—Two Paths

"Why not?" a young white man in his early 20s said as he examined a recruiting brochure for the Dayton, Ohio, Police Department, (DPD). Dan Baker's desire to be a cop in the mid-1960s was fostered by life where he grew up in a busy working-class neighborhood where cops walked a beat. As a young boy, he knew quite a few cops. He had seen them at work in one of the city's toughest white areas on Dayton's East Side. For Baker, the choice felt natural.

Baker was reared in a conservative Baptist home by plainspoken parents. His parents were from large families, and their early years were spent in hardscrabble parts of Eastern and Southern Kentucky. Life was harsh in their remote childhood homes. Except for electricity, everything else was as if in the early 1900s. Lump coal and wood were burned in potbelly stoves as their only source of heat. Cooking was done on a cast iron kitchen stove. Buckets of fresh water were hand carried from a spring that flowed out of rock in the hillside. They walked behind mules and farmed tobacco and corn crops on steeply sloping fields that provided their main source of income. The main food source was a few barnyard animals that were supplemented with routine hunting of deer, rabbit and squirrel. A loaded 12-gauge shotgun always rested against the wall at the front door.

Baker's father, Marion, was from Climax, Kentucky, Rockcastle County, about forty-five miles from Campton. Marion attended a one-room schoolhouse where he did not go beyond the seventh grade. Baker's mother, Nell, hailed from a small junction in the road near Monticello, Kentucky. She dropped out of elementary school to work after the early death of her father. His parents' hometowns were not really towns at all. They were tiny remote dots on a map and always referred to fondly as "down home." Rockcastle County's history also included slavery. Three-hundred-and-ninety slaves were owned by whites in 1860.

Marion and Nell lived frugally and got by with little. They eventually migrated to Cincinnati, Ohio, in the late 1930s to find work. Born out of their lifestyle was toughness known to the folks from the hills and the South. Strict values were bred into their three boys: Bruce, Dan, the middle child, and his younger brother Jerry. The entire family embraced the straightforward thinking, "work hard, be honest and stand up for yourself."

Due to lack of work in Cincinnati, the family moved again. In 1945, they moved fifty miles further north to Dayton, Ohio's East Side and chased rumors of good jobs. After a few low paying factory jobs, Baker's father sought work outdoors. He despised being tied to a machine on an assembly line. He ultimately found a job pumping gasoline at the Red Head Oil Company, a discount gas station that was open 24/7. It was in a tough area of East Dayton at Fifth Street and Wayne Avenue. The locals called the intersection "Filth and Wine."

Four rowdy hillbilly bars; the Blazing Stump, the Beer Barrel, the Sun Bar and Samu's Bar, were located near the Red Head gas station. The bars served cheap liquor and cold beer to hard workers and veterans mustered out of military service after World War II.

Marion Baker became the station manager. He got to know the police officers who walked and patrolled the four beats that converged at Filth and Wine. Some officers stopped at the gas station all hours of the day or night to take a break or use the telephone in the small back office. Marion gained the respect of the police officers, and years later, those contacts helped his son Dan, when he applied to join the DPD.

When Marion worked long shifts, Dan and his older brother Bruce often carried their dad's black metal lunch pail ten blocks to the gas station. The boys hung around and enjoyed a bottle of ice cold Coke.

Sometimes Dan talked to the police and listened to their fascinating stories about arrests or lighthearted moments when they helped people in need. He thoroughly enjoyed being around the officers. A few police officers helped the Baker family and got them bulk packages of flour, lard and cheese they somehow acquired.

In the early days, the family did not have a car and some of the officers were kind enough to provide transportation for the Bakers in their police cars. They took them to the grocery store or worship service at Emmanuel Baptist Church on East Third Street.

As a teenager, Dan Baker worked part-time and pumped gas at the Red Head Station, and he witnessed firsthand the goodness and compassion of the police. He also saw rough and tough policing on the streets at Filth and Wine.

———◄●►———

Another young white man came of age on Dayton's East Side but he was on a different path. His Appalachian roots in Eastern Kentucky were also mired in poverty but with little hope for opportunity. The Long family moved to Dayton, Ohio, in the early 1940s when Carma Long was a young teenager. The adjustment to the busy city was difficult for the family, particularly for Carma. He had little parental support. His father was not an outgoing person, described by some as detached. Long did not fit in with others his age in the neighborhood. His quiet and reclusive behavior only led to teasing from other youth. He withdrew even more. Though Long did not finish grade school, he could read. At times, it felt like a burden, as most adults in his family could not read. They looked to Carma to help them with their mail and important papers.

The busy city was massive in size compared to down home. Around the clock, dark plumes rose from scores of smokestacks at steel foundries, utility and auto plants. Warehouses, stores, shops and rail lines hummed with activity. Police cars often sped through the city as their sirens wailed. Downtown was crowded and busy, and the pace of life in the city was fast. After he dropped out of school, Long realized that his seventh grade education was going to hold him back. He faced stiff competition for low paying jobs.

The Long family had never seen so many colored people before. Thousands of them lived on the West Side and traveled through the city during the day. Whites never knew when they might run into 'one' downtown or in a factory. Hundreds of blacks from the south also flooded into Dayton's West Side every month seeking work.

Young Carma Long did not adjust well to the hectic pace of the city.

He was deeply troubled at the thought of sharing his life and space with colored people. Too many dark faces.

Eventually, Long found a series of menial part-time and full-time warehouse jobs in Dayton. His family hovered at the poverty line, and they could not see anything better on the horizon.

Generations of racism resided in Long's DNA. His lack of success was fertile ground for jealousy and revenge.

————◁◦▷————

Long was drafted into the U.S. Army in 1945, but he was honorably discharged in less than six months. He returned to Dayton to care for his father who had a nervous breakdown. As a loner, the rigor of military life was hard on Long, but he enjoyed one aspect of Army life: training with handguns and rifles.

————◁◦▷————

On February 25, 1948, at the age of twenty, Carma Long married a young woman named Grace Keith. She was also from rural Eastern Kentucky. Grace was a plain woman who moved to the city with her family. She was profoundly ashamed of being illiterate. She could neither read nor write. Her husband was already the go-to person in his family since so many could not read or write, and he took on the responsibility to help his wife with the most basic of daily decisions. Eventually, the burden of being needed by everyone was overpowering to Carma. Soon after marriage, the couple began to have children, and their responsibilities to support their family grew.

In 1962, Carma Long had an uncontrollable fixation with authority and he was deeply troubled by the efforts of the United States Government to restrict the individual rights of citizens. He read about accusations made by the Federal Bureau of Investigation (FBI), that some citizens, groups and publications were associated with Communists.

Long frequently spent time alone in the public library and he browsed newspapers and magazines. He discovered anti-government stories and teachings in a monthly publication called the *Daily Worker*. It was first published in 1924 in Chicago by the American Communist Party-USA.

During the turmoil of the 1950s and 60s, circulation of the *Daily Worker* grew rapidly.

Unknown to Long, the *Daily Worker* and many other similar publications and organizations were under surveillance by the FBI. The Internal Security Act of 1950, better known as the McCarran Act, established the Subversive Activities Control Board. Organizations that had any association with Communism were required to register with the U.S. Attorney General. The Board and the FBI also had the power to investigate groups and individuals suspected of even the slightest connection with Communism.

Long subscribed to the *Daily Worker* in December 1961 and saw an article in the February 1962 publication that upset him. FBI Director, J. Edgar Hoover, was quoted by excerpts from an article he published in the *American Bar Association Journal* in February 1962. The title was, "Shall it be Law or Tyranny?" Hoover argued that dissidents were disloyal to America and that "left leaning Supreme Court Justices" and some attorneys were unpatriotic in their representation of so-called "Free Speech" clients, who were placed on the Subversive Board's Watch List. Thousands of people were quickly labeled as Communists or Communist sympathizers.

February 22, 1962, Carma Long wrote a letter to United States Attorney General Robert F. Kennedy and expressed his dislike of Director Hoover's war on those who disagreed with the policies and actions of the U.S. Government. He included his name and address. At the time, Long lived at 327 Maeder Avenue, Dayton, Ohio.

The FBI immediately placed a mail cover on Carma Long's mail with the U.S. Postal Inspector and verified Long's regular receipt of mail from the *Daily Worker*. The mail cover tracked the sender and recipient information. Through investigation, they discovered that Long began to receive the *Daily Worker* publication in January 1962, and they continued to track his mail. Long was unaware that the FBI tracked his mail through the end of 1966. The Confidential FBI Indices reports documented the FBI's tracking activities.

The Confidential FBI files documented:

CINCINNATI INDICES FURTHER REFLECTS BUREAU BY ROUTING SLIP, DATED MARCH 2, 1962, CAPTIONED, MR.

CARMA LONG, 327 MAEDER AVENUE, DAYTON 27, OHIO, PROVIDED LETTER WRITTEN BY SUBJECT TO ATTORNEY GENERAL ROBERT KENNEDY IN WHICH HE CRITICIZED FORMER DIRECTOR HOOVER FOR ARTICLE PUBLISHED IN AMERICAN BAR ASSOCIATION JOURNAL. CINCINNATI INDICES FURTHER REFLECT SUBJECT SUBSCRIBED TO THE *DAILY WORKER* IN 1962 THROUGH 1966.

When the FBI evaluated the Indices entry, an FBI Analyst wrote two comments in the margin of the document that indicated the FBI's opinion of Carma Long:

"Rights of Free Speech, Communist."

"Communist, 4 yrs."

The FBI did not share Long's name and address with Dayton Police nor the fact that he was investigated since 1962 and tracked in their Indices.

———◄○►———

In 1965, Carma Long abruptly decided to change his name to Neal Bradley Long. He was not a person who shared his inner thoughts, feelings and decisions with anyone. He never explained why he did so. He simply told his wife after the fact. Despite the change, Long still went by the name of "Carma" Long.

Neal Bradley Long found a steady job in October 1965. He was hired as a chrome plater helper. Long worked at a small manufacturing plant on the fringe of Dayton's West Side at the Stolle Company located at 1525 River Rd., near South Broadway Street. He earned $65.00 a week. It was tough to make ends meet for his wife and six children, four boys and two girls.

Long hated driving to and from work through the West Side. It was 'nigger-town' to him. He heard rumors of whites being attacked and robbed by Negroes at traffic lights. His insides churned at the news but his outward appearance never telegraphed his growing hate toward Negroes.

THREE

Whites Only

In 1966, the City of Dayton was a divided city. Whites controlled the economy, city and county government, city schools and law enforcement. The Negro voice was barely heard in the halls of power.

West Third Street, fifty-five blocks long from the Great Miami River to the city limits, was the backbone of the West Side. People were drowning in poverty and crime-infested Negro ghettos. The absentee landlord rate was the highest in the city. The large Veterans Administration Center, (VA), located at the city limits on Dayton's West Side at Gettysburg and West Third Street drew thousands of visitors each year. Directly across from the main entrance was over a dozen residential structures divided into small apartments or rental rooms. Most posted "White Only" signs. White landlords flaunted their disdain for the Civil Rights Act and refused to rent to Negroes. Not only was this an insult to visitors, it was an ugly and constant reminder to thousands of Negroes who drove by the busy VA Center every day. The old South was still alive, even in the urban North.

With the Great Migration from the South to the North that began in the 1930s, Dayton grew rapidly in the mid-1940s and 50s. Word spread throughout Kentucky, Tennessee, Georgia, Mississippi and Alabama that good-paying factory jobs were plentiful in Dayton. The result was a massive influx of Negroes from the deep South and many whites from Appalachia. They came from southern towns such as Black Hawk, Mississippi; Berea, Hazard, Rockcastle County and Wolfe County, Kentucky; Kodak, Tennessee and many other dots on the map.

A who's-who of manufacturing companies employed thousands of production line workers. General Motors, *McCall's Magazine*, The National Cash Register Company, Dayton Tire & Rubber, Delco, Chrysler,

Frigidaire, steel foundries, printing companies, and tool companies had large production plants. A variety of other businesses and suppliers were sprinkled across the industrial pockets of the city, many on the West Side. Numerous warehouses, rail spurs and trucking terminals surrounded the facilities.

Whites who settled in the city flooded into the east and northern parts of Dayton. They rented sleeping rooms and multi-family houses or small apartments. Appalachians, Italians, Polish, Greeks, Hungarians, Irish and Germans dominated the white areas of the city. Most Negroes were relegated to live in the southwest quadrant of the city known as the West Side. The influx of Negroes swelled the population in the West Side. However, opportunity for them to find work was far less and the work was more menial. Many labor unions did not welcome Negroes and skill-based jobs were automatically blocked, due to lack of experience. Apprenticeships were restricted. Southern Negroes did not fit in well with the prevailing white culture.

Enactment of the Civil Rights Act in 1964 raised hopes of equality for Negroes but real change moved at a glacial pace. The *Dayton Daily News* reported, "A Negro Dayton high school principal, John Harewood, summed it up, 'People expected a lot more than has happened. The Civil Rights Act and other measures said things would be different. These people have been denied all these years and they are impatient now.'"

On May 8, 1966, the *Dayton Daily News* ran a series of articles entitled, "West Side 1966." Dave Allbaugh, a well-known reporter used a historic reference in his opening sentence.

"The first Negro came to Dayton in 1798. History gives him no name; the only trace is a list of taxpayers with the description, William Maxwell, including his Negro."

Perhaps foretelling of the smoldering discontent, the article captured four major areas of complaints by Negroes in the early summer of 1966.

1. Education. Most Negroes deplore West Side Schools. They are more crowded, less well equipped than all-white schools. The quality of education is lower. Poverty added to the problem. People expect you to take kids from a home with no books, magazines

and no parent interest and have them perform well. It won't work. Another educator commented, These children (in poverty) often come to school unfed after wretched nights torn by screaming, fighting, bed-wetting. Many can't sleep because of the cold and the rats.

2.   Joblessness. Nobody has any reliable figures on Negro unemployment, but it is believed to be double that of whites. Need training to be qualified for jobs.

3.   Housing. Segregation in housing is the big symbolic thing. Negroes were isolated on the West Side.

4.   City Services. Negroes get less service from agencies and are treated brutally by police.

While the series of articles in the *Dayton Daily News* identified major problems and stirred much conversation on both sides of town, nothing of substance changed. The white leadership was tone-deaf to the overriding problem of racial discrimination. For people on the West Side, the articles were correct, but it only restated the problems they faced every day. The Negro people wanted change, and they were tired of waiting.

Thousands of Negro youths were restless and prone to act violently against the establishment rather than take a patient approach to push for change. Negro leaders led non-violent sit-ins at downtown Dayton department stores, City Hall and many other businesses as they protested the lack of Negro employment. White-owned downtown barbershops and stores were picketed. Allegations of police brutality mounted and confrontations were more frequent on the street.

The more "uppity" the Negroes became, the more some whites expected 'race riots' to erupt. The self-fulfilling prophesies of violence between Negroes and whites slowly inched toward fruition.

Throughout the "well-to-do" sections of Dayton and its wealthy suburbs like Oakwood, the "help" (women day workers and housekeepers) continued to ride the yellow and black trolley buses across bridges to work in large homes and estates. Many were lucky to earn $25.00 a week for their hard labor. Negro women peered from the trolley bus windows during the ride from the ghetto to the manicured neighborhoods. The passing scenery underscored what it meant to be a Negro in the white man's world. The help entered the whites' homes through a back door. They were not allowed to enter or leave through the front door.

As racial tension increased, some of the help overheard whispered household conversations about the "colored problems." At times, the help, who almost never went to high school, were asked by fearful white employers, "What's going on?"

The help also had their own personal concerns. They needed to work and earn money, yet proud Negro women also wanted to maintain their dignity.

Eventually, some whites and their day workers found ways to continue the facade that everything was normal. They chose to avoid open discussions about looming racial issues.

Although pay was meager, some whites donated expensive hand-me-down clothing to the help, clothing that was no longer needed or wanted by their own children. One Jewish woman, who had twin girls, gave her housekeeper nice frilly dresses. Miss Corina's only daughter, Gaither, enjoyed the windfall of fine clothes. She had two of each outfit in different colors. She got a taste of the finer clothing. Gaither wore the dresses to Zion Hill Church. Even so, she knew the clothing once belonged to two white girls who seemed to have everything.

The help provided care for the white children, prepared the white folks' food, cleaned their homes and washed their dirty underwear as their day job responsibilities. At the end of a long tiring day, they sat quietly on the city bus ride back to the West Side, as the help had a brief respite from their daily grind. The day worker knew she had a family at home to take care of and there was no rest until late into the night.

Conversely, in the evenings, the well-to-do whites retreated to their dens and had a few drinks while they watched the evening news. Stories about civil rights demonstrations, sit-ins and riots were more troublesome each day. They worried if the racial issues in Dayton would cause them to lose their help. A ghastly thought was mouthed, "My goodness! Who will clean the toilets if Miss Corina isn't here anymore?"

————◄○►————

Activists in Dayton became more visible and spoke out loudly about the racial tension. A Negro man named William Sumpter McIntosh, known on the street as Sumpter McIntosh, emerged in West Dayton as a strong leader and an advocate of non-violent protests. He headed the local chapter of the Congress for Racial Equality (CORE) and spent time in Atlanta, Georgia, with Dr. Martin Luther King, Jr. McIntosh shared King's visions and helped shape the Civil Rights Movement when he shared his own non-violent approach and challenged the status quo. McIntosh led numerous protests and sit-ins in Dayton and showed no sign of backing down.

Many mature Negroes who worked every day and supported families experienced the burden of discrimination. However, they worried that restless youths and the new black militants would pull them all into a fearful and more dangerous future. There was little doubt that things needed to change, but those with families walked a fine line to keep a job, too.

Some looked to God and their churches for guidance. Increased racial tension and fear challenged their faith. At times, it seemed God had turned his face away and did not hear their prayers. They kept low profiles and hoped not to get caught up in police activity or a violent street situation.

Sunday worship services offered a day of predictability to many Negroes. At least there was a familiar routine, friendly faces and they felt God was present. At one church, late comers entered the one story previously abandoned and converted grocery store building that served as a place of worship. The church was situated just one block from West Third Street and Western Avenue. Minister Matthews sat in his usual place near the podium. Attired in his purple and gold floor length robe with an embroidered cross over his heart, he cradled the well-worn bible in his lap while he clapped his hands and tapped his feet along with the music.

An old Hammond organ sounded the first bars of "Peace Be Still," a song made popular by the Reverend James Cleveland. The organ screamed as the organist tickled the ivories up to high treble notes. No one needed a hymnal; the choir and musicians learned their songs by ear. The organ, along with guitars and drums accompanied the choir as the congregation swayed with the rhythm and stood when the spirit moved and raised their hands in praise to God.

The congregation of about one hundred working class people was mostly women with a smattering of children and a few men from the surrounding neighborhoods and a small number who had moved to better neighborhoods on the West Side. They wore their Sunday best outfits. In Negro churches, women's hats were often viewed as a primary component of the entire outfit. Beautiful and ornate hats ranged from small pillboxes to large wide-brims and high profiles. The colorful stylish works of art bobbed with the rhythm of the music.

Historically, religion sustained Negroes as they endured centuries of slavery, oppression and discrimination. In the 1960s, the church was the major institution in Negro communities. Some ministers struggled with decisions about their involvement in civil rights activities, while others became very active. A handful of the larger Negro churches took on the mantle of social change and risked life and limb to be part of demonstrations. In rare cases, some even partnered with a handful of white churches in joint demonstrations and sit-ins.

Increasingly, young adult Negro men and teenagers turned away from the old school belief that an unseen God could fix things. The powerful call of the streets to fight oppression was their reality. They saw police as the most hated symbol of authority and oppression.

———◦———

Police manpower in the United States shrank during the mid 1960s, partly due to the military draft. The fact that 831 police officers died in the line of duty from 1960 through 1965 did not help with recruitment of new police. In Dayton, the day-to-day pressures of policing were compounded by increased racial tensions that swept the country. Every time an officer reported for duty, it was impossible to know from one day to the next what major event might take place. The growing number of riots, civil rights demonstrations, militant groups and demonstrations about the Vietnam War strained the ability of authorities to maintain order in the homeland. The turmoil finally reached a crescendo that stretched police manpower and resources to the breaking point. As a result, many police and fire departments in America, including Dayton, successfully obtained approval from local Selective Services Boards for "2-A" Military Deferments based on "critical need." The Deferments allowed cities to keep key public safety employees rather than lose them to the draft.

In 1966, the DPD had 380 officers. Only fourteen were Negro. Seven women were police officers, but they were not allowed to work in uniform and usually worked the Juvenile Squad. Previous efforts to recruit minorities were tepid. Only one Negro was in a supervisory position. Sergeant. J.B. Hogan supervised the West Side Residential Burglary Squad in the Detective Section.

Efforts were intensified to hire Negroes but the undercurrent of racism among some whites was quick to find fault with Negro candidates or actual hires. In some cases, a handful of Negro police recruits had previously been active in non-violent sit-ins and demonstrations as citizens before they applied for a job with DPD. As a result, peer pressure among some white officers kept them from giving a "hand-up" to the new Negro cops. Predictably, some Negroes quit the job within a year or so. Those who remained stuck together professionally and socially.

At the end of a shift, most white officers drove to the suburbs or the white neighborhoods in Dayton and left the inner city and its problems in their rear view mirror. Not so, for most Negro officers who lived in the West Side. Away from work, they were frequently drawn into conversations about the troubles and racism in the city. Being a cop made them an easy target for harassment and some were called "Uncle Tom" and "house nigger." It was painful for the officers who experienced hostility in the station house and on the street.

———◁◦▷———

Police were required to adjust to new legal requirements that significantly affected the day-to-day operations of law enforcement. New United States Supreme Court decisions focused on alleged violations of Constitutional Amendments that protected the rights of citizens and bound the authority of police. It was change that some of the "old dogs" found hard, if not impossible to accept. As a result, some officers quit or retired early because they were angry at the way the law and policing changed for the worse, as they saw it.

In June 1964, the U. S. Supreme Court issued the Escobedo v. Illinois decision that prohibited police from denying a defendant access to an attorney. In June 1966, the Supreme Court ruled on another important case, Miranda v. Arizona that protected suspects and defendants from involuntarily waiving their Fifth Amendment right against self-incrimination. Both cases dramatically changed police practices. Persons in custody were afforded the right to legal counsel when they became the focus of a criminal investigation, even if they could not afford an attorney. The famous Miranda Rights warning, *"You have the right to remain silent..."* was hurriedly taught to all police officers and wallet-size Miranda Warning Cards were issued to officers across America. When the new laws came along, many cops complained, "Now we gotta read *them* their *rights*? Holy shit! Read a Miranda Warning? What the hell, we can't do our job anymore!"

The days were gone when a police officer simply went to work, put in eight hours on patrol and then went home. On the job, they were under constant pressure and often second-guessed by the "brass" and community activists. Cops were on the front line of dramatic changes in society.

———◦———

Negroes coined a new phrase, "Soul Brother!" When the term was used, it bolstered a feeling of unity. The colors of Africa, red, black and green, were prominently displayed on signs, caps, jackets, flags and other items. The message displayed newfound roots and pride by Negroes who often raised their fists in defiance. In June 1966, Stokley Carmichael of the Student Nonviolent Coordinating Committee (SNCC) spoke at a rally in Mississippi. He angrily shouted a new phrase that became the clarion call of the 1960s and changed how Negroes viewed themselves. Carmichael yelled, "Black Power!" during his speech and raised a single clenched fist in defiance. He challenged Negroes to shake off their slave names and embrace their color and their history and to fight the white power structure. He urged them to stand up to government and resist when necessary, particularly the police. The new phrase was heard around the U.S. and the world. Carmichael later became Honorary Prime Minister of the Black Panther Party and his message became more militant.

To many Negroes, the simple link of the word "black" to the word "power" enabled them to see a new horizon. "Black Power" was repeated by blacks of all ages. They often gathered and chanted, "Black Power" when police were on the street and made arrests or wrote tickets.

Signs that read "Black Power" appeared in windows of black owned businesses. DPD instructed officers to keep track of which businesses displayed the new provocative signs. At first, they believed it was a code or a secret signal. Many no longer referred to themselves as "Negro" or "colored." One thing was sure, "Black Power" did not sound friendly to cops when it was yelled in their faces. Unfortunately, Dayton was already one of the meanest cities in the United States and it was about to get meaner and a lot more violent.

FOUR

The Rookie Cop

"Look kid, when it comes to dealing with people out
here on the street, forget what they told you in the
academy. I'll show you how the job is really done."

—Unwritten axiom usually said on
"Day 1" to rookie police officers by veteran cops

SHIFT CHANGE: The second floor Patrol Section of the DPD Central
Police Station buzzed with activity three times a day. One patrol shift
went off duty while another prepared to mount up for duty.

It was 11:00 p.m. August 31, 1966. Officers had only twelve minutes
to attend roll call and hit the street. The assembly room clock granted no
mercy. Radio calls backed up and the dispatcher was anxious to unload
an avalanche of dispatches on the graveyard shift. The on-coming shift
of about forty officers was due out at 11:12 p.m. Shotguns were checked
out, supplies were squirreled away in individual boxes carried by each
officer and new batteries were loaded into long metal flashlights. Quite a
few officers were already tired. They had been in court during the day or
worked part-time jobs and did not get enough sleep.

A few officers told stories of highlights on their shift as they prepared
to go off duty. Others were simply worn out from their call load and the
heat on the 3:00 p.m. to 11:00 p.m. shift. None of the patrol vehicles was
air conditioned. A few men laughed as they shared morgue humor, common to cops. Officer Bud Turner told a story to a few officers as they
waited at the desk sergeant's table to turn in traffic tickets and reports.

Turner launched into his story, "Hey, listen to this. Crew 521 went on
a prowler call on Grand Avenue at a vacant house. A woman suddenly
jumped out of the shadows with a knife and tried to stab Larry Welch!"

He demonstrated with his right hand in the air. Turner acted as if he had a knife and dramatically thrust it downward. Turner continued, "Larry fell backward, drew his gun and shot her in the chest. What else could he do?"

The officers crowded around Turner and listened intently. "Yeah, after Larry shot her, he realized it was Leapin' Laura. She has tried to commit suicide for years, divin' and jumpin' in front of cars and buses on Salem Avenue. Then she tried to stab a cop . . . and BANG! Larry nailed her!" Turner paused for a second, and then added, "and, I'll be damned, she lived!" He waved his hands in the air in mock disbelief. "These mental cases, they got better luck than us. They won't even die when you shoot 'em. The emergency room doctor has sewn her up a bunch of times and he was tired of seeing her. Guess what?" he said. "Doc said, 'Shit floats!' meaning Laura. She got shot and lived! Any other poor son-of-a-bitch woulda died!" The group broke out in raucous laughter and then went on their way.

Some officers wanted to check out and leave ASAP. Others had reports to finish or evidence to tag and worked overtime until they finished. The small Reports Room was crowded, and the officers used Royal typewriters to hunt and peck with two fingers. The silver grey haze of cigarette smoke was thick in the air. Curses were hurled as an officer messed up his carbon paper or used an eraser and tore a hole in the onionskin copy. The black rotary dial telephones mounted on the wall were in full use. Some officers called home and others called lady friends to arrange a late-night visit.

As officers reported for duty, they lined up in three ranks for uniform inspection. Before they crushed out cigarettes, some officers burned off a loose thread on their shirt.

A new officer, rookie Dan Baker, just made it into the Assembly Room and squeezed in the front row of formation. A sergeant walked past each officer, stopped occasionally, and pointed to dirty shoes, a missing button, or stains on a uniform.

Another sergeant sat at a desk at the front of the room and barked out announcements. With an un-lit stub of a cigar in the corner of his mouth, he looked over his glasses that rested halfway down his nose. "With the hot weather, large crowds of Negroes have been a problem around bars and clubs on the West Side. Get out on foot more in the business districts. Watch your ass!"

After a pause, and on a more serious note he said, "We need to donate blood for Sergeant Kavloski's son, who was in a bad accident. St. Elizabeth Hospital (St. E.) will take your donations. Give it up for a good cause, boys. I'm sure some of you will be glad to go see the nurses."

A few men chuckled at the thought of Shirley, the redhead nurse with big tits, who worked the night shift in the Emergency Room. Giving blood provided the perfect excuse for a flirtatious visit. "Shirley has a real friendly way about her," one officer whispered to another, who smiled knowingly.

So much to learn, Baker thought. *And so little time to get wise and make it through probation.* His head swam with all the details they taught in the Police Academy, including lessons that covered history and the geographic layout of the City of Dayton.

In 1966, the City of Dayton, Ohio, was a racially segregated city of 265,000 residents. Most residents were white, and 70,000 were black. The *Dayton Daily News* and its sister morning paper, The *Dayton Journal Herald*, described the black population on the West Side as "The major Negro ghetto, 80 percent black."

Located in Montgomery County, Dayton's forty square miles was surrounded by a nearly all-white suburban ring of another 275,000 residents in dozens of small cities, towns, villages and townships that brought the metropolitan area population to over a half million.

Dayton's downtown was busy and vibrant with major full-service department stores. Federal, state and city office buildings clustered together. Large hotels were in the heart of town. The RKO and Colonial theaters were popular movie venues and lured patrons with signs on their marquis: "Cool Inside." The center city was also home to banks, major office buildings and a large historic and ornate indoor public arcade. The Dayton Arcade was full of counters that sold fresh baked goods, vegetables, fresh fish, meats and dry goods. High-end jewelry stores, restaurants and shops catered to thousands who filled downtown streets each day.

Dayton's skid row was on the southeastern edge of downtown along East Fifth Street. The marquee of The Mayfair Burlesque Theatre heralded, "Live, On Stage" matinee and evening shows by notorious burlesque queens who traveled the circuit throughout the Midwest. A half-dozen pawnshops, used bookstores and cut-rate clothing stores enjoyed a brisk business. Cheap movie houses, the Ohio and Rialto, were located across the street from the Pony House, a famous bar at 125 South Jefferson Street.

The Pony House was first opened in 1882; a hand-carved Honduran mahogany wood bar thirty-seven feet long and twelve feet in height was the focal point. Legend said "Buffalo Bill" Cody actually rode his horse up to the long bar, which had many old bullet holes from gunfights and celebrations of days gone by. Customers who once leaned on the dark wooden bar included gangster John Dillinger, who was arrested in Dayton, and the world famous boxer, Jack Dempsey. True to its name, the Pony House remained a place where an illegal horseracing bet could be placed with small-time bookies.

During the daytime, yellow and black City Transit electric trolley buses jammed the downtown streets and drew power from a complex web of overhead lines attached to thousands of steel poles in the city. Bus drivers often backed up traffic while they got out of the bus, donned gloves, went to the rear of the bus and reconnected poles that had jumped off the overhead wires. Electric sparks sprayed as bright as popping flash bulbs and danced in the air as the electrical poles and wires seemed to fight being reconnected.

The Great Miami River snaked its way through Dayton from the north and ultimately emptied into the Ohio River fifty miles south near Cincinnati. The Great Miami River was joined midway through Dayton by the much smaller Wolf Creek, widening the river as it passed beneath the city's best-known bridge that brought traffic into the West Side.

The West Third Street Bridge crossed from downtown Dayton into the largest business district on the Negro side of town. Eleven other bridges also granted access to the West Side. The West Third Street Bridge was an immense separation of two cultures, one white and one Negro. The wide river represented the 'glass ceiling' of segregation. The bridge separated Negroes from power and a better life they could see on the other side.

————◦————

In Montgomery County, there were more than twenty-five different police departments, which included the Montgomery County Sheriff's Office.

Most were medium and small police departments in cities, townships and villages. Except for one small township police department west of Dayton's city limits, neighboring departments were nearly 100% white. Even the Ohio State Highway Patrol, with its force of eight hundred Troopers, had fewer than fifteen black officers.

Traffic flow through Dayton was disrupted due to major construction on the brand new Interstate 75 highway project that slowly linked Detroit, Michigan, to south Florida. The I-75 route cut straight through Dayton in a north/south direction and paralleled the Great Miami River. The highway further separated the east and west sides of the city.

All police patrol operations emanated from the Central Police Station, also called Dayton Police Headquarters, in downtown Dayton. The Third Police District covered the largest portion of the West Side.

The Fourth Police District boundary covered the north side of the Great Miami River and lower Dayton View, which trended toward a racially mixed population. Along with the rapid change in demographics came a dramatic increase in absentee landlords and degraded property values along Wolf Creek as blacks inched across the creek.

The Fifth Police District was the northwestern portion of the city with a vibrant 40-block-long business strip on Salem Avenue. A large Jewish population and upper-level income white professionals shared a well-to-do section of large homes called the "Golden Triangle."

———◦———

Baker's reminiscence of lessons in the Academy about Police District boundaries and demographics was interrupted when he heard the sergeant bellow, "Listen up, I have a special announcement to make."

The sergeant announced that a new officer had joined C Platoon, one of four platoons in patrol operations. "Everybody knows that Officer Malone was transferred off C Platoon after he shot and killed a Negro in McCabe Park on the West Side a few days ago. What happened to Malone is a reminder to us all to be more alert. He had no choice. He was attacked with a hammer and he had to shoot the guy. The case will go to the Grand Jury, but he should be okay."

The sergeant paused for effect. "Tension is still high on the West Side. There has already been one Negro protest downtown at City Hall about the shooting. Malone is on desk duty and will be transferred to East Dayton in a week or so...for a change of scenery."

The Sergeant stood up. "We have a new officer, Dan Baker, joining us tonight. He's a probationary rookie from the last recruit class and he will fill Malone's slot." The sergeant smiled and looked across the room directly at Baker, as he stood in rank with the rest of the men. "This young man was top in his class. We'll see how he stacks up on C Platoon." A few veterans cast a wary eye and chuckled. Feeling self-conscious about the sergeant's remark, Baker knew that all new officers learned one very important thing about police culture: until an officer proved himself to be a good partner and one not to rock the boat, the jury was still out about his acceptance.

Last minute changes to the crew assignments were announced by the sergeant, "Walters: foot patrol, four hours, Sector 404 Downtown. We've had a rash of break-ins, so make sure you shake the doors. Gibson: relieve an afternoon crew at St. E. Hospital. He's guarding a prisoner from a homicide arrest."

The sergeant continued, "Baker! You go to the Third District, Beat 336 and ride with Officer Billy Crawford. Take the paddy wagon tonight."

Crawford stood at the opposite end of the formation and looked down the line at Baker. He shrugged as if he had been handed a shit detail, but knew there was no benefit in complaining. After being dismissed by the sergeant, Crawford walked over to Baker and said, "I'll meet you downstairs." He tossed the keys to Baker for wagon #674. "Check it over for weapons and drugs. Sometimes prisoners hide shit in the back, behind the bench seats."

So much for hello, Baker thought.

As Baker walked down the stairs to the parking lot, he felt self-conscious in his brand new light blue uniform shirt and hat with a shiny black visor and silver shield on the front. His black leather Sam Brown belt and swivel holster were well polished and creaked as he moved. Baker thought about his good rookie wages, $99.00 a week.

While he waited outside for Crawford, Baker realized he was uneasy about going to work on the West Side. He knew it was the toughest district and he remembered his Academy training. The Defensive Tactics Course made it clear that officers were expected to be able to use their wits, hands, body, billy club and firearm, if necessary, to handle difficult situations.

FIVE

Never Give Up

"Be civil to everyone, courteous to no one. If he uses
a fist, use your stick. If he uses a knife, use your gun.
Cancel his ticket right then and there."

—*Kilvinski's Law*
The New Centurions *by Joseph Wambaugh*
January 30, 1971

Baker thought back to the first hour of each morning in the Dayton Police Academy that started with one hour of Defensive Tactics. He vividly remembered the third week of class when students were told to sit down on the gym mat after their warm-up exercises. They welcomed the sit-down. Their t-shirts were already soaked with sweat from the hand-to-hand combat.

Officer Bob Noyes, the Defensive Tactics Instructor, wore a white Judo gi and Black Belt as he entered the room. He stepped into the middle of the group. He looked impressive and confident. Hands on his hips and bare footed, he was fit and tough for a 45-year-old man. Noyes began, "Many of you will be alone when you walk patrol beats or patrol in a car. When you are out of your car, *you are on your own*! The brass tell me that someday we'll have portable radios for everyone, but not yet. So, I'll teach you what cops have had to know for a hundred years: how to fight.

"Gentlemen, you will only have a few tools other than your wits and your hands to defend yourself on the street and gain control of people who resist or fight. You'll have a billy club and your gun. That's it." Noyes continued, "When you get in a tight spot, it will probably occur to you that you have *nothing* protecting your body other than your uniform shirt and maybe a leather jacket. You'll even see some of the old-timers who carry a small metal-backed New Testament Bible in their left shirt pocket over their heart. They hope it may help stop a bullet, but it ain't much to hide behind. That is precisely why we spend a lot of time showing you take-downs, hip throws, pressure points, how to use the billy club and how to use your fists and fingers as weapons. God forbid, if somebody ever gets the drop on you, so I'll teach you some handgun take-away moves, too."

The instructor moved as he talked but never broke eye contact with the men on the floor. "On this job, you'll be confronted with all kinds of people who don't want to go to jail. Men, women, juveniles, killers, drunks; you name it, you'll have to deal with 'em. Old, young, big, little, tough, armed, unarmed and mental. Some of them will even want a piece of you, for God knows why." He paused for effect. "You have to be ready to do your job and protect yourself at all times.

"The Department is experimenting with small personal-size mace spray, and it may be issued to you in a year or so. I'm not so sure it works that well. It damn sure makes people mad and it can overspray on you, too! Anyways, with or without mace, it's up to you to control people you arrest or have to fight.

"Here's how it really works on the street. Look-it, you basically have four choices to handle difficult people. You can use voice commands to urge a person to comply; as he made gestures with his elbows, hands and fingers," Noyes added, "Sometimes, you will have to use your hands and feet to push, twist, pinch, employ 'come-along' holds, apply pressure, hit, slap, poke, gouge, restrain, trip or just plain wrestle with someone. The police baton, billy club, nightstick, whatever you wanna' call it, will become your best friend. You can use the club to thrust, deflect, disarm, hit, twist a limb or strike someone to get their attention. Your last resort is to draw and may-be even use your firearm." A pause followed to let it all sink in.

"You really shouldn't draw your weapon unless you are ready to use it. Once the gun is out of your holster, your ability to use your hands or the nightstick is limited and if you are not ready to shoot, the gun could be taken away from you if you're fighting. I'm not your firearms instructor, but I have to tell you what I think, too."

Instructor Noyes wrapped up with a final speech. "Once you have that blue uniform on fellas', you represent law and order, and by God, that's a heavy responsibility. If it takes more than one of you to get the job done, we'll send as many officers as we need to get it done! I know you all aren't boxers and fighters, but once you graduate and hit the streets, you are expected to do whatever it takes to bring someone in. You can't turn your back. If you do, you'll never be able to face your partners or the street again.

"If you are not comfortable putting your hands on someone and fighting, you won't make it at DPD. If that's the case, I don't want to work with you on the street and nobody else will either."

Noyes slowed his speech and looked down at the floor before adding something very sobering. "A few of my friends have been killed on this job and a whole hell-of-a-lot of others have been hurt." He clapped his hands and said, "Get on the mats, fella's!"

———◦———

Occasionally, Captain Grover O'Connor, commander of the Police Academy walked into the classroom and observed the recruits as they practiced their tactics. O'Connor's storied career was replete with dramatic episodes, sensational cases and a reputation for knocking heads. He stood off to the side, arms folded, and personally evaluated which recruit would make a good tough cop on the street. Afterward, he reminded the Academy staff to make sure that each recruit was unofficially tested in a real physical altercation on the street during their field duty weeks.

———◦———

Baker paid close attention to his daily defensive tactics workouts, and from the rumors he heard, he anticipated more action working the West Side. Not only was the radio call load high, but situations cops dealt with in the West Side were difficult and more dangerous. Baker knew that as a rookie, he would be tested in ways he could not even imagine, and violence would be part of the job.

Crime problems on the West Side were more visible and widespread than the rest of the city. The West Side led in homicides and violent crimes. Over seventy-five illegal gambling joints and illegal bootleg liquor houses attracted workers who gambled away their paychecks on the weekend as they mingled with gangsters, pimps and drug dealers at the craps tables.

Street-level drug sales, dope houses and shooting galleries full of junkies were spread around. Poverty, coupled with access to fewer stores and services, encouraged an underground economy of second-hand stores and "fences" that sold and bartered stolen goods. During the day, large-scale illegal numbers betting operations thrived. Some of the best officers and detectives in the entire department spent their first years on the West Side as new street officers in uniform.

—◄o►—

As the late night shift came to life, police officers streamed out of Roll Call and picked up their cars. Baker gazed over the parking lot crowded with blue 1960s Chevrolet four-door sedans with DPD markings. Many of the single bubble gum machine size emergency lights atop the cars were being tested and their bright red rotation cast an urgent glow. Veteran officers were used to the sight but Baker felt his pulse quicken. The sights and sounds were rich. The sounds of shotguns being loaded and loud rough talk filled the air as cops readied for street duty.

SIX

The Thin Blue Line

"People sleep peaceably in their beds at night only because
rough men stand ready to do violence on their behalf."

—George Orwell

Officer Crawford finally came outside and told Baker that the Desk Sergeant ordered some foot patrol duty on West Third Street, between Broadway and Williams Streets after bars close at 2:30 a.m. "Sarge wants the paddy wagon to be seen there tonight." Crawford added, "Maybe it will keep trouble down."

Crawford, a five-year veteran patrolman, was one of the best officers on C Platoon. His deep Louisiana accent was noticeable. Some blacks called him a "cracker" right away when he spoke. Those who chose to confront Crawford's authority risked learning a hard lesson. His reply to aggressors was simple, "We can do this the easy way or the hard way."

Crawford stood about six feet tall. He was very athletic and in good shape and he could back it up. Baker at 6'3" and 220 pounds could probably handle his end, too Crawford thought.

Before they got into the wagon, Crawford told Baker, "Take off your name tag. You don't need to make it easy for anybody to complain about you. You won't drive, touch the radio or unlock the shotgun unless I say so. If the sergeant comes around tonight, I'll do the talking. Any questions?" he asked with a wry grin on his face.

"No," Baker said, and he thought to himself, I guess I'll just be a pull-toy for a while.

Crawford and Baker finished checking the equipment in the wagon, including the Remington 12-gauge shotgun mounted upright on the passenger side. Crawford held the microphone and notified the dispatcher, "Crew 336 is signal 200," an indication they were available for calls.

Dispatch responded, "11:16" and added, "Go to the Palace Bowling Lanes at 1420 West Third Street; report of two men fighting in the parking lot." Crawford acknowledged the radio call and the wagon headed out toward the West Third Street Bridge.

Baker noticed Crawford also carried an eight-inch long black leather Texas Slapper blackjack. It had a small amount of lead in the flexible tip. Other officers carried the unauthorized weapon and the sergeants ignored them.

The only official equipment carried by the two officers included a .38 caliber four-inch barrel Colt Police Revolver, loaded with six rounds. Twelve more rounds, for a total of eighteen, were in individual six round pouches on their gun belts. Each officer carried a hickory billy club. Baker's club was new and polished. Crawford's club was scuffed and nicked. That was it. There was no protective gear and no personal radio. Baker thought, *No wonder so many guys carry a slapper and an extra sturdy flashlight that also made a nice club.*

Aside from the police radio mounted on the dashboard in the wagon, a few of the old-timers liked to use the handful of police call boxes mounted on telephone poles at key intersections. A black telephone provided a direct ring-down-line to the dispatcher.

DPD experimented with hand-held portable radios that were large, heavy and carried in a belt holster. The antenna stretched out 12 inches, but reception remained poor in many areas. Only a few such radios, nicknamed the "brick," were available for trial use. Crew 336 did not carry a "brick," and that was okay with Crawford and other older cops who did not want to be on a short leash.

Whenever Crawford and Baker were outside of the police vehicle, they were on their own and out of radio contact. Crawford was used to it. Other communication options were also limited. A stop by a fire station on the late shift to use the telephone was not welcomed by sleeping firemen. Beat cops had to rely on getting along with storeowners, bar keepers, emergency departments at hospitals, security shacks at large factories and a handful of twenty-four-hour neighborhood gas stations if they needed to use a free telephone.

As Crawford and Baker headed west to the West Third Street Bridge, Baker felt large sweat rings beneath his armpits and wondered, do I have what it takes to do the job out here? Will I get along with my partner?

About two-dozen Negro prostitutes slowly walked along a 10-block stretch of West Third Street as several pimps kept watch over their ladies. Hookers liked to work near the river since a lot of white men, referred to as "tricks," ventured across the bridge. There were plenty of alleys to duck into or rooms to rent for thirty minutes or so in cheap and dangerous whorehouses. The ladies knew how to turn a trick quickly, clean up and get back to the street. Prostitutes often carried mouthwash and a rag to wipe up. Those who spent more time with a client often carried a douche bag and powder. Most hookers carried a straight razor or shortened ice pick in case they had to get violent with some of the crazy men that came their way.

Flashy Cadillacs, Lincoln Continentals and Deuce & a Quarter Buicks (Electra 225s) driven by pimps and drug dealers prowled the streets. The street life was new to Baker. He noticed cold hostile stares from some people. Perhaps the police presence slowed their nighttime activities or they simply did not mask their dislike for cops.

Upon arrival at the Palace Bowling Lanes, there was no sign of a fight. There was the usual large crowd of about fifty men and women out front on the sidewalk. Crawford made a u-turn in the street and came alongside the curb. He knew a few of the folks and asked if anyone knew what happened. A small-time street pimp wearing red bell bottom pants, shiny patent leather shoes and a open collar shirt with long gold chains around his neck approached the driver side of the wagon and spoke to Crawford through the window, "Hey man, there ain't nothin' to it."

Crawford responded, "John-John, What's happenin' tonight?"

Before he responded, the tall thin black man looked at Baker, smiled slightly and said to Crawford, "You got you a rookie tonight?"

Before Crawford could answer, the man named Ernie John-John said there was no fight. "Hey man, it was Carl. Man, you know him. He been drinkin' and he had a athletic fit."

Crawford seemed to know who Carl was and what John-John meant, but Baker didn't have a clue. Crawford laughed and asked if Carl was okay.

John-John said, "They held him down on the ground and put a spoon in his mouth to keep him from swallowin' his tongue, man. He finally calmed down."

John-John asked one more question, "Man, you gonna give my ladies some slack tonight?"

Crawford chuckled and said, "We'll see."

John-John grinned and said, "Aw- shit, man" and he walked back onto the sidewalk.

Crawford could see the puzzled look on Baker's face.

Finally, Baker said, "I've got a question. What is an athletic fit?"

Crawford could not hold back his laughter anymore and answered, "Out here, a lot of things are said differently. John-John meant the man had an epileptic seizure. You know, a athletic fit."

Baker grinned and shook his head. He felt like a fish out of water. Then he asked, "Why does the guy have a name like John-John?"

Crawford replied, "Well, John-John told me that when he was born, his daddy was going to name him John and he was so excited that he stuttered and yelled out JOHN-JOHN and the name stuck."

Crawford laughed at Baker's puzzled face and said, "Stay loose, you'll get used to it." Baker realized he had a lot to learn when it came to street language and how Negroes talked.

Crawford said, "Take a look around every time we stop like this. Get familiar with who you usually see. It'll help you later when you are looking for someone." Crawford pulled away from the curb, very slowly, as he let the presence of the paddy wagon do the talking.

Baker had little exposure to Negroes thus far in his life. He grew up in East Dayton, attended a white-only school and seldom interacted with Negroes. As a police officer, he noticed that many physical descriptions of blacks used in police work were hard to understand. Sometimes suspects were listed as Negroes, blacks, colored males, light-skinned, brown-skinned, dark-skinned or medium-brown skinned. At first, Baker wondered how he would ever be able to recognize suspects based on descriptions of wanted persons. Older cops said physical descriptions of Negro suspects were almost useless; "Colored Male, 20s to 30s, six feet tall, black hair, brown eyes. Shit, that fit half the West Side."

Baker was an amateur artist. He constantly doodled and drew since he was old enough to hold a pencil. He took art classes at the Dayton Art Institute before he joined DPD. Baker determined that if he applied his observation skills of a sketch artist and studied police mug shots, he would recognize individual facial characteristics of Negro and white suspects.

Crawford guided the wagon through high crime areas on West Fifth and Germantown Streets at Five Points. He pointed out bars and flophouses that the police responded to on a nightly basis. The Converted Bar was on a busy intersection called Five Points. Crawford said, "The owner is Sam Slaughter. He knows his customers and will handle the drunks himself when we go in. That's okay by me, but sometimes we have to take a few to jail."

Crawford pulled to the curb and parked on the sidewalk in front of the bar and glanced at Baker, "That's why I'll park the wagon at the front door. Let's stop in and check on the social life."

The Converted Bar was a dilapidated joint in an old one-story frame building that had not seen paint for decades. The customers were poor and most lived close enough to walk to the bar. Drinks were cheap liquor and beer on tap. "You need to see this place. You'll be here a lot," Crawford said.

Both officers grabbed their billy clubs and headed for the front door that stood open due to summer heat and no air conditioning. Crawford paused before they entered. He dropped his cigarette on the sidewalk and crushed it out with his foot in a twisting motion.

The entire bar was dimly lit with a few light bulbs that hung from the ceiling on a single wire. The only other light came from a well-worn and abused jukebox that loudly played B.B. King's song, "Three O'clock in the Morning." The place smelled of stale beer and body odor. The bar was packed with people. Many had been drinking heavily and nursing their painkiller.

The officers were joined by the owner. Crawford introduced Baker to Sam and they shook hands. Sam eyeballed Baker then looked at Crawford and said, "Gotcha' a new one again, huh?" Baker wondered how many times he had to hear that line.

As they walked back to the paddy wagon, Crawford told Baker, "Sam's an okay guy. Whenever he tells you something, it's good. I ain't too hard on him either. Those folks back there in the bar, they gotta' have a place to go, too."

Crawford and Baker decided to do some foot patrol in the area and they walked up and back for a block and stayed close to the paddy wagon. On the way, Crawford cautioned Baker about how things could turn violent quickly on the West Side. He said, "One of the worst stories I've heard was from one of the old timers. It happened in the 800 block of West Fifth Street, back in 1955. It was a hot September night, kinda' like we're having now, when a large crowd of Negroes gathered in front of the YMCA building on West Fifth Street. They blocked streets and shut down traffic. They were pissed off about the murder of a young colored teenager named Emmet Till in Mississippi. They say after he flirted with a white woman, he was kidnapped and murdered by two white guys in Mississippi. They beat him, shot him in the head, tied his body to something heavy and threw him in the river. The white guys were acquitted by an all-white jury. Rumors and news spread through the West Side like wildfire."

Crawford and Baker stood under a street light. Baker listened as the story continued. "The crowd grew bigger as more officers arrived and Negroes poured out of every nook and cranny in the District. Before it was all over, the sheriff's men and all of DPD was there. A lot of tear gas was used and some ass whoopin' happened for sure. The mob got to be about five thousand people, they said. People threw rocks, bottles and firebombs. Finally, after a few hours and about fifty arrests, the mob slowly broke up."

Crawford took a long drag off a cigarette and said, "That shit can happen so fast. We can get caught up in a bad spot before we know what hit us, so be extra careful out here. Things have been extra tense for a long time. Hell, it seems everybody is pissed off about something and they are ready to explode. We don't need that shit here."

Crawford and Baker resumed patrol and the paddy wagon groaned as the oppressive summer heat tested its power train. With every bump and lurch, a dozen pairs of handcuffs that hung near Baker's passenger door by a single chain clanged against the rear of the right front seat. Crawford was used to the noisy racket, but to Baker, it underscored the mission of a wagon crew: to take a lot of people to jail.

With the windows rolled down, Crawford and Baker could hear most everything going on in the street. Patrol tactics in the wagon were different from regular street patrol. Crawford liked high visibility, slow driving in curb lanes. He often paused in front of known trouble spots. Some officers did not enjoy being so visible on patrol. Not Crawford; he wanted to see who was out on the street.

SEVEN

The Hunter

"When daylight is gone, the murderer rises up, kills the
poor and needy, and in the night steals forth like a thief."

—*Job 24:14*

(New International Version Bible)

The driver sat alone behind the steering wheel of a dirty dark brown 1960 Oldsmobile. The paint had worn thin and dull. His face was fixed in a blank, wide-eyed stare that hinted of a troubled mind haunted by dark and disturbing thoughts. It was 2:15 a.m. September 1, 1966. He was parked on South Terry Street on the east side of Dayton, Ohio, beneath a cluster of towering old maple trees burdened by large heavy leaves. He preferred the shadows of the huge drooping trees. They shielded him from the streetlights.

The all-white working class neighborhood was full of houses converted to cheap apartments and sleeping rooms. Emmanuel Baptist Church, with its looming bell tower, stood at the intersection of East Third and Terry Streets. Its presence seemed to call out to sinners and the needy. The church meant little to the lone man. He had his own method to communicate with God. The man had always harbored racist thoughts about Negroes and he was obsessed with hate toward the coloreds. He'd heard about "them" all of his life. Now in the city, the bitter and lonely man was ready to act on his hatred. The hot and humid night was miserable. The air was still. It was like being in a cast iron frying pan and the driver felt like he had cooked all day. The Oldsmobile was not air conditioned, and all four windows were rolled down.

The man's life at age thirty-eight was one of disappointment. Menial low-paying labor jobs were the only work he had been able to land. None provided stability. His co-workers and neighbors thought he was a bland person, a loner, detached and even creepy. He never socialized, not even a bit.

The man often felt out of control, and at times, he believed that God guided his thoughts and actions. The godly commands blocked any feeling of responsibility for his acts.

Life had not dealt him a good hand. Bitterness reigned.

———◄○►———

The man fretted and opened another Pabst Blue Ribbon beer bottle with his church key. He pondered his convoluted thoughts and sank deeper into an angry delusional depression. After the beer bottle was emptied, he placed it in a paper sack along with a few other empties. He opened the car door, dropped the sack in the gutter and got out of the car. A bit unsteady, the man took a leak under the shadow of a tree as he readied himself to do something very important.

He sat behind the steering wheel again and rested his right hand on a long hard object on the bench seat beside him. It was covered with a blanket and he was comforted as he stroked the blanket and started his car.

The driver turned onto the 1500 block of East Third Street and headed west on the four- lane street toward downtown. He went down a quarter-mile-long grade and saw streetlights that glistened straight ahead for miles. Third Street, also known as U.S. Route 35, crossed the entire city, due west, through the heart of town into the West Side, then on to Richmond, Indiana, and points beyond.

As he gripped the steering wheel a bit tighter, the driver looked ahead to his destination. Streetlights lined the path, crossed the Great Miami River and merged into a single blurry line far away on West Third Street.

Aside from patrons that stood outside bars scattered along his route through downtown, there was little activity on East Third Street. All-night squat-and-gobble restaurants were busy. Many of the patrons hoped to avoid a hangover and had a late night meal and strong coffee. Wympee's Fat Boy Hamburger, The White Tower Restaurant, famous for its Double Butter Burger, and The Hot Shoppe, with its counter stools in the window, all hosted the night hawks.

As the driver of the Olds passed through the East Side, he barely noticed the white people, as if they did not exist. His focus was much darker. The vehicle continued on its journey through downtown and passed in front of the DPD Central Police Station at 335 West Third Street. Police cars were parked along the curb lane, but the driver paid little attention. He headed west.

As the Olds crossed the bridge over the Great Miami River, the driver grew more alert despite the beer that flowed through his body. There was an excited anticipation in his heart and mind. As he reached the midpoint crown of the 230-yard long bridge, he knew he was in "nigger-town." He smirked bitterly.

A bulge beneath the blanket on the front seat bolstered the driver's feeling of power as he slowed his car and observed people that walked the streets. *Unlike East Dayton*, he said to himself, *these coloreds are outside, all over the place!* People were loud, drunk and acted like fools; he mulled and curled his lips in disgust.

———◦———

During his young life, the driver hunted with his father in the hills and valleys of the Daniel Boone Forest in Eastern Kentucky. His upbringing included introduction to the best hunting weapon in those parts, a 12-gauge shotgun. He was well schooled on how to chamber a round and how to activate the safety switch at the start of an early morning hunt. He knew the racking of a shotgun was a fearful sound to all prey and warned of impending doom. The man had learned that his aim did not have to be perfect; the pattern of the blast would spread. A relatively close shot at the target still delivered the power to bring down a large animal like a deer or even a man. Death might not have been instant, but it surely came.

Finally, the Olds drifted off West Third Street into a neighborhood. The man adjusted his sitting position. He leaned forward with both hands on the steering wheel at the twelve o'clock position. The driver looked over his knuckles and peered out the windshield. He strained his eyes to see more clearly. He was in his full hunting mode.

The hunter's moves were more deliberate, just as if he was on foot in the woods tracking an animal. He looked for an opportunity to find, aim, fire and kill. He searched for unsuspecting prey, perhaps a vulnerable colored man, alone on the street. The thought of bringing down his victim in a few minutes sent tingling sensations through his testicles. He relished what was ahead. The plain-looking man felt powerful. He would decide who would die.

EIGHT

"Call a Amalance!"

At about 3:15 a.m. September 1, 1966, the hunter drove his Oldsmobile slowly through West Side streets near the Great Miami River. He was acutely aware that his white skin was noticeable as he penetrated black neighborhoods. He tilted the visor down on both sides of the windshield in a futile attempt to hide his pale face. Tall trees along the curbs cast heavy shadows and periodically blocked some streetlight. The vehicle looked ghostlike as it passed in and out of cones of light.

The driver scanned neighborhood streets. He made mental notes of his proximity to bridges he needed to cross to get back to safety on the white side of town when his hunting was over.

Once the driver was familiar with his escape routes, he looked for targets of opportunity. He passed through the business district near Broadway and West Third Streets, about six blocks inside the ghetto. Dozens of black men and women stood alongside parked cars while they talked and openly drank alcohol. Streetlights in front of businesses were bright and the hunter was anxious to get out of such a busy area.

While the white man waited at a red traffic light, a black prostitute approached the Olds on the passenger side and looked in through the open window. The woman was short, heavy, dark skinned and wore a messy blond wig. She wore tight fitting red shorts and a shiny top. The man saw other women on the street corners and he did not like it that so many people saw him, even though they seemed not to care. The hooker placed her right hand on the window ledge and addressed the driver: "Going out tonight, honey?"

He saw her dark skin more clearly and noticed her long red fingernails. The driver instinctively rested his right hand on the object beneath the blanket on the seat of the car. He just stared blankly at the woman. She said, "Half-n-half? $15.00?" The driver looked straight ahead and did not respond. The woman stepped back from the car. The traffic light changed to green and the Olds turned right on West Third Street. As the car disappeared around the corner, the hooker said, "Probably a crazy mother-fucker anyways," and she turned her attention to other white men who circled the block.

As the Olds approached the next intersection, the driver saw a Dayton Police paddy wagon parked at the curb. He saw two white officers on foot. He turned right on South Williams Street and headed toward West Fifth Street to get away from the paddy wagon, lights and so many people.

The Flamingo Pool Hall at Hawthorn and West Fifth Streets was still open at 3:30 a.m. and a half-dozen men engaged in a game of pool as they drank from bottles inside crumpled brown paper sacks. The owner, nicknamed Pops, was a black man in his 60s. He was a large, street-wise man who knew how to handle young bucks who came into his hall. A few drug addicts, already high after shooting up narcotic Paregoric cough syrup, loitered around outside in the alley behind the Flamingo. Addicts cooked the narcotic cough syrup down over a flame in a spoon to a potent hit suitable for injection.

Across the street from the Flamingo Pool Hall was the Clean Kitchen, a run-down walk-up lunch counter that sold cheap meals. A beer and wine carryout and auto repair shop occupied the other two corners. All of the businesses were closed. A few illegal alcohol joints in houses remained open and operated quietly.

At 1022 West Fifth Street, a small storefront church was dark, but its presence was a faint lifeline in the midst of the ghetto. The church name was hand painted on a window: "Christ Holy Temple Apostolic Faith." About fifteen people were outside on the sidewalks as they talked and drank cheap wine and beer. A bootleg liquor joint operated by a man named Lester Mitchell was next door to the church. Like the others, he was outside since it was hotter than hell inside his small place. Mitchell lived in the back of his joint, along a lane called Trash Alley. He swept the sidewalk with a broom as he talked with friends.

The hunter paused at the corner of South Williams and West Fifth

Streets and looked east toward the 1000 block of West Fifth. He saw the black people and his nostrils flared as he instinctively sucked in a deep breath. His opportunity had arrived.

The hunter made his turn east on West Fifth Street. As his right hand rested on the blanket next to him, he drove past the people on the sidewalk. No one paid him any attention and probably thought he was just another white trick looking for prostitutes. The hunter wondered, *Why is a guy sweeping with a broom at this time of the morning?*

The Olds stopped and turned around in the YMCA parking lot two blocks away. The hunter sat quietly as he surveyed the area. He had the implement of death resting on the seat next to him. "I'll teach these Niggers. God told me that I will decide who will die!" he muttered aloud.

The hunter slid the blanket away and exposed his 12-gauge shotgun. He chambered a round, then flicked the safety off. The end of the barrel was sawed off to make the weapon easier to handle in the car. The feel of the weapon stiffened his spine.

The man drove west on West Fifth Street toward the people on the sidewalk. He slowed as he approached the 1000 block of the two-lane street. The Olds crossed the center line about seventy feet behind Mitchell as he swept the sidewalk with his back to the car. Other people outside barely noticed the car as it approached.

At about 3:35 a.m., the thirty-nine-year-old Mitchell felt an uncanny sensation. Danger. As Mitchell turned to his left in response to his gut feeling, a sawed-off shotgun barrel protruded from the driver's side of an Olds. In a split second, the vehicle came within about forty feet of him. Horrified, and with no time to react, Lester Mitchell saw and felt the hot painful blast from the shotgun at the same time. He let out a blood-curdling scream in horror and pain. The left side of Mitchell's face absorbed a terrible barrage of shotgun pellets that entered his body at a slight upward angle since the shooter was seated and the victim was standing. Pellets penetrated Mitchell's eyes and shoved bone fragments into the frontal lobe of his brain. Simultaneously, the left side of his neck, shoulder and upper chest were shredded by shotgun pellets that tore into his skin and muscles. Lester Mitchell collapsed.

The shooter quickly pulled the shotgun back inside his moving vehicle and sped away. He turned onto a side street and headed to the West Fifth Street Bridge and back across the Great Miami River. He disappeared into the hot summer night.

While the sound of gunshots was not uncommon in the ghetto, the sound of a shotgun blast drew attention. People came out of illegal joints and the pool hall and saw Lester Mitchell as he lay on the sidewalk along side his broom. He was barely alive. He bled heavily. His life slowly drained into the filthy gutter.

Someone screamed, "Call the police! Call a amalance! Call a amalance!"

A friend of Mitchell's, Leonard Cantrell, stood on the street not far from Mitchell. He saw a white man in a car with a shotgun barrel that stuck out of the driver's side window. He heard the blast and dove for cover. Cantrell saw Mitchell fall and he yelled, "Some white honkey mother fucker just shot Lester." Immediately he ran to his car that was parked nearby. Cantrell tried to follow the shooter but lost sight of him. Cantrell turned around and went back to where Mitchell was shot.

Even though Cantrell was drinking before Mitchell was shot, his senses were not dulled to the tragedy. He joined the angry crowd that grew frustrated as they waited for the police to arrive.

Rumors of the shooting spread rapidly by telephone calls from nearby phone booths and by phone from the Flamingo Pool Hall. Men from the Flamingo and other bootleg joints ran to their cars and sped away to tell the news. As people flocked to the scene to see what happened, they heard shouts. "A white man just drove by and shot Lester! Mitch wasn't doing nothin'! He was sweepin' his sidewalk and he was shot for nothin' by a honkey!"

Immediately, different accounts of what happened surfaced. Cantrell and others said the shot came from a white man in a moving car. There were several different descriptions of the car, the number of occupants, from one to three people, and different colors and makes of the vehicle. Some said the car had California license plates and others said Ohio plates. Perhaps the darkness, alcohol and drugs and the blast of a shotgun that shattered the hot night caused so many different stories. However, two things the witnesses said were consistent: the shooter was a white male, and he fired a shotgun from his car.

Several men tried to comfort Mitchell and stem the bleeding from his jagged wounds. People anxiously looked up and down the street in search of the emergency vehicle. None was in sight. It seemed like time stood still as they waited for help for Mitchell.

NINE

"Signal 0-0"

Prior to the shooting, the poor crime infested inner-city neighborhood was already like a time bomb that waited to explode. Years of segregation, discrimination, poverty, violent crime and a myriad of social ills had grown worse. The shooting of Mitchell by a white man became the spark that lit a long smoldering fuse.

Amid the confusion, rumors spread that more blacks might be shot by whites. Although a few people ran away, others stayed on Fifth Street. They watched and waited with their concealed "Saturday-night specials." They were ready, just in case "whitey" returned.

The Dayton Police and Fire Departments each operated their own communication centers. Each department had only one main telephone number listed for all calls. The PBX Switchboard Operators sat in a room next to the dispatchers. They were overwhelmed with incoming calls as they plugged and pulled lines as fast as they could transfer calls to the Dispatch Office.

At 3:39 a.m., the first police crews were dispatched to the scene. "Bleeeeeeep!" The high-pitched emergency tone interrupted normal radio traffic. "Crew 331, 332 and District Sergeant 310, go to the 1000 block of West Fifth on a man shot on the street. The suspect is a white male who fired a shotgun from his car, tan in color, and no license number. Fled headed west on West Fifth Street." The dispatcher called Crawford and Baker, "Crew 336? Crew 336?"

The police dispatcher received no answer. The dispatcher wanted to send the wagon to the scene but remembered that the officers were off the air and out on foot at West Third and Broadway. The dispatcher sent all other available police crews to look for the suspect's vehicle. The fire department also dispatched an ambulance and a supervisor.

The first police officers approached the scene and radioed that a large crowd was at the intersections of West Fifth, Shannon, Hawthorn Streets and Trash Alley. People waved and pointed as they directed officers to 1020 West Fifth Street. Officers found a few men who attempted to comfort Mitchell and prop him up. The crowd grew larger and became extremely restless. Some took their frustration out on white police officers and demanded officers "Do something! You pigs wouldn't let a white man lay here like this!"

The sergeant recognized the situation was difficult to control and radioed for help. Within less than a minute, he heard sirens as they drew close to the scene. He was glad to see red emergency lights as backup forces approached from all directions. Officers got out of their vehicles and ran to the scene. They carried their billy clubs and pushed through the crowd.

DPD Shift Lieutenant Bill Stevens responded to the scene and joined the District Sergeant. He directed officers to protect the crime scene as best they could while others worked to disperse the crowd. The police dispatcher informed the Lieutenant that on-call Homicide Detectives, commonly referred to as 'Dick's', had been notified to respond to the scene since initial reports indicated death was likely.

Lieutenant Stevens radioed to the dispatch center. "I need that ambulance now! Check their status!" Almost immediately, Stevens saw red lights as an emergency vehicle approached from the direction of Fire Station No.13 at West Third and Euclid, a dozen blocks away. Stevens ordered officers to surround Mitchell as they pushed onlookers back to clear a path for firemen to bring in a stretcher. Mitchell was close to death. A woman on the street shouted in a shrill voice, "Here comes that damn Cadillac amalance!" The Dayton Fire Department ambulance, a red and white 1963 Cadillac Super Royal Rescuer with its elaborate pointy red taillights and elongated body, arrived with two firemen.

The ambulance crews were trained in advanced first aid, but they had no significant triage training, medications or extraordinary monitoring devices. Dayton's ambulance service was basically "grab and go," and that they did, as fast as they could.

The disorderly crowd grew quickly to over one hundred people on West Fifth Street and police made a few arrests for disorderly conduct, assault and resisting as the situation continued to deteriorate. Bottles and rocks flew toward the police. Among those who threw bottles was Leonard Cantrell, key witness to the shooting. Within moments, a large plate glass window was broken on West Fifth Street. The sound of shattered glass energized the crowd and kicked them into high gear.

Six police officers were ordered to form a ring around as much of the crime scene as they could while other officers continued to hold the larger crowd at bay. Two Homicide Detectives arrived about twenty minutes later, and officers made a path for their cars to get close to the scene. The seasoned detectives looked the part, and, despite the heat, they wore blue sport coats, white shirts and ties. The detectives realized they had very little time at the scene due to rising tension. They knew that it was a drive-by shooting and there was little chance that there would be much physical evidence to collect. Detectives made basic measurements, drew a quick sketch, collected some possible items of evidence and took a few photos with a Polaroid Land Camera. The bright flash from each flashbulb in the night froze stark black and white images of detectives and onlookers in an eerie scene.

The crowd morphed into a large mob that set out to destroy property, loot and attack the police. The mob started north on Shannon and South Williams Streets, toward the West Third Street business district. It was a busy commercial area with around a hundred stores, shops and businesses, mostly owned by whites and Jews. Police feared for businesses like Rubenstein's Furniture, May Company Furniture and the Ohio Loan & Pawn Shop. Large businesses such as The Central Oldsmobile new car dealership and the Gem City ice cream plant were in their path.

The mob threw glass bottles and smashed automobile windshields with metal garbage cans and rocks. A fire was lit in old furniture that sat on a curb for trash pick-up. Even though flames were small at first, the blazing fire in the night was foretelling as it stirred man's primeval behaviors.

Ironically, the destruction of the West Side began on the same street where, decades ago, two brothers and inventors named Orville and Wilbur Wright grew up in a house at 7 Hawthorn Street. They opened their first bicycle shop near West Third and Williams Streets. Their dreams of flying and their craftsmanship in the tiny bicycle shop ultimately liberated the human race from earth's gravity and changed the world for all generations to come.

On the night of September 1, 1966, the same streets once graced by the presence of the Wright brothers were pathways of hate and anger. Streets were littered with broken glass. Lieutenant Stevens radioed police dispatch and ordered all available units to a staging area on the fringe of the trouble area to await orders.

All West Dayton fire stations were placed on active standby. Dayton Police Dispatcher Sergeant Folkereth used a call signal not used since the riot in 1955 as he directed officers to their staging areas. "All cars responding to the West Side, we have a possible 'Signal 0-0' in progress. Repeat, '0-0'. Use caution." Older officers immediately recognized the designation as "race riot." They braced for trouble.

Crawford and Baker were on foot on West Third Street and out of radio contact. They were totally unaware of the shooting on West Fifth Street. They heard sounds of sirens from all directions and saw police cruisers race by and turn toward West Fifth Street. Cars sped by and people ran toward West Fifth Street. Crawford yelled, "Let's get back to the wagon and see what the hell is going on!" Clusters of people gathered in the street: hookers, pimps and motorists. Many were angry and waived their arms and shouted obscenities.

The paddy wagon was parked mid-block on West Third Street. Crawford and Baker were close to it when a car stopped in the street and several black males yelled, "A brother's been killed by a honkey!" A bottle was thrown from the car as it sped away. One man hung from the window and yelled, "Die you fucking Pigs!"

The officers reached their wagon at about the same time they heard the shattering of large storefront plate glass windows down the street. To their rear, they heard crowd noise as it grew louder. The sound of shots echoed on the street. There was no way to tell if shots were aimed at the officers or if fired randomly.

Once inside the paddy wagon, Crawford tried to call dispatch but radio chatter was so heavy he could not get through. DPD had only two radio channels. Channel A was for direct two-way communications with the Dispatch Center that all cars heard simultaneously. Car-to-car communications occurred on Channel B, and it was not recorded. Channel B was also jammed with radio traffic of officers who attempted to coordinate a response.

Officer Crawford drove west on West Third Street, headed away from the mob just as another leaderless crowd swirled around the corner at Broadway and into the intersection and blocked the street. The paddy wagon was pelted with rocks and bottles as it made its way past the surging crowd.

Crawford and Baker finally heard the dispatcher as he told Third District officers to report to a staging area at West Fifth and Conover Streets. When the paddy wagon joined a half-dozen other cruisers, Crawford and Baker heard the story about the Mitchell drive-by shooting by a white man who got away. Crawford muttered to Baker, "We're in deep shit."

At about 4:30 a.m., the Dayton Police PBX switchboard operator received two frantic telephone calls from Baltimore and Ohio Railroad gatekeepers located in two separate towers at West Third Street at Conover and West Fifth Street at Broadway Street. The gatekeepers were terrified as they witnessed the beginning of the riot from their nests. Each man worked in a ten foot by ten foot wooden tower built in 1907. The towers were perched twenty feet in the air on a single pole and afforded a vantage point that allowed gatekeepers to oversee railroad traffic on two sets of tracks. A gatekeepers' job was to operate large drop-down crossing gates when freight and passenger trains occupied the rail crossings at street level at the busy intersection.

A hastily organized group of officers rushed toward the towers. Billy clubs in hand, police rescued the two gatekeepers. Rioters scattered only to regroup a short distance away.

————◦————

Saint Elizabeth Hospital, Dayton's largest Catholic hospital, routinely treated more gunshot wounds than any other hospital in the city. St. E., as it was commonly called, was an imposing structure located in West Dayton on the banks of the Great Miami River at the intersection of the Washington Street Bridge at Cincinnati Street. It was Dayton's first hospital, dedicated August 15, 1868.

In 1966, St. E. was the largest hospital in the city with hundreds of doctors. Nurses wore white dress uniforms, white shoes and stockings and bright white nurse caps with two wings perched atop their heads. Dayton Police officers spent a lot of time at St. E. Routinely, officers used St. E. as a place to eat, take coffee breaks and use telephones to call in crime reports or to call home. Homicide Detectives were known on sight by the Emergency Room trauma staff due to their frequent call-outs at all hours and trips to see crime victims who were near death from stabbings, gunshot wounds or beatings.

The Dayton Fire Department's red Cadillac ambulance pulled into the St. E. Emergency entrance at about 4:20 a.m. A trail of blood dripped beneath Lester Mitchell's stretcher as it was wheeled inside. Doctors immediately assessed his wounds and initiated an endotracheal intubation for suction and oxygen. Mitchell was in grave condition and Surgery was placed on standby. In the gritty world of homicide investigation, detectives generally rushed to the hospital if the victim was still alive and tried to obtain a statement from even gravely wounded crime victims. This often happened in the hospital's trauma room while the medical team worked on the patient. The detectives' goal was to obtain a firsthand verbal statement, no matter how brief, as to circumstances of the violence or the name of any persons responsible. In order for a victim's statement to be admitted into court testimony, the victim had to believe he or she was about to die, and in fact later die. Under an exception to the Hearsay Testimony Rule, called a "Dying Declaration," courts permitted detectives who heard or took such statements to testify about what the victim said.

TEN

Mr. Beu-tell

A living legend: "An extremely famous person, especially in a particular field."

—Oxford Dictionary, *2013*

O n Dayton's north side, an unmarked Dayton Police detective car was parked in a driveway. The house was dark. A yard marker near the front door displayed an 82nd Airborne Screaming Eagle logo that the man inside the house was proud of but seldom spoke about.

A new pink princess style telephone sat on the nightstand in the bedroom. Ring—Ring—Ring—*Ring!* As usual, a tablet and pencil were by the phone. The big man in bed tried to pick up the pink noisemaker smoothly, but his large hands fumbled with the new phone his wife insisted on buying. When he took the dainty phone off the cradle, its handset rotary dial illuminated the dark room and he winced at the bright light. He hated it. He muttered, "Siss, siss, sissy phone."

His headache reminded him of gin and tonics he consumed about four hours earlier at the trendy Tropics Nite Club on North Main Street. Homicide Detective Ralph Beutle, Sr. tried mightily to sound lucid. Detective Beutle was known to criminals and cops alike as "Mr. Beu-tell." He was a living legend, an old-school cop. He had scores of "snitches" all over the city.

"Ye, ye, yeah, Beu, Beu, Be, Beutle here," he stuttered.

"Mr. Beu-tell," said DPD Dispatch Sergeant Folkereth, "It's 4:10 a.m. and all hell's breaking loose on the West Side. We got a male, black, shot at 1020 West Fifth Street, supposedly by a white guy who drove by with a shotgun." Can you go?"

Mr. Beu-tell said "Uh-huh, yeah su,su,sure."

"The suspect got away and there is a large disorderly crowd at the scene," added Sergeant Folkereth.

The big guy scribbled notes, jotted down the time of notification and a few facts. The Sergeant added, "Lieutenant Stevens said you may want to try to get a statement from the victim at St. E. first. A few other Homicide Dicks will go straight to the scene."

Mr. Beu-tell sat on the side of the bed and came out of the fog. As he cradled the pink telephone receiver, he nudged his wife, Jo, as she awakened. "Hon, hon, honey, I got, gotta go. I'll ca, ca, call you later. Go ba, ba, back to sleep."

Jo was used to late night calls from Homicide, missed engagements, a moody man who returned home after he saw untold violence. She never stopped worrying that each time he left home, he may never come back from the streets. The rest of her night was restless.

Beu-tell always left his "call out" clothes at the ready: a pair of grey slacks, a blue summer sport jacket, white short-sleeve shirt and a tie. His .38 caliber Colt Detective Special, with a two-inch barrel and holster fit nicely under his coat along with his handcuffs.

Once inside his detective car, Beu-tell plugged the cord from a portable red emergency light into the cigarette lighter. As he had done many times, he placed the red flashing globe with a magnetic base atop the car's roof with his left hand and sped out of the neighborhood. As his taillights disappeared, Jo stood at the window and peered through an opening in the curtain, watching her man leave again.

On his drive to St. E., Detective Beu-tell listened to heavy police radio chatter about the shotgun shooting and growing crowds. Tense voices crowded the airwaves as police crews urgently called for help on the West Side. He knew this was no ordinary call-out for Homicide. He braced himself for a long shift as he arrived at St. E. at about 4:45 a.m. to check on Lester Mitchell.

Beu-tell's reputation as an investigator was excellent, and he was known far and wide. Beu-tell was a tough man and he used his physical strength in vicious ways, if it became necessary, but he was also a very confident and approachable man. Beu-tell's stuttering was something he dealt with without embarrassment. Cops, criminals and witnesses alike had to listen carefully to Mr. Beu-tell, which meant he had their full attention. His imposing six-foot four-inch ramrod straight frame was softened by his speech pattern. It made him smooth. When Beu-tell spoke, he often began with "Le-mee, Le-mee, see..."

Beu-tell walked past the St. E. Hospital Security Office and directly into the Emergency Room. No one bothered to stop him; Beu-tell was well known to everyone. The detective saw Lester Mitchell on a gurney surrounded by doctors and nurses. The medical team worked frantically.

Beu-tell peered over the shoulder of the senior doctor and saw Mitchell's wounds. The doctor gave a knowing look to Beu-tell and moved his head slightly left and right. Mitchell was going to die soon.

Detective Beu-tell knew it was unlikely Mitchell could speak. Nevertheless, he tried to communicate. He hoped for some sound, grunt or acknowledgement. He donned a white cotton gown over his clothes and left the straps undone in the back. Beu-tell moved close to Mitchell's face and spoke gently.

Beu-tell summed up his questions very well, despite his stuttering. "Lee-me see, te, te, tell me Lester, who di, di, did this to you? Where can I fi, fi, fi, find him?"

The doctors and nurses watched Beu-tell. Everyone around the gurney had seen horrible violent death many times and they paused to watch the big cop tenderly speak to a dying man. After a minute of trying, Beu-tell whispered, "Ga, Ga, God, b, be with you, Le, Les." He gently placed his hand on Mitchell's shoulder, then walked away.

Beu-tell washed his hands in silence. Despite his years of witnessing violent deaths, the big cop was always bothered by senseless murder.

Beu-tell used the telephone in the security office and called the new Chief of Detectives, Captain Grover O'Conner, who was in his office. "Hey Cap, he ain't gon, gon, gonna make it boss, shot in the hea, hea, head. When he dies, the sha, sha, shit will hit the fa, fa, fan." Beu-tell described Mitchell's wounds. They were from a shotgun blast, probably pellets. After the update, Beu-tell grabbed a paper cup of hot black coffee and hit the street.

The old school detective believed there was a short window of time in which homicides were solved. Detective Beu-tell knew the Mitchell case appeared to be a random racial stranger- on-stranger shooting, and it was one of the hardest types of cases to solve.

By 5:00 a.m., Dayton's all night radio stations, WING, WHIO and WDAO FM caught up with the story of a large disturbance that followed a shooting, but information was scant. WDAO radio was one of America's first stations that offered a majority of programming to the black community. It emerged as an important voice for people on the West Side.

The Dayton metropolitan area soon learned of the explosive situation on the West Side. Lester Mitchell was reported as alive but in grave condition. News that a defenseless black man was the victim of a drive-by shooting by a white man touched a raw nerve. It was certain that Dayton would not be exempt from the already broiling racial tensions that spread throughout the United States. The DPD was about to encounter its biggest challenge since it was established in 1873, and it was not well-prepared. In the early morning hours of September 1, 1966, seedlings of hatred and violence matured on the streets of West Dayton and neared full bloom.

ELEVEN

"Burn Baby, Burn!"

"You jus' take an' run," he said, "an' you burn when they
ain't nothin 'to take. You burn whitey, man. You burn
his tail up so he know what it's all about."

—*Quote of a rioter during the Watts Riot*
Los Angeles, California
Newsweek, *August 1965*

September 1, 1966. The early morning sunlight was bright and hot. It trended toward another above-ninety-degree day. There was not a cloud in the sky. Blacktop streets were hot from days of unyielding scorching heat.

There was a brief lull in riot activity during early morning hours. Meanwhile, large crowds gathered and moved about many of the West Side streets, almost at will. Police commanders decided to avoid confrontation with rioters and they backed away and sealed off access to a few areas. City officials foolishly hoped rioters would simply run out of gas; however, the rioting was fueled by beer and liquor looted from stores, bars and drive-thru carryouts that were plentiful on the streets. Drug users traded stolen goods for heroin, narcotic drugs, pills and needles looted from pharmacies, which fueled false courage and whet appetites for more violence.

Daylight revealed the extent of damage to stores, automobiles, warehouses, businesses and neighborhoods. Plumes of smoke were in the air, visible from structure fires in many locations. The Dayton Fire Department, with help from a few mutual aid fire companies outside the city, fought to extinguish fires.

Epicenter of the worst rioting was a thirty-block-long stretch of West

Third Street between the Great Miami River. Dayton Police officers were deployed to dozens of other pockets of trouble throughout the West Side. Unfortunately, wild lawlessness continued and many innocent citizens had to fend for themselves.

DPD held over its night shift and called in all off-duty personnel. Scores of officers reported for duty and flowed through the Central Police Station for assignment. Police radio communications were on primary Channel A, a frequency that was easily monitored by citizens and news media with radio scanners. Only a few officers who were sent out to the streets received a portable police radio.

The DPD was in new territory. Never before were they required to respond to a riot of that magnitude. It was a "gen-u-wine aw-shit" moment. All available police vehicles were in use and teams of three or four officers were assigned to one car. Basic logistics was a major problem impeding timely deployment of officers. The tiny one-lane gasoline station at the Central Police Station was not equipped or staffed to service over one hundred vehicles on twelve-hour shifts. City of Dayton's "bean counters" were slow to support the need to open charge accounts at privately owned gas stations and further delayed mobilization of forces.

Riot helmets were in demand, but Dayton Police did not have enough for even half of the officers. Chief Caylor called upon one of his colleagues, Dr. Will Grossman of Dayton's Federal Civil Defense Agency (FCDA). His agency maintained a large storage facility in the East First Street warehouse district. President Truman established the FCDA in the 1950s for protection of civilians in the event of an enemy attack or an atomic bomb attack by another country. The FCDA amassed emergency food, water, medical supplies, tents, folding cots and air-raid helmets.

After many years of non-use, the heavy, musty, wide-brimmed white steel helmets were in terrible shape with old rotted cloth sweatbands and chinstraps that were ill fitting. Nevertheless, one hundred helmets and other supplies were rushed to the Central Police Station under police escort. The Dayton Police Firearms Armory had an inventory of about one hundred and ten 12-gauge shotguns, but was not able to provide enough for the increased number of officers on the street. Most of DPD's riot shotguns were able to affix bayonets. However, officers were not trained to use a bayonet. One police officer asked a sergeant who handed out equipment, "What are rules of engagement for use of the bayonet?"

The sergeant barked, "Son, get your ass on the street. If somebody needs stickin', stick em'. If he needs a shootin', shoot em." He looked past the young officer and yelled to another in line, "Next!"

The three Dayton Police firearms range officers were all expert marksmen. They were placed on standby as a counter-sniper team. The trio enlisted a few other marksmen in the department and formed two teams so one team could be on duty at all times.

Due to a shortage of shotguns, DPD took another bold and unusual step. They asked a half-dozen pawnshop owners to loan their inventory of pawned 12-gauge shotguns to DPD for assignment to officers on riot duty. The wide assortment of over one hundred old shotguns was more than police expected. Many were in questionable, if not poor, condition. Some officers received old, full-choke shotguns that looked like Jed Clampet's shotgun on *The Beverly Hillbillies* TV show.

Officers were given one of everything: an ill-fitting helmet, a borrowed shotgun and in some cases, a bayonet. It was done in such a hurry, no one signed for anything they received.

In 1966, Ohio State law allowed use of deadly force to stop the commission of a felony. Dayton followed the law and officers generally did not use deadly force in non-violent property crimes. However, shots fired at fleeing stolen cars and burglars were still rubber stamped during normal police operations. "Holy shit," said a sergeant to a commanding officer. "What do we expect officers to do. What are the rules of engagement for shooting at felons?" A tired looking veteran Lieutenant replied, "I don't have a clue, ok! Just you guys get on the street, NOW! Put on a show of force until we figure out what to do!"

Chief of Police Lawrence Caylor made a formal Mutual Aid Request to the Montgomery County Sheriff's Office (MCSO) headquartered in Dayton. The sheriff's office was the second largest police agency in the metropolitan area with about 280 full and part-time officers. Over half were assigned to operate the county jail. The rest were on road patrol and in the detective bureau.

Sheriff Keiter immediately ordered all available personnel to assemble at the Montgomery County Fairgrounds, just east of the Great Miami River and the Stewart Street Bridge. DPD commanders coordinated with the deputies and began an initial deployment. Two groups of about seventy-five deputies were assigned to twelve-hour shifts. Most were assigned to the perimeter of trouble areas and downtown to combat random looting.

A few police officers from small towns came into Dayton's West Side without invitation and caused problems. Most were unaware or did not care how DPD responded to the riot. Some brandished their own personal weapons, M-1 carbines and long rifles, and it was as if they had won a prize for a free day of "ass-whooping some Negroes." That attitude pissed off many DPD officers, and it led to a few shoving matches and explosive arguments. Baker witnessed more than one confrontation when rogue outsider cops were told to leave or they would get their own "ass whooping." Dayton cops had to live with their own use of force decisions and tactics. No outside cop was allowed to come into town, cause problems and then leave with no regard for the consequences.

Cities and townships that surrounded Dayton took action to seal their borders. White upscale cities like Oakwood and Kettering made sure the "colored problem" did not spill over into their area. Roadblocks were set up and heavily staffed with armed officers who checked all cars that contained Negroes. A few yellow and black City Transit buses that ran the routes were checked when they entered suburban enclaves. Middle-aged and older black women who were day workers and a few black men who made it out of the West Side were singled out and questioned. White bus passengers did not receive the same scrutiny. Blacks were used to being looked upon with suspicion by white cops. In the face of heavily armed police, blacks quietly suffered indignation.

Dayton Police officers on West Third Street were confronted with large mobs. They went in and out of shattered storefronts and ran away with anything they could carry. Hit-and-run attacks by rioters spread throughout West Dayton as far away as fifty blocks from the Great Miami River. Westown Shopping Center across from the Dayton Veterans Administration Center was looted. Stores and dumpsters were set afire. Police who responded were attacked with glass bottles, pieces of wood with nails, rocks and bricks torn from the streets. Police fought back as fiercely and violently as necessary. Occasionally, shots were heard. Police had no idea where the shooter was. A few bullet holes were later discovered in police vehicles.

While violence continued and escalated on the streets, the general public and news media believed Lester Mitchell clung to life at St. E. Hospital. Dayton Police officials knew that when he died, the situation on the streets would worsen.

TWELVE

Call the National Guard!

By approximately 9:00 a.m., September 1, 1966, mobs again roamed the streets in large numbers. They took their anger out on their own neighborhoods and business districts. They rebelled against years of real and perceived oppression by a dual system controlled by white and Jewish business owners. Rioters rationalized that they could steal and burn at will and show "the man" they would not be pushed any further.

As police officers entered the riot zone, they saw marauders who destroyed their own area. A veteran officer watched the self-destruction. He said sarcastically, "These dumb shits! They got pissed off and tore up their own backyard. They looted their own neighbors!"

"Who gives a rat's ass?" said another officer. "They can burn the ghetto to the ground for all I care!"

In one effort to stop a violent mob, thirty Dayton Police officers on foot moved slowly down South Williams Street toward West Fifth Street. The officers moved forward in a line stretched from curb to curb and fended off rocks and bottles. They moved a mob of about one hundred rioters back toward West Fifth Street. Two arrest teams followed right behind the police line. Crawford and Baker trailed the entire group of officers in the paddy wagon. If a rioter was targeted for arrest, one of the arrest teams stepped forward and collared the rioter. The prisoner was pulled behind the police line and stuffed in the paddy wagon.

Some rioters saw the tactics of the police and peeled away from the larger drug- and alcohol-fueled mob. They hid between houses and believed they could conceal their location and launched bricks, bottles and rocks over buildings and from narrow spaces between houses. A street thug nicknamed Jiggs was among those who lobbed rocks at the police.

He thought he was safe from sight and capture. Jiggs and others laughed and cursed as they hurled anything they could at the police. Little did they know, two small squads of police moved on foot through the alleys to protect the flanks of officers in the street. With a great deal of energy and revenge, police officers surprised rock throwers from behind.

Jiggs suddenly felt his big afro nearly pulled out at its roots from behind. He was spun around. Then he saw a big meaty-gloved fist just before it smashed his nose and teeth. A cop who was hit several times that day with things thrown at him delivered the blow.

"You son-of-a-bitch!" the cop said through gritted teeth as he smashed his fist into Jiggs' face a second time. He delivered a kick to Jiggs' testicles as he slithered to the ground. Other officers laid wood to rioters who were caught in the same surprising predicament. Most of those rioters were not arrested. Officers shut down rock "snipers" and moved on. They could not afford to bog down in formality of numerous arrests. They had more streets to clear, and, most importantly, they had to watch their brother-officers' back.

As street clearing operations took place all over the West Side, police officers encountered many blacks who did not riot. People stood on porches, in their yards or behind window curtains and peered out. Men and women, young and old watched the sad sight of police and citizens in open combat. At the other end of the spectrum were people who cautiously told police they were glad for protection. Children mirrored the full range of reactions and emotions. Some played as if it was a game, others threw small rocks harmlessly toward the police. Still others cowered and cried or stood and stared with fear on their faces. Unforgettable images and memories were seared into their subconscious.

Baker and Crawford saw faces of elderly blacks who feared loss or damage to their property. One elderly woman valiantly stood on her porch. It was a very small old wooden house on Hawthorn Street, one block from the Mitchell crime scene. She held a broom across her body with both hands. She held up the straw end in the air and wielded it as if it was a weapon. Her bib apron covered her long dress from another era. It was soiled and her white hair was in disarray. She appeared to have endured a long and fearful night without sleep. The woman was in her

80s. She watched as a group of police officers on foot in the middle of the street herded the hostile mob. She screamed at the rioters and police alike, "Stop! Stop! Stop! Please . . . , Lord God, Stop!"

Her head dropped. She was spent. Her body suddenly sagged, bowed over with grief. The broom slid from her feeble hands and fell to the porch. Tears flowed and she collapsed.

Two white Dayton Police officers in the street saw the old woman fall. They broke ranks from the group of officers and ran to her aid. They helped her stand up, then onto an old wooden chair on the porch. In the midst of all the shit going on in the street, an isolated moment of compassion shined as bright as the sun. With smoke in the air from nearby fires, noise and cursing all around, the elderly woman, perhaps only a generation or two removed from slavery, leaned forward in the chair. She sobbed and wailed a sad sound. She was taken into the arms of a cop twice her size. Her worn arthritic hands clutched his blue uniform shirt for dear life as she broke down with grief and fear.

Crawford and Baker drove by and watched the trio on the porch. Both men stared at the sad, yet compassionate scene. The woman's loud wail was like an echo from an ugly past. Given her age and appearance, Baker thought about what she must have seen in her long years on earth. Baker said to Crawford, "You know, she doesn't deserve this."

Crawford did not speak. He turned his face away for a few seconds, as if to gather his thoughts or emotions. He turned back toward the windshield, obviously pissed off, then he growled, "When we get a chance, let's get out of this god-damned wagon." Baker knew what that really meant.

The chance to get out of the paddy wagon was at hand. Suddenly, officers yelled for help over the police radio. They were only a few blocks away on Germantown Street. Crawford was instantly energized and he kicked the wagon in the ass. The old paddy wagon lurched forward and belched blue smoke out of the exhaust. It found new speed.

As the paddy wagon got close, Baker and Crawford saw rioters as they pelted a police car with rocks as officers struggled with a few men. Baker, the rookie, and Crawford, the seasoned veteran, were on the same page. Within seconds, they were on foot with the other offices and waded into the mob. They swung away with their billy clubs until the crowd broke up.

As Baker headed back to the paddy wagon, he felt something wet on his billy club. It was blood. He wiped it off and readied for more.

—◦—

A block from the Lester Mitchell crime scene, Reverend Lowell, pastor of the Hawthorn Street Apostolic Church, protected it as much as possible. The church sat in the midst of the ghetto, just down the street from the Converted Bar. Reverend Lowell and a hand full of black men stood outside and surrounded the small concrete block church. They pleaded with rioters to stop the violence. Some held their Bibles with outstretched arms and yelled to the rioters, "Please stop! In God's name, please stop!"

The Reverend shouted to the paddy wagon as Crawford and Baker drove by, "God bless you officers! We are prayin' for you, too!"

Crawford waved and said to Baker, "There are a lotta' good people out here. It's a damn shame they have to deal with this."

—◦—

Dayton's Mayor, Dave Hall, a small white man in his sixties, and other leaders huddled at City Hall with Dayton Police Chief Lawrence Caylor and other officials to assess the situation in West Dayton. Mayor Hall was a well-known local politician, and he was a successful businessman who owned a chain of dry cleaning stores in the city.

Black community leaders who attended the meeting at City Hall were outraged at the apparent racially-motivated drive-by shooting. The air was hot with complaints and ultimatums. Demands were made for police to retreat from the West Side and allow black leaders to take to the streets and talk people down from their anger. On the other hand, the Police Chief was adamant he would perform his duty and stop the riot with all necessary force.

Black leaders believed that if police addressed two main issues immediately, somehow the riots would stop. Their first demand was for release of five prisoners who alleged they had been "roughed up and falsely arrested" during a disturbance at the Mitchell crime scene. Police were accused of overreaction that started the riot. Chief Caylor angrily denounced the accusation.

The second demand dealt with a long, festering issue. Blacks wanted two Vice Squad Detectives, Bill Riley and Dick Walley, nicknamed Batman and Robin, banned from ever working on the West Side again. While the two detectives were not connected in any way to the riot, they had been the subject of citizen complaints for years. They were accused of police brutality during various vice and narcotics raids.

One example cited as to why Batman and Robin were hated so much was the alleged total violent destruction of Cozey Williams' large illegal bootleg joint on West Third Street after a "buy-bust" three months earlier by an undercover state liquor agent. It was true; there was bad blood. Batman hated Cozey so much that he had a clear glass ashtray in his office and on the bar at his home with a picture of Cozey's face taped to the bottom. Every time he put out a cigarette, he smashed it in Cozey's face and added a few choice words as he did so.

Over strenuous objections by Police Chief Caylor, Mayor Dave Hall agreed to their demand to release the five prisoners immediately, one of whom was a notorious criminal nicknamed Frog. In addition, Mayor Hall agreed to transfer Batman and Robin to the east side of town and banned them from any activity on the West Side. Black leaders immediately went to the streets and spread the word that their demands had been met. It did nothing to calm the rioting.

Police Chief Caylor was not one to air disagreements with the Mayor in public, but he knew he had to set the record straight or lose all credibility as a leader of police officers. The Chief angrily told the *Dayton Daily News*, "The agreements [to the demands] were made, but not by me!"

Rumors spread like wildfire that city leaders made the Police Chief cave in to demands. It was a blow to the rank and file members of DPD and damaged morale of those in the line of fire. Officers were angry about being "stabbed in the back" by politicians. Many officers asked, "What's the use in arresting looters?"

A local powerful black activist, C.J. McLin, Jr., who was planning his first run for the Ohio Legislature, demanded that the Mayor remove police officers from the riot zone. He further pressed and demanded that he and other black leaders be allowed to "go walk the streets and calm the riot." Mayor Hall denied the offer and decided that the ability to end the riot was beyond control of the Dayton Police. McLin was livid.

Mayor Hall then held a meeting with Police Chief Caylor and a few other city officials. The Mayor recalled that Cleveland, Ohio, needed 1,600 guardsmen over eight days to quell riots that began June 18, 1966. Based on Cleveland's experience, and in consultation with Police Chief Caylor, Mayor Hall decided to ask for approximately one thousand Ohio National Guard soldiers.

At about 10:45 a.m., Mayor Hall directed his staff to initiate a call to Ohio Governor James A. Rhodes. A telephone call was made to the Governor's office, but he was not in. The Mayor described his request to the Governor's aide, hung up, and waited in his office for a response. As time passed ever so slowly, Mayor Hall agonized about what the riot meant to Dayton's future.

With the upcoming 1966 governor's election in November, the Governor was glad to attend the Stark County Fair in Canton, Ohio. It took a chain of telephone calls and police radio messages to track him down as he enjoyed his walk among fair goers. Before he was located, Governor Rhodes made it to his speaking engagement with the local chapter of the 4-H Club in a large circular cattle barn. He spoke before a capacity crowd of about 250 people. The Governor was dressed for the occasion in western clothing that related well to farmers and ranchers.

Just as the Governor began to speak, the Ohio State Patrol (OSP) Executive Protection Team supervisor, Sergeant Vincent Sheehan, received an urgent radio message to call headquarters.

Sergeant Sheehan called OSP Headquarters and was patched through to Mayor Hall in Dayton. After he received the verbal request from the Mayor for activation of the Ohio National Guard, Sergeant Sheehan told the Mayor to have DPD send an emergency Tele-Type ASAP to OSP Headquarters to document the request.

When the Governor finished his fifteen-minute speech, he waved and posed for photos as Sergeant Sheehan walked onto the low platform. He handed the Governor a note, and Rhodes knew it was urgent when he saw the tense expression on Sheehan's face. The Governor paused yet he kept a smile on his face so as not to alarm anyone. He glanced at the note.

The handwritten message was simple:

> Riot in Dayton, Ohio. Negroes looting. Negro man near death
> in random shooting from a car early this a.m. by white man.
> Large riot out of control since 5 a.m. Mayor Dave Hall called,
> wants Ohio National Guard activated. Tele-Type on way.

Mayor Hall directed Police Chief Caylor to send a Tele-Type immediately to the Governor through the terminal at OSP Headquarters. The handwritten copy was rushed to DPD records section where a clerk entered the following information on the Tele-Type terminal:

> Urgent. Dayton Mayor Dave Hall declares a Public Emergency.
> Citizens are in violation of the Civil Disorder and Public Riot
> provisions of the law. Rioting began at approximately 4:30
> a.m. September 1, 1966, after a Negro man was shot at random
> in West Dayton by an unknown white man in a passing car
> who escaped. Victim likely to die. All available Dayton Police
> Officers and Montgomery County Sheriff's Deputies are on
> duty. We are unable to control the riot involving thousands of
> people. Looting, fires and criminal assaults are occurring over
> a large area. The general public is at risk. Request activation of
> Ohio National Guard Units to be sent to Dayton to help quell
> the violence. Request approximately 1000 National Guard.
> Dayton Police Chief L. Caylor is the Commanding Officer in
> Charge for all civilian law enforcement operations.
>   Mayor Dave Hall, City of Dayton. (EOM)

The Mayor received word at 12:30 p.m. that the Governor approved activation of several Ohio Army National Guard Units, also referred to as Ohio National Guard, totaling one thousand personnel for immediate deployment. With the commitment in hand, police drove the Mayor to West Third and Williams Streets in West Dayton, one of the worst areas of the rioting and just a few blocks from the Great Miami River. From the intersection, hundreds of people could be seen in the streets. Debris and broken glass littered the area. Plumes of smoke rose in the air. Police surrounded the Mayor. He was visibly shaken by sight of the violence and screams directed at him. "You silly bastard! Go back to your dry cleaner shop before you get shot."

Another shouted, "We gonna' burn this place down."

Mayor Hall was taken aback. As a long-time resident of Dayton and a prominent businessman in the community, the scene cut to his heart. Nevertheless, he performed his duty.

At about 12:45 p.m., as many looked on, Mayor Hall sat in a Dayton Police car equipped with a loud speaker and read the Ohio Riot Act. Although he was nearly drowned out by angry voices from the large disorderly crowd on the street, Mayor Hall fulfilled requirements of the law. He read a proclamation that ordered rioters to "cease and desist" violence and disorder. Further, he declared an "Emergency" as required by law and announced he had asked the governor for the Ohio National Guard. The mob at West Third and Williams Street seemed indifferent at first, but soon many rioters buzzed with surprise that the Mayor had called in the National Guard.

The Mayor's voice cracked with emotion over the shrill tenor of the loud speaker when he added an unplanned and personal message, "Please citizens of Dayton, stay away from this area. I don't want anyone to get hurt or shot." His words rang hollow.

With tears on his face, Mayor Hall got out of the car. He had little time to gather his emotions before he was immediately confronted by Sumpter McIntosh, the well-known black civil rights activist. McIntosh's impromptu confrontation on the sidewalk with the Mayor included C.J. McLin, Jr. and Judge Arthur O. Fisher, who was Dayton's first black judge.

Fisher, a well-respected man, was generally able to bridge divides in the community. He was the son of a shoeshine man. Fisher was no stranger to racial discrimination. He rose to serve with distinction as navigator-bombardier with the all-Negro U.S. Army Air Corps, Tuskegee Airman Group during WWII. Major Harry Book, DPD Field Operations Commander, also joined the group.

The street meeting took an ugly and desperate turn. Mayor Hall and McIntosh argued openly in front of others including reporters from the

Dayton Daily News and the *Dayton Journal Herald* who captured the confrontation. McIntosh, with his white shirt sleeves rolled up and a cigarette in hand, objected to reading the Riot Act and activation of the National Guard. He blamed Mayor Hall. McIntosh said, "This is the city's fault." He spoke loudly again, so others could hear when he added, "You can blame the Mayor and the Chief of Police!"

An hour before, McIntosh met with a number of rioters and talked down the violence, but it did not work. Some of the men who attended the meeting at McIntosh's West Third Street office near the riot area abruptly left the meeting and returned to their acts of destruction.

Mayor Hall angrily responded to McIntosh, "Some of those same people left your meeting and went back to looting right away. You, sir, have no control over the rioters!"

That infuriated McIntosh who waved his arms wildly and proclaimed, "How can I control them?"

Mayor Hall snapped back at McIntosh, "Precisely! We did what you asked and it didn't work! We did all we could."

McIntosh retorted, "I am holding Dayton officials responsible for the riot!"

Judge Fisher edged to the police perimeter and held his arms high. He called out to the mob, "Citizens of West Dayton, please leave punishment of wrongdoers and the murderer of Mitchell to the law." The air was thick with pent-up hate and profanity. Fisher's plea for calm was drowned out.

Roiling violence in the streets grew more dangerous and spread rapidly. Sumpter McIntosh angrily disagreed with Judge Fisher and defiantly shouted, "No! The people should arm themselves!" McIntosh's words were so startling, the group stopped talking for a moment.

Police Major Book stood near the group and listened to Hall and McIntosh argue. He heard McIntosh bitterly announce that people should arm themselves. Book had heard enough.

He forcefully interjected himself into the conversation, "Gentlemen! I will not stand here and listen to calls for people to arm themselves. The decision has been made. The Guard is coming." Major Book emphatically added, "The Chief of Police *will* control the rioters and with the help of the Guard, we'll get this under control. That's it!" Major Book then looked straight at McIntosh and said, "I ask you to help if you *can* help to control this. If you choose not to help, I'll take it from here."

McIntosh did not respond. His non-answer spoke volumes to Major Book and the others. Unfortunately, command and control of police operations and morale on the streets was already weakened by political interference and rumors. Those who heard the Major probably did not like what he said, but it was clear. Major Book followed the Chief's orders to clamp down on the streets in preparation for arrival of the Ohio National Guard.

As conversations between Mayor Hall, McIntosh, Major Book and others continued, looting erupted anew on West Third Street. Hundreds of people swarmed stores and businesses within clear view of officials on the sidewalk. Police officers were prepared to fire weapons toward the charging rioters, but they were immediately ordered to "Hold your fire. If you can't hold your position, back off."

A *Dayton Journal Herald* newspaper reporter, Ann Heller, was told by Dayton Police officers, "Outside interference by amateurs, particularly those in City Hall, seriously hampered police efforts to control rioting."

Heller reported, "The criticism from high commanding officers to the patrolmen on the street was followed by charges that control was wrestled away from police."

A high-ranking officer complained over the police radio, "There's *NO* word from the top."

Another replied, "I have no idea who's runnin' the show. Everyone has been left to his own devices."

Captains, lieutenants and sergeants in the field decided not to wait any longer for orders from "on high." They decided to act as commanders, and they took necessary actions to protect their men as they saw fit.

The die was cast. Roles were muddied. A path forward had been chosen. A riot had been legally declared and one thousand Ohio Army National Guard troops were on the way to the West Side.

THIRTEEN

All Hell Is Breakin' Loose!

"At Third and Williams, the street was full of colored
people throwing bricks and bottles—anything they
could get their hands on. I drove right into it. The
first thing hit the right door. I ducked down as far as
I could. The next one hit the windshield and broke it.
Then one connected with my jaw."

—Charles Stockdale, truck driver
The Dayton Daily News
September 1, 1966

Activation of the Ohio National Guard on September 1, 1966 to help
quell violence was the second time in Dayton's history. The other
time was in 1948, during a bitter and violent three-month long labor strike
at Univis Lens Company in Dayton. The strike grew so large that Governor Thomas J. Herbert sent several hundred Ohio National Guardsmen
to the strike zone.

Pursuant to the request of Mayor Hall and the order of Governor
Rhodes of Ohio, Ohio National Guardsmen were notified by their commanders to report to their respective unit headquarters to prepare for
deployment to Dayton. Most members came from small communities
within a one-hundred-mile radius of the City of Dayton.

Sudden activation required time for each guardsman and commander
to notify employers, adjust to the impact to their families and prepare
themselves for deployment of unknown duration and risk. A lengthy
checklist had to be completed before guard units could leave their respective armories. Although much had been pre-planned, it still took time to
arrange logistics for a riot mission. A great deal was required for a military

bivouac to be self-sustaining, including food, medical support, communications gear and tons of equipment. Jeeps, trucks and other vehicles that had been in storage were prepared for a stay of a week or longer. Weapons and ammunition had to be transported and tracked for accountability. While response by the National Guard took shape, a serious change occurred in Lester Mitchell's medical condition at St. E.

———◄◇►———

September 1st, at 7:55 p.m., sixteen hours after being shot in the 1000 block of West Fifth Street, Lester Mitchell died.

St. E. Nurse Sierschilla went into a private office and made a telephone call. She contacted the DPD operator and left a message for Detective Beu-tell to phone her right away. Within minutes, the phone rang and she told the detective that Mitchell had expired. She did not call the Montgomery County Coroner's Office, which was the required protocol. The nurse knew that she had violated procedures, but the police insisted that she *not* call the coroner.

Two hours later, the on-call coroner investigator, B.E. Tumblison, heard unconfirmed rumors of Lester Mitchell's death at St. E. Since he had not received official notification, he was concerned that St. E. had not followed the law on required notification of a violent death. While Tumblison understood the desire to delay publicity of Mitchell's death, he chose to do his job by the book. Tumblison documented events for his report to the Coroner, Robert Zipf, M.D. Investigator Tumblison's notes stated,

> On 9-1-66 at 9:45 p.m. the below signed investigator contacted St. Elizabeth Hospital re: the demise of the aforementioned (Mitchell). I had received information that the deceased had expired. I talked to NURSE SIERSCHILLA and she advised that the Dayton Police Dept. was contacted and they advised the hospital not to tell anyone that the deceased had expired. The Dayton Police advised them that they would contact our office. As of this report, I've received no word from the Dayton Police Dept. re: the demise of Mitchell. Respectfully submitted, B.E. Tumblison

Investigator Tumblison was required to make formal notification of Mitchell's death to his next of kin. He searched for nearly three hours and tracked down Lester Mitchell's mother, Mrs. Eckles, who lived in Ann Arbor, Michigan. The sad message was delivered by Ann Arbor Police.

Dayton Police and the local media outlets agreed to delay the story of Mitchell's death for another six hours so rioters would not be further inflamed as nighttime approached. The purposeful deception carried significant risk as police deflected questions from black leaders about Mitchell's condition.

———◄○►———

Traditionally, the first weekend of September marked the beginning of a long Labor Day holiday weekend in Dayton. Public schools normally commenced classes the day after Labor Day, which was September 6. As a precaution, classes were cancelled in advance. The Dayton School Board was concerned about potential mini-riots in schools on the West Side. The board was particularly concerned about Roosevelt High School on West Third Street that served a population of black and white students. It was one of the largest high schools in the region. Roosevelt had a rapidly declining white student population. Even though at first glance it appeared to be an integrated school, Roosevelt was deeply segregated with separate athletic programs and separate gymnasiums and swimming pools. Separate proms were also mandated. Even within Roosevelt High School, there was a dual education system—one for whites and one for blacks with second class standards for blacks. When compared to white high schools in the rest of the City of Dayton, lower standards existed for blacks. White schools had better buildings, the most recent textbooks, new equipment and plenty of supplies, an overall superior educational opportunity for white students.

Black schools attracted fewer high quality white teachers. Buildings were old and in need of repair. Textbooks were outdated hand-me-downs from white schools, and many had pages missing. It was not uncommon for blacks to find books defaced with derogatory racial comments such as "niggers," "Go back to Africa," and "Can you read this, shine boy?"

———◄○►———

Rioting continued into the night of September 1st. Looters employed hit and run tactics. They gathered in large crowds at intersections and blocked streets with debris and abandoned vehicles. Police moved in and cleared and occupied the area as long as they could.

Police swept through the West Side and closed illegal alcohol bootleg joints and gambling houses to cut down on gathering places and availability of alcohol and drugs.

The message was, "Close, now! If we come back and you're open, we'll bring the paddy wagon and everybody goes to jail." Despite the dragnet approach to shutting down illegal joints, some dealers still found a way to sell alcohol and illegal drugs. The damage to some illegal joints at the hands of police was substantial, but complaints were not likely. Old-time bootleggers knew if they complained, the police would come back with a vengeance.

"Let 'em call the Mayor or Sumpter McIntosh," dared one detective as he left Big Man's bootleg joint in shambles. The detective clutched the necks of two unopened cold beer bottles between his fingers as he walked out.

◄○►

Under command of the Ohio National Guard General Erwin Hostettler, Battalion Commanders Colonel Thomas Mulcahy, Colonel Edgar Griton and Colonel James Clem led the forces to Dayton. They assembled a force of one thousand men on short notice to work in an unfamiliar city on twelve hour shifts. It was a daunting task. Their base camp settled on the five hundred acre grounds of the United States Veterans Administration (VA) Center at West Third Street and Gettysburg Avenue.

Some guardsmen had to make personal sacrifices to meet their obligation. Sergeant Olan Rohrer had already bought several kegs of beer for his bachelor party. He was scheduled to be married in a few days. Although he was pissed off when he received his activation notice, his "supportive" friends happily offered to "take care of his beer" during his deployment.

Captain Ray Trickler, Battery Commander, had finished his production line shift at a local plant when he received an urgent telephone call. The Captain was notified of his activation and told to pick up his equipment at the Dayton Armory. As he drove on West Third Street near Gettysburg

Avenue in route to the armory, Trickler got a taste of the violence that spread throughout the city. He told the *Dayton Daily News*, "A car with five Negroes in it bumped my car in the rear. I didn't bother to get out to see what damage was done, I just kept going," he said.

———◄○►———

Word spread quickly about activation of the National Guard for a riot on the West Side of Dayton. Many soldiers responded from nearly all-white small towns and farming communities in counties adjacent to Montgomery County such as Miami, Darke and Preble. Many guardsmen called their relatives and neighbors and told them the routes and times they would convoy to Dayton. Activation of forces from rural areas was the biggest thing to happen in the region in anyone's memory. Virtually everyone knew a guardsman. Farms and businesses stopped work as people wanted to see the convoys. Main routes out of surrounding rural counties were soon lined with people in cars, pickup trucks, farm tractors and hay wagons as they watched the troops pass.

Children were excited and adults felt a mixture of fear and pride as they waited for first sign of the convoy. Some elderly veterans quickly found their old military uniforms in attics and dusty trunks and wore whatever still fit. American flags were mounted hastily along the road.

While most white guardsmen and their families had little, if any, regular contact with blacks, they believed the West Side was a dirty and violent place, commonly referred to as "nigger town." Despite racist views of the West Side, some white men, old and young, had dark secrets about going to the West Side without knowledge of their parents, wives, children and ministers. A good number of the soldiers couldn't help but think about their secret trips to the West Side for sex with black prostitutes. It was true that major parts of the West Side were high crime areas, but not enough to deter a lone white man or a group of guys out on a drunken night in the "big city" of Dayton. Men looking for a "good time" could leave home and be sitting at the corner of West Third and Broadway in about ninety minutes or less. Pimps like John-John relied on white men from out of town.

With dirty secrets fresh in mind, some guardsmen had a hard time holding their heads high as they passed by their proud neighbors on the same route they secretly took to the West Side a few nights a year. A few soldiers who were regular visitors to the black side of town hoped they would not be recognized as a trick.

———◦———

Over 150 jeeps, troop trucks and scores of other military vehicles rushed toward Dayton. The OSP provided escorts.

At the VA campsite, commanding officers immediately prepared for incoming units. The 371st Sustainment Brigade assessed the VA grounds and modified their plans to accommodate power generation, water, fuel depots, latrines, vehicle maintenance and erection of tents. Communications networks were established and space was made ready to receive and safely store weapons and ammunition. Unit commanders were briefed by the general's command staff and assignments were made. An advance team immediately began liaison with Dayton Police on deployment plans and rules of engagement. Dayton Police planned to assign an officer with each team of soldiers to provide local knowledge and coordination.

At 11:30 p.m. on September 1st, the first platoon of Ohio National Guardsmen traveled under escort by Dayton Police to DPD Command Post at the rear of the Central Police Station in downtown. Although the first deployment was small, it had an exclamation point. A Browning Model 1919 .30 caliber light machine gun was mounted on a tripod on the hood of the lead jeep. The belt-fed weapon was loaded.

FOURTEEN

Back To Square One

At about 1:30 a.m. Friday, September 2, 1966, a plain black Cadillac hearse backed into a parking space at the rear of an old two-story barn-like building. It was escorted by two Dayton Police cruisers that parked a short distance away. Officers kept a watchful eye on the delivery. Two men, who wore dark clothing, got out of the vehicle and opened the large rear hearse door. They removed a gurney that carried a body covered by a white sheet and pushed it up to a set of double doors.

The partially faded sign above the doors read in bold black letters, "Montgomery County Coroner's Office." A very bright light bulb with a metal shade hung over the rear entrance to the building. A man in a white wraparound smock with three-quarter length sleeves answered the doorbell. The double doors opened slowly and the gurney was rolled inside.

The man in the smock was Larry Cushman, one of three dieners on staff. His job was to receive bodies and ensure proper handling and preparation of a corpse for autopsy. In known or suspected criminal cases, he took precautions to protect traces of physical evidence. Cushman was also qualified to assist the pathologist with autopsies as he weighed organs and dissected samples.

The Montgomery County Coroner's Office and Morgue, located behind the large Miami Valley Hospital near downtown, was in need of repairs. Many people passed by the morgue each day but did not realize what macabre work was performed inside. The coroner, Dr. Robert Zipf, an elected official, tried for many years to obtain funds for a new facility. He saw the need to improve their ability to determine time and cause of death and he advocated for more advanced toxicology and laboratory analysis. However, no technology could replace skilled hands and observations of an experienced pathologist and coroner.

The gurney was rolled into a large holding area where the diener reviewed paperwork sent along from St. Elizabeth Hospital. A coroner's ID tag was attached to the big toe of the body's right foot. Other bodies were in the holding room, some ready for pick-up by funeral homes, and some awaited toxicology results. There were others simply parked until the day shift came in. At any given time, there were usually thirty or more bodies in the building.

Two gurneys were parked along a corridor that caught the attention of one hearse driver. Two mangled and unidentified bodies were concealed beneath white sheets that were soiled with rusty colored stains. A strong burnt odor wafted in the air.

The driver asked the diener, "What the hell happened with these?" as he pointed to the two bodies.

The diener answered without looking up, "DPD Homicide's got a hold on them. Two men were mixed up in arson at a warehouse. They accidentally set themselves on fire!"

Beneath the loose cover sheets were twisted and grotesque bodies on their backs. The heads jutted forward, arms bent and knees thrust upward. The hearse driver was fascinated with the odd positions of the bodies that poked upward beneath the sheets. He said, "Hells bells, those SOB's must have been boxing before they died!"

The diener laughed and said, "Who do you think won the fight? Let's look!"

He suddenly yanked the sheet off one body and the two hearse drivers gasped and stepped back. The blackened body was hideous. Any skin left on the torso looked like a blackened hotdog left on a charcoal grill far too long. The skull was void of hair. The eye sockets and teeth protruded from the skinless face. Organs that were somewhat protected in the mass of the body's thick trunk had burst open and burned in sections. Fluid seeped from the organ cavity onto the bottom sheets of the gurney and collected into pools of brownish coagulated liquid. Several fingers, cooked away in the fire, were totally missing from the hands.

Suddenly the hearse driver made terrible noises and doubled over,

"Urrrh! Urrh! I can't hold it!" He puked all over the floor. He slipped in his own vomit and fell against the gurneys as he accidentally touched crispy tissue when he stumbled.

The diener laughed at his own practical joke until he realized he had to hose off the slimy vomit that covered the floor. "Holy shit! Can't you guys take a joke?"

Without saying another word, the hearse crew got out of there as quickly as they could. A single set of vomit footprints trailed out the door.

———◄○►———

Lester Mitchell's autopsy began at 9:00 a.m. Pathologist James Funkhouser, M.D. paused a moment and narrated his initial observations of the body. The body was placed on its back on a stainless steel examination table, tilted slightly so body fluids drained away at one end. A faucet at the opposite end of the table was used to rinse body parts or wash blood and small pieces of human debris away. Various size jars, bottles and labels were ready for collection of specimens and organs as needed. Surgical knives and a variety of saws and clamps were pre-positioned. Two coroner investigators attended the autopsy along with a staff photographer. Traditionally, a homicide detective attended all crime-related autopsies. This was one of the most important cases of the century in Dayton, yet strangely absent was anyone from the Dayton Police Homicide Squad.

From the beginning to the end of the autopsy, Funkhouser dictated as he examined the body from head to toe. He used a microphone that hung directly above the autopsy table and described each step in a clear but matter-of-fact tone, and the diener assisted with the organs and collection of tissue samples. His comments were recorded on a RCA cassette tape recorder that sat on a nearby counter.

When Dr. Funkhouser first observed the body, it was clad in a hospital gown with a Curlex bandage around the upper face and eyes. The doctor made the first autopsy opening of the body with two incisions that began at the shoulders and converged in the upper chest area. A third incision was made down to the pubic bone area. He carefully went around the naval. When connected, the three incisions permitted easy access to the entire chest cavity and exposed internal organs. The ribs were cut open at the sternum with a large tool that looked like an outdoor pruning tool. Individual ribs were clipped loose and pulled apart to completely open the chest. Dr. Funkhouser read the identification tag, reciting all identifying information: "Male, Negro, Name: Lester Mitchell." He noted that Mitchell was short in stature and weighed an estimated 210 pounds. The doctor's monotone voice continued:

> Head and Facies: There are fifty-eight abrasions and pellet (puncture) wounds of the face, left neck and left shoulder area. The most concentrated area involved the left side of the face. There are a few pellet wounds of the forehead with a few involving the right side of the forehead, cheek and nose. There are several pellet wounds of the left eye with puncture of the globe and collapse of this eye.

The autopsy continued until the entire body was examined and the Final Pathological Findings were noted:

1. Shotgun wound to left face and shoulder with:
   (a) Fracture of both orbital plates.
   (b) Laceration, hemorrhage and edema of brain with pellet tracts (two), left cerebrum
   (c) Left neck hemorrhage
   (d) Laceration of left eye

Cause of death: Cerebral anexoria, cerebral hemorrhage and edema due to shotgun wound to the head, homicide. The Certificate of Death listed Lester Mitchell, Negro Male. Age 39. Date of Death, September 1, 1966.

———◦———

As morning broke over Dayton's skyline Friday, September 2nd, the blazing sunrise dawned on a wounded city. The entire city was gripped in uncertainty as the Labor Day holiday period approached. Radio and TV stations announced Mitchell's death, and, as predicted, it inflamed emotions and fear.

The Today Show, a national morning television show, broadcast a story about the Dayton riot and added it to the list of cities around the U.S. in the midst of riots.

A dozen Dayton detectives worked around the clock trying to find the vehicle or person responsible for shooting Lester Mitchell. Detectives wrestled with possible motives. Was Mitchell the victim of a hit? Was this a random murder? If so, was racial hatred the motive? Aside from the pellets and a shotgun shell wadding recovered from Mitchell's body, there was little physical evidence to go on.

Unlike many homicide investigations within a racial group, when a suspect is identified or an arrest is made within twenty-four hours, the Mitchell homicide presented a greater challenge. A white-on-black drive-by shooting, especially in the heart of the ghetto, was not a run-of-the-mill crime for Dayton. Detectives could not recall any similar crime. Due to the riot, detectives were unable to connect with many of their black informants. Their white snitches knew nothing as most avoided dealing with blacks. Eyewitnesses were certain that a white man fired a shotgun from a moving car. Without basis, some detectives were skeptical that a white man was the suspect. They discounted the witnesses and believed some were covering for a black suspect. The reality was that no solid leads turned up. It was as though the killer was an invisible ghost. Homicide Detectives could not move beyond square one.

FIFTEEN

Fix Bayonets

By 9:00 a.m., September 2nd, after word of Lester Mitchell's death spread, rioting became more vicious. Rioters chanted Mitchell's name and threw rocks, looted and set fires. Words spray painted on several burned-out buildings focused anger. "Les was killed cause he was black!" Rumors circulated that police delayed telling the public of Mitchell's death as part of a cover-up. Police officials realized the short-term gain by delay of the announcement only added to distrust of DPD.

Carloads of young black males adopted a new tactic; intersections were blocked by hastily erected barricades. Some motorists, mostly white, were car-jacked. Delivery trucks were hijacked and taken to isolated locations and emptied. Everything was stolen, no matter what it happened to be, from cupcakes to car parts.

Dayton hospitals received scores of injured patients. St. E. bore the brunt of the surge and recorded over sixty people with injuries in the first twenty-four hours of the riot. Some claimed they were injured by police billy clubs; others were treated for exposure to effects of the Triple Chaser CS Gas tear gas canisters used by DPD to disperse large crowds.

Numerous patients were injured when they looted stores. Doctors treated severe gashes and wounds in arms, hands and feet caused by broken plate glass store windows and glass display counters. Eight people arrived with gunshot wounds as a result of wild random shootings on the streets. Miami Valley Hospital, located just across the Great Miami River from St. E., also received about thirty patients with similar injuries. Dayton Police officers did not escape injury. A dozen officers required treatment for cuts, bruises and concussions; two had broken bones. Many other police officers tended to their own minor cuts and bruises and chose to stay on the street.

Residents in white neighborhoods close to the Great Miami River and Wolf Creek feared blacks had crossed the bridges into downtown and into East Side neighborhoods. Scores of police officers were diverted to white areas to handle calls. Carloads of white youths became vigilantes and scoured for blacks who might cross the river. Some adults who openly brandished shotguns, rifles and handguns on the streets were arrested.

———◦———

Local criminals capitalized on looting underway on the West Side. They traded loot for drugs. 'Fences' managed to operate for a while as they took in jewelry, tires, fashionable clothing and anything they could turn for a good profit. Detectives tried to disrupt the trade and raided every 'fence' they knew of. Doors were kicked in and brute force was used if anyone resisted. Narcotics Squad Detectives focused on hard-core rioters who were drug addicts. As carloads of detectives fanned out, they played out a narc's dream to clean up the streets.

A veteran narcotics detective coined a popular phrase on that special 'ass-kickin' day. *"No Search Warrant? No problem!"* Detectives loved the freedom to do as they saw fit, to whom they saw fit, in a manner they saw fit to shut down drug traffic.

Over the eight hours that followed, more than twenty-five drug sweeps struck like bolts of lightning. Detectives hit the West Side hard. The narcs also branched out and performed impromptu raids on the East Side and in Dayton View as they conducted raids they had been itching to make. DPD command staff turned a blind eye and ignored technicalities of lawful search and seizure requirements. Even though the narcs conducted violent and destructive raids, many neighbors were happy to see the dope houses raided. Some residents came out of their homes, applauded and waved to the detectives.

———◦———

Dayton Police and the Ohio National Guard achieved full deployment by 1:00 p.m. on September 2nd. The deployment plan, supplemented by the county sheriff, included police officers, deputy sheriffs and guardsmen.

They were split into twelve-hour shifts. Even with all their manpower, authorities could not cover all of the trouble areas.

Rules of engagement for the National Guard were not consistent at first. Some guardsmen were not permitted to load their weapons. They were ordered to carry ammunition magazines in their pockets. However, for a period of time, Colonel Crim ordered his men to load their weapons. He told an *AP* reporter, "Guardsmen are armed and will shoot if fired upon."

The sight of loaded .30 caliber machine guns mounted on the hoods of jeeps scared the hell out of many would-be snipers.

————◄o►————

At a checkpoint at Germantown and Euclid Avenue, DPD officers blocked the street. One officer, "Big John" Heck, wore a helmet and carried a Model 12 Winchester shotgun that was fully loaded and mounted with a fixed bayonet. He was an imposing sight at 6'5" and 260 pounds. He stood his post and stopped traffic at the roadblock.

Around 9:00 p.m., a vehicle approached the roadblock and a black man got out. He said he needed to pass through the roadblock. Sergeant Sam Morris, who manned the post with Big John, said to the motorist, "Sorry sir, this street is closed; you cannot pass."

"Well," the man muttered belligerently, "I'm coming through anyway."

Officer Heck stood nearby with his shotgun at port arms. Heck saw the man suddenly grab Sergeant Morris' shotgun and try to wrestle it away. Heck yelled, "Holy shit, damn!" He got behind the man as he continued to try to take Sergeant Morris' shotgun. Heck pointed the bayonet at the man's ass and pushed it into one ass cheek and the attacker screamed bloody murder. He immediately let go of the sergeant's shotgun and was arrested without further incident. The man was transported to St. E. to attend to the very bloody and painful two-inch stab wound to his "non-compliant ass."

Bystanders and cops alike saw the bayonet incident. Word traveled fast on the street that "Those Dayton Police are crazy. They'll stab your ass!"

Officer Heck, normally a gentle and peaceable person, immediately came to the aid of his sergeant. He handled a dangerous situation. For weeks afterward, officers joked that Big John "made that guy's asshole a bit bigger" with the bayonet. Police humor told the story a different way. "Got a hemorrhoid? Don't see a proctologist! See Dr. John; he can fix ya'!"

A few blocks away from Big John's decisive action, a large mob turned ugly in a confrontation with a white business owner. At Germantown and Williams Streets, numerous stores were attacked by rock-throwing looters. They attempted to start a fire at the rear of the R&K Market on the corner to force the owner outside so they could loot his store. All surrounding businesses had already been looted. The only one that remained was the market, occupied by the owner, his wife, three sons and a few friends. They were determined to protect their store. The owner and his small army were armed with shotguns and handguns. Shots had been exchanged earlier, and it was a standoff with the looters.

Crawford and Baker parked the paddy wagon near the scene. They were joined by a dozen other officers who were ordered to take back the intersections and restore order. Crawford carried a 12-gauge shotgun. Rioters encircled the location and were perched on rooftops and hid between buildings. Rocks rained down on the officers. A large street light arched out over the intersection and illuminated the entire street. It made the police an easy target. Rock throwing continued and Crawford yelled to the sergeant, "Let's shoot out the light!"

The sergeant responded, "We're under orders not to open fire."

Crawford, in his southern drawl said to Baker, "Hooorrrsse shit! We're not going to stand here and take these rocks like pigeons."

When the sergeant moved away, Crawford looked up at the bright street light and shouldered his shotgun. He took steady aim and fired one round. He quickly racked his weapon and fired again. The entire street light standard exploded and crashed to the street. The intersection was immediately plunged into darkness.

The sergeant yelled, "Who fired that shot?" His question was drowned out by cheers from the cordon of officers on the street. The sergeant knew it was the right thing to do. He let it drop and decided he would just take his ass chewing by his lieutenant later.

The shotgun blasts echoed off the street so loudly, rioters immediately stopped throwing rocks and scattered like rats. Crawford reloaded and said, "I guess all those years of runnin' and huntin' wild hogs and chasin' varmits up trees down home paid off tonight." Baker and Crawford laughed so loud it hurt. It felt good to take control of a small piece of turf.

On September 2nd and 3rd, deployment by the Ohio National Guard was in full swing. The total number of guardsmen, Dayton police officers and sheriff deputies peaked at 525 per twelve-hour shift. The remaining Ohio National Guard forces comprised a reserve force, command and control staff, logistics and bivouac duties.

Sunday, September 4th, the Ohio National Guard reduced its numbers to three hundred soldiers on each shift; the number continued to decline as the days passed, and order was restored.

◄o►

During the first two days of riots on the West Side, over 175 people were arrested and booked in jail. A large number of juvenile offenders were arrested, but because the juvenile detention facilities were overcrowded, many were released for later hearing dates. The city and county jails were barely able to cope with hundreds of arrests that were coupled with their normal jail population in custody prior to the riots. The Dayton Municipal Court and the County Common Pleas Courts worked double shifts to formally charge and prosecute arrestees.

◄o►

The riot of 1966 proved to be a turning point for the City of Dayton, and more so for blacks. Previously isolated by the river and its twelve bridges, major portions of the West Side were reduced to shells of what they used to be. Nearly fifty blocks of West Third Street, the main artery on the West Side, suffered damage. A dozen other business districts on the West Side had been hit hard as well. Those core areas provided the majority of retail goods and services. After the riot, blacks had fewer places to go for their everyday needs.

◄o►

The riots left deep scars, but, the determination to gain equality for black people was hardened with the urban conflict. The desire to rise up in the face of discrimination grew stronger. America, including Dayton, could no longer ignore the powder kegs in cities.

SIXTEEN

Laid To Rest

Six days after a drive-by sniper murdered Lester Mitchell, the Chapel at Loritts Funeral Home at 3924 West Third Street grew quiet. Reverend James Flannigan, the pastor of Wayman AME Church, rose and addressed the congregation. He spoke to nearly two hundred people who came to celebrate Mitchell's life and to mourn his death. Soft whispers were exchanged. Several older black women dressed in white nurse's uniforms stood scattered throughout the sanctuary, volunteers ready to attend to anyone who needed assistance.

The large crowd strained the old window air conditioners. It was extremely warm inside the sanctuary. Movement of many hand-held fans stirred the air and provided scant relief. The prayerful face of a bearded white Jesus was on one side of the fan and Loritts Funeral Home on the other.

Reverend Flannigan opened the service with his head bowed in a brief silent prayer. He then quoted Carl Sandburg's poem, "Prayers of Steel," as the centerpiece of his message.

> Lay me on an anvil, O God.
> Beat me and hammer me into a crowbar.
> Let me pry loose old walls.
> Let me lift and loosen old foundations.

Reverend Flannigan said, "I predict a new foundation of better relations among Negro and white Daytonians will be built in the aftermath of the riot. God moves in mysterious ways. Dayton will not be the same Dayton it was a few days ago." The words fell upon the largely black audience.

Some in the audience murmured in doubt of a new beginning. Their cup of optimism was empty.

Lester Mitchell's burial followed at Greencastle Cemetery in West Dayton. Many unanswered questions remained. Hundreds of people arrested during the riot were processed through the court system. Despite Reverend Flannigan's words, many people worried that Dayton would never get better.

DPD continued to work the Mitchell case using the traditional approach to developing leads through informants. It seemed that every drug addict, thief and jailbird called with information about Lester Mitchell. Many admitted they did not have any solid information but if they just had the chance to deal a little dope, get back on the street, or have a few days to "work off a case," they could provide information. Criminals used all their wily tricks to get a free pass. Nothing panned out.

SEVENTEEN

Just Another "Black-On-Black" Crime

A small impromptu memorial was stacked against the stoop in front of 1020 West Fifth Street. The few flowers that remained were wilted and faded. A white homemade cross was propped up and inscribed with "RIP Lester Mitchell." Several empty whiskey bottles were arranged by the flowers. An unopened Stroh's beer, Lester Mitchell's favorite, sat among the items.

Dayton Police Homicide Detectives admitted they did not have a clear picture of what happened during the early morning hours when Lester Mitchell was shot. The crime scene was overrun by a large disorderly group, and the riot prohibited detectives from diagramming the scene in detail. Eyewitness, Leonard Cantrell, and others insisted that a lone white male fired a shotgun blast from the driver side of a passing automobile.

Captain O'Conner wanted to make a detailed diagram of the scene, and he enlisted help from the city's Engineering Department to ascertain exactly where the shot originated that killed Mitchell. Engineers and surveyors met detectives in the 1000 block of West Fifth Street on September 13, 1966 at 10:00 a.m., twelve days after Mitchell's death. Six Dayton Police officers in uniform arrived first to set up security. The fact that detectives were going to the crime scene again was leaked to the news media by an ego-driven detective. Photographers from the *Dayton Daily News* and television reporters arrived and film crews angled for the best background shots. Radio station reporters carried cassette tape recorders on shoulder straps and talked into hand-held microphones. Crowd control quickly became an issue when about 125 onlookers gathered.

The Clean Kitchen walk-up food stand was back in operation. People bought plates of food and watched the "show" while they ate. The crowd watched curiously as engineers diagrammed and measured the scene from several different angles. A few people in the crowd talked angrily about Mitchell's murder not being solved.

One character, well known to the police, yelled, "What you pigs doing now? Drawin' pictures? You bastards probably already know who did it! Right? Yeah!"

Officer David Michael had heard enough. As he walked toward the man known on the street as Mac, the crowd parted and backed away. Mac stood alone, face to face with Officer Michael.

Officer Michael was a thick man who stood 6 feet, 2 inches tall. He had an eighteen-inch neck and massive hands. Michael carried a billy club and folded his arms across his chest with the club in his right hand. He stood close to Mac and quietly spoke one-on-one with him. After a brief pause, Mac turned and ambled down the street, not another word was said. Officer Michael walked back to his post.

Finally, curiosity got the best of his partner and he asked, "What happened?" Michael said, "I just told him an ambulance would be here in a minute. He could either shut the hell up and go on down the street, or keep on runnin' his mouth and get a ride to the hospital in one of those shiny red Cadillacs."

The surveyors and detectives took measurements from a point they believed Lester Mitchell stood when he was shot. Dayton Police Detective Sergeant Burns believed they could establish a pattern of pellets that missed Mitchell and hit the front of the storefront church behind and to the right of the victim. They measured from the curb in front of 1020 West Fifth Street, where witnesses claimed a car slowed and from which the shot was fired. Measurements were also made from across the street and from an alley alongside the Flamingo Pool Hall. Surveyors also took measurements of the widest range of pellet holes found in the storefront and the height of pellets from street level.

The engineering team left after two hours at the crime scene. The news media promptly reported that police used engineers as a "modern and fresh approach to analyze a crime scene."

A headline in the September 13th evening edition of the *Dayton Daily News* proclaimed doubt that Lester Mitchell was shot by a drive-by killer: "Was Lester Mitchell Shot by Pedestrian?"

———◦▸———

September 20, 1966, nineteen days after Lester Mitchell was murdered and a week after engineers visited the Mitchell crime scene, the *Dayton Daily News* published a story with large bold black headlines that surprised many readers. "Shots fired from across street in Mitchell Case, Engineering tests determine location."

A photo of engineers and a detective at work with a ladder and measuring tape accompanied the article. The story was in direct contradiction to the September 1st report that Mitchell was shot by a white male suspect from a passing car.

After the engineering survey, DPD officially changed their story that Mitchell had been shot from a passing car. They insisted that the shot that killed Mitchell was fired from across the street, not by a drive-by shooter's car. The *Dayton Daily News* article stated:

> Ballistics and engineering tests show the shot that killed Lester Mitchell was fired from across the street, not from a passing car, police reported today.
>
> It was the Mitchell shooting that touched off rioting on Dayton's West Side on Sept. 1.
>
> Some half-dozen witnesses to the shooting, all of them negro, earlier told police the fatal shot was fired from a passing car carrying two or three white men. It was the rumor of that apparently wanton shooting that spread through the city's West Side and inflamed the rioters.
>
> "Based on as much scientific evidence as we can bring to bear on the case, we are 99 per cent sure Mitchell was shot from across the street," Lt. Robert Swartz said today.
>
> In fact, police have pinpointed a walkway beside 1017 as the spot from which the fatal shotgun blast was fired.
>
> That walkway leads between two buildings into an alley

that parallel Fifth St. and would have provided an excellent escape route, police added.

... The pattern tests indicated the shot was fired from between 50 and 60 feet, Swartz said. Officers then measured that distance along the line of the shot ... and found it placed Mitchell's assassin in the mouth of the walkway across the street.

"At the point where the car would have been (according to witness' statements), the shot would have passed over the roof of the car," Sergeant Burns reported.

"The shot was just too high as it passed over the street to have come from an auto," he added.

"Witnesses may have seen a car pass just before or after the shot was fired, but the shot didn't come from it," Burns added. Police tests also revealed that Mitchell may have seen his killer just as he was shot.

... Police also said the shotgun used number five shot, a relatively small pellet size used for rabbit or pheasant hunting. From the number of pellets, they theorized the gun was probably a 12-gauge. In their tests, detectives fired hundreds of shots from the four guns. Each gun was tested for pattern at least once at each five feet from 10 to 65 feet, Burns said.

Statements by Dayton Police in the newspaper article dismissed the drive-by shooting theory and that a white male in a vehicle committed the crime. Not one witness told the police they saw a white man on foot in the heart of the black ghetto area when Mitchell was shot at 3:35 in the morning.

According to Dayton Police, the entire blame for the devastating riot shifted to an unsubstantiated "wanton rumor" started by black witnesses who were mistaken that a white man in a passing car murdered Lester Mitchell.

Police did not discuss how the new "99 percent sure" theory affected their next steps in the investigation. One thing was sure: black witnesses out on the street at 3:35 a.m. were not believed in the face of "science." "Whitey" was no longer a prime suspect.

The FBI, with its sophisticated capabilities in analysis of firearms and bullet trajectory, remained silent as they had done throughout the entire Mitchell case and the riot. In the midst of the highly publicized story, they did not offer or provide any expertise, even though they knew DPD planned to perform technical analysis at the scene. DPD was left to use in-house capabilities of engineers who normally designed streets and sewers. Although the city engineers were well intentioned, they were not experienced in criminal matters and they had no experience testifying in criminal court.

Reactions of a few detectives close to the investigation were mixed. A handful of detectives still believed the eyewitnesses who said Mitchell was killed in a drive-by shooting by a white male who fired from the driver's side. Many seasoned patrol officers on the street were incredulous, too.

The new theory accepted by police pointed the finger at a black-on-black crime. It raised the possibility that the shooting may have been committed by a person who knew and targeted Mitchell. A veteran detective referred to Detective Lieutenant Schwartz and Sergeant Burns' news quotes about the engineering study and quipped sarcastically, "Who can argue with *science*? Now all of a sudden WE give a shit about *science*? What happened to good old-fashioned police work? From now on, if you want to solve a murder, don't call a cop. Call a damn engineer and surveyor."

Following publicity that police were ninety-nine percent sure about results of their engineering study, news coverage of the case was placed on the back burner. No more news releases from DPD, no newspaper editorials, in-depth articles or detailed TV stories demanded to know status of the Lester Mitchell murder case.

Some leaders in Dayton's black community were outspoken and did not believe the new shooting theory at all. Sumpter McIntosh and a handful of other black activists held numerous meetings where people vented anger and distrust at the new story told by DPD.

Areas devastated by the riots remained a mess while city and community leaders focused on finger pointing about the underlying causes. City officials and leaders in the black community made proposals for immediate federal and state funding for education, welfare, health services, better city services and drug programs. Some black leaders shifted their focus into high gear as they learned federal money was projected to soon flood into Dayton. A few self-appointed black power brokers made sure they were first in line with ideas about new programs and organizations they could lead and from which they would profit.

Cops had simplistic barometers of their own that determined when the West Side returned to normal. Two activities slowly returned as sure as the sun rose each morning. The daytime illegal numbers rackets were back in business. Bookies, or "hand books," as they were known, prowled the streets with their small multi-color Rainbow tablets and pencils in their pockets and took small cash or credit bets from poor people and those who worked along the streets in stores, lumberyards and delivery trucks.

Another sign things returned to near-normal at night on the West Side was the return of prostitutes. White "tricks" gradually returned to the streets. Hookers shuffled slowly along the sidewalk with the flow of traffic and cautiously peered into cars. The memory of Lester Mitchell's murder had grown dim. As far as DPD was concerned, it was considered just another black-on-black crime and relegated to the status of a less-important homicide.

———◁◦▷———

Neal Bradley Long sat in his dingy room and read the story in the *Dayton Daily News* about the engineering study. Statements made by Dayton Police saying Mitchell was not killed by a drive-by shotgun shooter amazed even his troubled mind. He, of all people, knew better. A rare, seldom-seen grin softened his face for a moment.

Long's personal problems continued to mount and he projected his resentment toward black people and his belief they "got more" than whites. He believed he had to stand up for white people and stop the coloreds from taking over.

When he hunted, when he fired, when he killed, Neal Bradley Long felt like a vigilante; a good guy making things right.

EIGHTEEN

The Bell Tolls

During the moderate fall weather, in an attempt to lure more people in for worship services, many churches often left their front doors wide open. Some posted deacons at the doors to greet people on the street and invite them inside.

Neal Bradley Long stopped at the gas station at East Third and June Street. He took a swig of cheap Saint Charles California Brandy, wiped his mouth with the back of his hand and slid the bottle under his seat. He got out of the car and pumped gas. His attention was drawn to the sound of the large Verdin Tolling Bell atop the stone tower of Emmanuel Baptist Church a block away. It signaled like a costal lighthouse as the bell called to all who needed guidance to a safe port.

Long heard the bell as it rhythmically tolled. He stopped in his tracks. He changed course and walked to the church as if the tolling bell reeled him in. Long did not care much for church or being told by a preacher man what to do in life. He had his own communications with God.

Long moved toward the open doors, still unsure if he would enter. He was greeted by a deacon who motioned to the open door. "Come inside, my friend," the deacon urged. The deacon's handshake was returned with a damp, limp hand. The deacon gently nudged Long inside and followed as he entered the sanctuary.

Neal Bradley Long was dressed in his soiled work clothes. He shuffled to a seat in the last pew. Long sat alone and eyed his escape route back to the door. The majority of the congregation of about two hundred white people clustered in front of the sanctuary. They were dressed in common everyday clothing that looked clean and ironed. A few people in the church wore their Sunday best. Long could not relate to the fellowship he saw among the friendly and smiling congregation. A few members greeted him after the welcome song and he felt uneasy rather than included.

The minister, Pastor Nile Fisher, a fundamentalist Baptist, took the podium and paused a moment. He stood before the choir and a large wooden cross mounted on the wall.

The son of a farmer from Toppenish, Washington on the Yakama Indian Nation Reservation, Pastor Fisher was a handsome plainspoken man with a deep voice and jet black hair combed straight back. The pastor knew about a hard life. As a child, he lived on a farm in the rich Yakama Valley. His family grew cherries and Yukon Gold potatoes. The farms used irrigation canals fed by cold mountain water from the gigantic snow-capped Mt. Rainer, about twenty miles away.

After the choir finished a song before the sermon, Pastor Fisher was moved by God's spirit to lay aside his prepared sermon. He believed he needed to speak out immediately. The minister bellowed, "There are sinners here who need to get right with God today! This morning, I feel an unusual burden to speak strongly. There are some here, this very minute, who are tormented by the devil and need to get right with God, RIGHT NOW!"

A long pause followed as the Pastor surveyed the crowd. He held his arms outstretched with his well worn black leather King James Version Bible in his right hand. Deacons, seated in front of the church, rose and stood quietly, ready to assist individuals in the audience. Pastor Fisher prayed aloud and asked those in need to raise their hand as the elaborate pipe organ bellowed and the choir softly sang the heart-tugging song, "Just as I am, Without One Plea." The words extolled God's goodness and universal forgiveness.

The plaintive sound of the organ and voices of the choir irritated Long. He believed everyone stared at him as the hymn continued.

"Just as I am, and wanting not, to rid my soul of one dark blot."

Long was convinced that the preacher addressed his message directly to him. Even if he wanted to raise his hand for spiritual help, his arms felt like they each weighed one hundred pounds.

"Oh Lamb of God; I come, I come."

Long suddenly bolted from the pew and stumbled to the floor. He got up and quickly staggered to the door and rushed out the church onto

Terry Street. The deacon followed him to the door. He saw Long cross East Third Street and disappear. Long hurried to his car and drove to his rented half-double house on Torrence Street. He rushed inside, drew the window shades and locked the door. He was alone; Grace and the children were not home. He removed a duffle bag from beneath his bed. Long was reassured when he pulled out his sawed-off shotgun. He laid back on the bed with the tool of the "death angel" beside him. Sleep came.

NINETEEN

Trick or Treat

Tuesday, September 20, 1966, tension in the West Side escalated once again when Stokely Carmichael, head of the Student Nonviolent Co-ordinating Committee (SNCC) spoke at a church on the West Side. The *Dayton Daily News* described the audience as "white intellectuals, Negro professionals, churchgoers and college students. Also in the crowd were Negroes who had been arrested during the riot earlier in the month."

Carmichael garnered national and world attention a few months earlier when he angrily coined the phrase, "Black Power." He emphasized "Black Pride" as he spoke to several thousand people at multiple events during his time in Dayton. Throughout Carmichael's visit, he was under covert surveillance by agents of the FBI and Dayton Police detectives. Publicity that surrounded Carmichael's visit and his "Black Power" phrase stirred emotions. Many blacks, particularly the young, were energized. Most whites heard his message as a threat.

———◄○►———

In mid-October 1966, six weeks after Lester Mitchell's murder, Neal Bradley Long suddenly took off work at Stolle Company for a "personal matter" and disappeared from Dayton. He did not tell his wife or children where he was going. During the previous months, Long drank excessively and had become withdrawn. He and his wife Grace grieved for years over the death of their four-year-old son, Larry, in 1958, and Long often relapsed into depression. Grace worried it had happened again. When his son died of rheumatic fever, Long was so distraught, he got down on his knees and cussed out God. Grace told others she had never heard Neal mad at God and it scared her.

"There were periods when he acted as if he was in another world," Grace reflected. "Neal had been getting messages from God for about fifteen years." When Neal disappeared in October, the family guessed he went down home to Kentucky, as he often did.

Near the end of October 1966, Long returned to Dayton from Kentucky and went back to work at Stolle Company. He was still estranged from his wife and children, but Grace found out her husband was back in town and had rented a sleeping room. She went to Long's workplace at lunchtime on Halloween, October 31, 1966 and asked to see him. Long was given permission to meet his wife in the parking lot, and Grace broke down when she saw him. His face was void of any semblance of caring emotion. Grace was alarmed that he had returned to Dayton without contacting her. She begged him to come home. Long told her flatly, "God told me to leave you and my family."

Grace left, broken hearted and worried how she would go on without her husband and take care of their children. She had little money. She was illiterate. As Grace had done many times before, she hoped that her husband would calm down and come home.

Neal Bradley Long was agitated inside and robot-like on the outside. Later that same day, Long told his supervisor he had to leave work. His negative self-talk dragged him deeper into resentment and self pity. He was convinced he would never have much of a life. As a young boy, he often heard his father in Campton, Kentucky utter a phrase that typified acceptance that the poor folks in the hills would never break the cycle of poverty and a hard life. The words took root in Long's subconscious and on Halloween, it was as if a tape recorder played the message over and over in his head.

"Once you're born in a shack, you'll die in a shack."

Long carried many burdens and disturbing thoughts. As he walked to his car in the Stolle parking lot; his life was out of control. Long continued to hear commands and voices he believed came from God. He was sick and tired of colored people like Martin Luther King, Jr. who demanded more rights at the expense of white people.

————◦————

On Halloween afternoon at about 4:00 p.m., the DPD and Dayton Jaycees, a community organization, prepared for their annual Halloween candy give away. After the riot that started September 1st, "begging" or "trick or treating" in the City of Dayton was moved to 5:00 p.m. to promote safety for the children.

Traditionally, members of the Jaycees rode along in police cars and handed out candy to children they saw on the street. In preparation for the annual Halloween Candy Patrol, Dayton Police cars lined the street in front of the Central Police Station at 335 West Third Street in downtown Dayton.

Exactly two months after Lester Mitchell's murder, Neal Bradley Long slowed a 1959 Plymouth station wagon he was driving in front of the police station as he looked for a parking space. He was startled to see so many police cars. He parked his car and hesitated before he got out. Long knew that going inside to see police was risky.

Long saw news reports that Dayton detectives used city engineers and surveyors and made measurements at the Lester Mitchell crime scene on the West Side. He wondered if police were close to catching the killer. As he stood outside the entrance to the police department, Long reviewed his plan to go inside and make a confession. He knew he could be arrested for murder. Although his reasoning was often detached from reality, Long was cunning, and he felt the urge to see if the Dayton Police knew of him.

———◄◦►———

The Central Police Station was a five story limestone structure that housed the entire Dayton Police operation, including the city jail. Neal Bradley Long entered the front door and located the Information Desk that was housed along with PBX switchboard operators and the dispatch center.

The desk was staffed by Sergeant Miller, also known to his friends as "Greek." He was a smart and experienced man, proud of his ethnic heritage. An injury left him with an assignment indoors, where he pushed paper and dealt with all sorts of walk-in visitors. Greek was near retirement and his twelve-month countdown calendar hung on the wall by his desk. Big X's marked off each day with December 31, 1966 circled.

Greek saw Long as he approached. "What can I do for you, sir?" Greek asked.

Long flinched at such a friendly comment from a uniformed sergeant and looked at Greek with a deadpan expression. Long spoke softly. "I need to confess to something. I may have killed a man."

Greek, a man who had heard all kinds of weird stories said, "Son, step a little closer, I can't hear too good. Say it again."

Long repeated, "I quit drinking and got religion." He then added, "I may have killed a man a long time ago."

The Greek, an unflappable man, replied in a matter-of-fact way, "Okay, son, have a seat, I'll call someone."

Greek called upstairs to Dick Section and asked for anyone on Homicide. While he waited for someone to answer, Greek thought to himself, "Damn, it's Halloween. All the crazies will probably come see me tonight."

Homicide Detective Howard Krisher answered his desk telephone and looked at his watch at the same time. Greek stood behind his desk and cradled the telephone on his shoulder against his ear while he shuffled papers. Greek said, "There's a guy down here who says he may have killed someone a long time ago. Since then, he's got religion and wants to talk to somebody."

Detective Krisher, an old school "gum shoe" cop of German lineage, said, "You gotta be shittin' me, Greek. Don't pull my chain, it's Halloween!" When Greek did not respond, both men chuckled and Krisher quickly added, "I'll be right down."

Detective Krisher was well-known because he frequently submitted articles to the tabloids *True Detective* and *Inside Detective* on some of his sensational homicide cases. He always looked to make the most out of what he knew, professionally and personally. Detective Krisher asked Detective Vernon "Red" Benson to go downstairs with him. Benson was called "Red" because he had a very fair complexion that quickly turned red if he was pissed off. Red was a little irritated since detectives got off work at 4:45 p.m., and he was about to leave early to meet other detectives for a few drinks at the Park Row Lounge, a favorite cozy hangout for veteran cops.

As they walked to the elevator, Red turned more pink at the thought that he was delayed having a "Scotch-pop," his favorite Cutty Sark drink. Both detectives were highly experienced and knew that seldom, if ever, did a person walk into a police station and say they may have killed someone.

The elevator doors opened and the detectives saw Long seated in a chair next to Greek's desk. Greek nodded in the direction of the man. Detective Krisher approached. "I'm Homicide Detective Krisher," he said as he extended his right hand. He grasped the man's hand, which was limp and cool. Krisher had already started to size up Long when he stood up.

"I'm Neal Long. My name used to be Carma Long, but I changed it a long time ago. You can call me Carma."

Red and Krisher escorted Long to the elevator. Their short ride upstairs went by silently as the detectives observed the supposed killer. Long had second thoughts if he should have gone to see the police, but it was too late to change his mind.

Neal Bradley Long saw about twenty detectives in Dick Section as they sat at old grey metal desks in rows in an open bullpen area. A blue haze of tobacco smoke hung in the air. Some detectives had removed their suit coats; their shoulder holsters and weapons were exposed.

They appeared to be wrapping up for the day.

In front of the large room was a raised stage about thirty feet long with a mesh screen from floor to ceiling. Behind the screen were bright lights and two solid steel cell doors. Long also noticed along one wall was a half-dozen doors with numbers on them. He was directed to Interrogation Room three and told to have a seat.

To help Long settle down, Krisher and Red asked a few basic questions about where he lived, about his family and his employment. Long had a question to ask as well. "What is that big stage for?"

Detective Krisher responded, "Sometimes we have prisoners locked up and witnesses come here to identify whoever robbed them or whatever. We turn the lights down in the big room and the suspect is lined up with other men that look kinda' like him. A witness can safely identify the guy without being seen."

Long listened intently and did not respond right away. Krisher paused. Long said blandly, "That's interesting," and his voice trailed off.

Detective Krisher asked an open ended question. "What brings you here today?"

Long answered, "I was in a fight a long time ago. I may have killed a man."

Krisher and Red glanced at one another and paused. They let the words sink in as Long squirmed in his chair. The detectives asked Long to tell his story. Long gave a sigh and sat with his hands clasped between his knees. He leaned forward slightly and looked at the floor as he avoided eye contact.

Long spoke about the year 1944, when he was seventeen years old. He and a friend walked on Washington Street, near the bridge that crossed into the West Side. Two scrap metal junk yards and warehouses lined the street. "It was a summer evening, a Saturday, around 9:00 p.m. It seemed the sidewalk wasn't big enough for all of us when we were approached by two men," Long told Krisher. He added, "The two men beat us in the head and face. My friend ran off, and I got a pocket knife out and cut this man across the face, and I think I cut him pretty bad." Long continued, "But then I ran away and I never found out how bad I cut him. My friends all knew I did it and I ducked around for a long time going back and forth to Kentucky." Long added, "I stopped drinking and then I got religion and felt God wanted me to confess about this."

When Long finished his story, the room was quiet as Krisher and Red used an interrogation ploy and sat quietly to see what came out next. Unprompted, Long said, "I was always afraid I killed a man. If I killed a man, I want to take my punishment."

The veteran detectives weighed whether or not to read Long his Miranda Rights. They hated the new U.S. Supreme Court Miranda decision that guarded against self-incrimination and they had a hard time adjusting to it. The Dicks relied on the fact that Long was not in custody and that there was no other evidence that the alleged crime even occurred. They decided not to read Long his Miranda Rights.

Neal Bradley Long gathered confidence since he had "confessed." He sat up straight on the chair and boldly stated, "Well, I've done my part, it's now up to you!" He added one more important thing, "Well, you know where I am, and if I have to get punished, you just come and get me."

Detectives Krisher and Benson excused themselves from the interrogation room on the ruse to make a quick telephone call and to get a paper cup of water for Long. As they exited, they locked the door from the outside. Krisher said, "What the hell . . . ?"

During the few moments outside the Interrogation Room, they checked to see if Long was wanted on warrants. None was found, only a record of a few drunken arrests and traffic tickets, some in the name of Carma Long. If the detectives decided to send a Tele-Type request to the State of Ohio Bureau of Criminal Identification in Columbus, Ohio and to the FBI to determine national level wanted bulletins, it would take several hours or longer to receive a response. They decided not to send any Tele-Types. In the meantime, they briefly discussed Long's confession with a few other detectives who were still in the office. No one took it seriously and it became a quirky story to pass on at the end of the workday, especially on Halloween. The "nut case" story traveled quickly.

Just outside the Detective Section and down the hall near the elevator was a small cramped room dedicated for use by newspaper reporters. The sign above the door read "PRESS ROOM." There were a few chairs, one desk, a black rotary telephone and an Olympia SG-1 typewriter. Police reporters from the morning *Dayton Journal Herald* and the evening *Dayton Daily News* newspapers hung out there. They were always hungry for scraps of news, tips or actual leaks of stories. The reporters cultivated relationships with potential newsmakers. Homicide Detectives were at the top of their list.

The story told by Long quickly made it to a reporter named Joe Eszterhas who happened to be in the police station. Eszterhas staked out the Dick Section and patiently waited in the hallway hoping to see Detective Krisher.

Krisher and Benson went into Interrogation Room two, directly next to Long's Interrogation Room. The two detectives quietly entered the dark room and closed the door. A large two-way mirror allowed them to observe Long without his knowledge. They studied his appearance and behavior. Long was not suspicious of the mirror in the room and he sat quietly, slouched down with his arms folded across his chest. Red said, "This guy looks like a flat tire. There ain't much we can do with this story, right?" Krisher nodded and watched for a few more moments.

The detectives joined Long again and asked him for more details of the vicious stabbing. Long described the men but was general and evasive. He said the man he cut was colored. Long was asked who else knew about the fight and he said he told his father and wife. Long said neither he nor his friend received medical attention even though he alleged they were beaten in the face and head. Long claimed he did not know where his unnamed friend from 1944 might be found. Long added that he did not suffer any hand wounds from the pocketknife he used as a weapon.

Usually both Homicide Detectives were very thorough in their quest for details. Perhaps it was the Halloween confession that threw them off stride. They gave little thought to pursuing the claim by Long. They did not take his picture or open a case folder.

Historically in Dayton, as all Homicide Detectives knew, murders rarely crossed racial lines, yet Long's story involved a serious stabbing or possible homicide. However, it did not arouse any unusual suspicion for the detectives despite the fact that the most sensational inter-racial murder in Dayton's history happened just sixty days prior to Long's very unusual confession.

After they spent a little time with Long, the detectives decided not to pursue his story and ended his visit with a thank you and a handshake. By 6:00 p.m., Long walked out of the Dayton Police Station. He reminded himself of what he told the detectives, "I did my part. I confessed."

A slight smile crossed Long's lips when he left with a wealth of inside knowledge about the Dayton Police Homicide Squad. He knew he was not a suspect in connection with the murder of Lester Mitchell, or any other case. Those thoughts soothed him momentarily. But messages from God returned and filled his troubled mind as he walked to his Plymouth station wagon.

Long drove south along the east side of the Great Miami River and parked on the roadside near Deeds Carillon Park. The sun had set, and a veil of darkness descended. His car was packed with clothing and some snacks. He did not need anything from anyone.

Despite what Long told detectives about not drinking alcohol, he never stopped drinking. It was a line of bullshit. He was glad to see the detectives accepted his story as the truth. Gulps of alcohol dulled Long's edginess.

Sergeant Krisher and Red Benson decided there was not much more they could do about the Halloween confession, given the age of the reported stabbing or homicide. "Hell's bells," Krisher said, "This is one of the weirdest stories I've heard in a long time."

As the detectives left for the day, they walked out of Dick Section and grinned at the Halloween skull figure taped to the door to the Homicide Office. How fitting, Red chuckled to himself. Detective Krisher saw reporter Joe Eszterhas in the Press Room and walked in his direction.

Krisher and Eszterhas spoke and walked together and Joe mentioned he had just written a "puff piece" story about how cops and Jaycees handed out goodies to kids on Halloween night. Krisher grunted in acknowledgement. Joe then said, "Speaking of Halloween, what's the story on the guy who walked in and said he killed somebody?"

Krisher stopped walking and feigned a lack of interest. He weighed the possibility; Krisher knew it was potentially a good Halloween news story and it would help highlight his career one more time.

Krisher answered, "Joe, you want to meet me at the Embassy in about fifteen minutes?" Joe happily agreed.

————◦————

The Moraine Embassy Bar, only two blocks from the police station, was next door to the *Dayton Daily News/Dayton Journal Herald* building in the heart of downtown. It was a hangout for newspaper reporters, editors, DPD detectives and lawyers. It was the kind of bar customers ducked into for a quick stiff drink to help get through the day. Beer mugs were frosty and cigarette and cigar smoke filled the air.

After a few sips of cold beer, Eszterhas and Krisher leaned over the table so they could hear each other and talk over the din of the crowd. The reporter pulled his narrow reporter's notebook from his back pocket and jotted down shorthand notes on the white lined paper. After about one hour, Krisher left and Eszterhaus quickly walked next door to the news building to find Joseph Fenley, newspaper City Editor. "Joe," he yelled, "I've got a great Halloween story for ya!"

In less than ten hours from the time Neal Bradley Long walked out of the Dayton Police station, the November 1st edition of the *Dayton*

Journal Herald morning newspaper carried a story with bold, black one-inch headlines:

"MAN CONFESSES TO 'STABBING' BACK IN 1944"

The byline reporter, Joe Eszterhaus, introduced the story and described the scene on Halloween night, October 31, 1966 when Neal Bradley Long, AKA Carma Long, admitted to police a possible murder in 1944. It was a popular local story for a few days and was also distributed nationally by the *Associated Press (AP)* and *United Press International (UPI)* wire services.

The Dayton FBI Field Office routinely kept newspaper articles in a clip file of all high profile crime-related media stories. Agents recognized Carma Long's name. However, the FBI did not notify police that Long's name was in their confidential Indices files. Had the FBI informed DPD, Homicide may have taken a second look at Long and his story. Detective Krisher was quoted throughout the *Dayton Journal Herald* story as he described Long's admission as "...too old to check out." In addition to many of Long's statements that were quoted in the article, the reporter also quoted Detective Krisher. The article stated:

> Detective Krisher told Long that if the facts were as he related them, it looked like a case of self-defense. "The man [Long] presents a special problem," Krisher said, "because we'd have to look through all the records to find a complainant who claimed he'd been cut. If these men did jump Long and his friend," Krisher said, "the chances are that a complaint was never turned in. All our records before 1963 have been micro-filmed," Krisher said, "and it would mean that we would have to look through all the microfilms to find this one complaint." Detective Krisher even waxed philosophical and told the re-porter, "He [Long] was 17 years old then." Krisher said. "Now he is a mature, religious man. A lot of things have changed since 1944, and so have a lot of people."

Detective Krisher had quickly accepted the statements by Long as true, about how he turned to religion and stopped drinking sometime between 1944 and 1966. Krisher saw no need for any more investigation. He said the possible murder was too old, too much trouble to assign a clerk to use the microfilm search capability for old cases, which was more efficient and faster than old methods. It was too hard to check with hospitals or interview a few of Long's family members such as his father and stepmother in Miamisburg, Ohio. While detectives did not pursue Long's confession, Krisher decided it was a good story to give to a newspaper reporter as soon as possible. Dayton Homicide Detectives were too busy to be sidetracked; they were busy with the unsolved murder of Lester Mitchell. They did not want to waste time on some old, amusing story told on Halloween night.

———◦———

Buried in a musty file cabinet in a storage room at the *Dayton Journal Herald* was a drawer full of newspaper clippings filed by year and date. The yellowed identification tag labeled a drawer "1944." One clipping was dated June 18, 1944, titled "Man Stabbed." The article written by a staff writer described a police report about the stabbing of a man on the Washington Street Bridge at 12:10 a.m. who was attacked by an unknown man and "taken to Miami Valley Hospital for treatment of serious wounds." No names were in the article that closed by saying, "police are investigating." Neither Detective Krisher nor reporter Eszterhaus bothered to check DPD records or the newspaper's clip file. Long's story was true.

———◦———

Dayton Police Supervising Detective Sergeant R. Burns completed a sixty-day review of the Lester Mitchell murder case. Ironically, it was the same day Neal Bradley Long boldly walked into the DPD homicide office and admitted to a rare white-on-black crime on a bridge leading into the West Side. Homicide Detectives did not collect a photograph, fingerprints, written statement, background information or arrange a Polygraph examination for Long.

DPD Homicide Complaint No. 197129 in the death of Lester Mitchell, "Colored Male (CM) age 39," was returned to file as "Inactive - Not Cleared." All investigative leads had been exhausted.

TWENTY

Hiding In Plain Sight

Neal Bradley Long woke from an alcohol-induced nap in his car. For the rest of Halloween night, Long drove around aimlessly in his car. He never understood Halloween as a fun night for children. As a child, he never went begging for candy in Campton, Kentucky. Long remembered the words of a country preacher in the Hardshell Baptist Church who rocked the one room church every October with his loud cadence and breathless messages about Halloween. "It's the devil's night! Not one for God-fearing believers!"

As light in the sky gave way to darkness, Long saw children dressed in their homemade costumes as they "celebrated the devil." He did not like it.

At about 1:00 a.m., November 1st, Long went to his wife's rented half-double house. She did not know he left work earlier in the day or that he had seen Dayton Police to confess to Homicide Detectives. Grace was apprehensive but glad to hear him come in the door. The children awoke and greeted their father.

Long was withdrawn and preoccupied with his own thoughts. He told Grace that he was sure God told him to leave his family. Grace and the children were stunned by Long's statement.

Long hastily gathered a few personal items and left the house. A light rain fell as Grace and the children stood at the door and clutched one another, as daddy drove away.

At about 2:00 a.m., Long stopped in a parking lot by the U.S. Post Office warehouse on East Fourth Street. He relived events of the afternoon and evening. His paranoia kicked in when he remembered that he went to the police station and admitted to possibly killing someone.

In the quiet of the night, Long heard voices in his mind. "Yes?" Long said out loud as he broke the silence. Long believed he heard God.

Long continued to dwell on his belief that white people did not have a fair chance in life. He blamed the "coloreds" who "acted up" all over the country, even in Dayton. When the colored guy was murdered by the shotgun blast on the West Side in September, Long thought that it would help "stop them from taking over." When the riots followed, Long hoped coloreds would finally be put in their place by the police, but it only got worse for white people.

Long felt woozy as he drove down East Third Street toward downtown and crossed the West Third Street Bridge. It was nearly 3:00 a.m. Light rain fell and chilled the night air. Windshield wipers on his Plymouth were worn and powered by a vacuum line to the carburetor. The wipers were erratic and noisy as they rapidly slapped the windshield when he let off the gas pedal. Rain transformed the streets into a shiny world that reflected the streetlights. As on-coming cars passed, a circular blinding glare of the headlights looked like an aurora behind Jesus Christ's head. Was it a sign from God?

Long's anger against colored people welled up inside as he drove on West Third Street and crossed Broadway Street. It was once a familiar place to him, but now it was difficult to recognize since destruction from the riot sixty days ago. City blocks of storefronts were boarded up. Some were covered in anti-white graffiti.

Long drove on West Fifth Street and passed the 1000 block. The area was quiet as it was salved by rain. He stared blankly as he slowly passed 1020 West Fifth. A small wooden cross and old flowers marked the spot where Lester Mitchell died from a shotgun blast. Neal Bradley Long sniffed the sweet smell of a righteous death that still hung in the air.

At 4:30 a.m., about the same time in the early morning that Lester Mitchell was gunned down exactly two months earlier, Neal Bradley Long drove across the Wolf Creek Bridge at Rosedale Avenue. As he crossed the bridge into the West Side in his intoxicated and delusional state, he lost control of his station wagon. It slid over the curb and into the concrete bridge. The crash injured Long's shoulders, ribs, neck and back as he was hurled sideways on his bench seat into the passenger side. Long was dazed and he bled from facial injuries. A motorist happened by and called police from a telephone booth.

Veteran Dayton Police officer Bill Rinehart arrived at the accident scene within a few minutes. Long was incoherent. He had a strong odor of alcohol on his breath and he was unable to stand due to his injuries. Long was taken by ambulance to Good Samaritan Hospital.

Officer Rinehart was unable to question him, but he noticed that Long's address on his operator's license was 39 S. Torrence Street in East Dayton. Rinehart wondered why Long was on the West Side at 4:30 in the morning. He observed a large pile of old clothes in the back of the wagon.

It started to rain harder and got close to shift change time, so Rinehart decided not to search the wagon. He left all the personal property inside and had it towed as-is so Long or his family could claim it later.

Officer Rinehart drove to the hospital where Long received treatment in the Emergency Room. He was stopped by a hospital security officer at the entrance. "Hey Rinehart, you here to see the nut case from the traffic accident on the West Side?" The security officer continued, "The guy from the bridge accident started talking crazy when they wheeled him in. Something about crossing the Jordan River, you know, like in the Bible."

Rinehart attended church whenever he could, despite his lousy work schedule. He paused and responded, "I think Jesus went to the Jordan River where John baptized him. Jesus hid from guys who wanted to capture him. It was a place of safety." The security guard looked at Rinehart and saw that he was serious. Rinehart continued, "It's too deep for me at this time of the mornin'. I gotta write up this accident report and get outta' here."

Rinehart wrote a traffic ticket for the accident and gave it to the nurse to keep for Long. As Rinehart walked away from Long's gurney, he heard Neal Bradley Long yell, "I'm in the promised land. I'm free. I crossed the Jordan River." Rinehart shook his head and chalked up another weird encounter story to tell his buddies on a slow night.

The Emergency Room medical doctor on duty interpreted Long's comment about "crossing the Jordan River" as a possible suicide attempt. Long's physical injuries required admission to the hospital where he remained under medical care for ten days. During his stay in the hospital,

Long's mental status was unstable. It became evident that he needed to be moved to a psychiatric facility for detailed evaluation.

The decision to hold him did not alarm Long because he wanted to be out of society for a while. There was too much pressure at home, at work and from his recent contact with Dayton Police detectives on Halloween night. The fewer people who knew of his whereabouts, the better, he thought. Long was hiding in plain sight.

On November 11th, Neal Bradley Long was transferred across town to St. E. Psychiatric Ward for further evaluation. The intake psychiatrist, Dr. Somsel, diagnosed Long as "Schizophrenic-paranoid type, very dangerous." During the intake, Long described himself as a loner without any friends. He talked about God's messages and that he had seen "God's wrath."

After being treated for two weeks, St. E. psychiatric staff noted Long's behavior was less erratic. He was considered for release because the medication worked and he had family support from his wife, Grace. Long could also resume employment at Stolle Company. Even though his initial diagnosis was significant and dangerous in nature, Grace agreed with the decision to release her husband to return home before the Christmas holiday season.

December 19, 1966, Long's employer at the Stolle plant allowed him to return to his old job as a chrome plater helper. Long settled into his old routines, continued his medication and did not have any significant new episodes of erratic behavior through early winter.

After a period of relative calm, Neal Bradley Long abruptly became violent again. Sunday, March 12, 1967 at 2:00 p.m., Dayton Police Officers Roger Ballinger and Gary Pysick were dispatched to 39 South Torrence Street in East Dayton on a family trouble call. When they arrived, Grace Long was upset and afraid of her husband. He threatened her and their children and in a fit of rage, Long had broken furniture. Grace said her husband picked up their children at church around noon and brought them home. He was in an agitated mood when he arrived. Long told his wife, "God told me to destroy myself and my family."

Grace told officers her husband was recently in the Psychiatric Ward at St. E. She provided his psychiatrist's name. Officers telephoned Dr. Somsel and discussed Long's rage and violent behavior. Dr. Somsel authorized police to take Long into custody for "safe keeping."

Before Neal Bradley Long arrived at Dayton State Hospital (DSH), March 12, 1967, Dr. Somsel notified DSH that Long was to be admitted on his order. Dr. Somsel indicated that he had diagnosed Long in November and wanted him admitted for the same illness, "Schizophrenic-Paranoid Type, with homicidal and suicidal tendencies and extremely dangerous." Neal Bradley Long was taken to DSH, one of Ohio's largest mental health institutions.

———◦———

DSH was a legendary place known by nearly everyone who lived in the ten county catchment areas. The hospital site was selected by a famous architect, Thomas Kirkbridge, who also founded the American Psychiatric Association. It was sited on the eastern edge of Dayton at Wayne Avenue. The massive building, completed in 1855, sat on a high hill in the countryside and overlooked Dayton. A long tree-lined road led up to the facility. The institution was originally named Southern Ohio Lunatic Asylum and opened with 162 patients. In early 1900, the name was changed to DSH.

DSH housed over 1200 patients in 1966. Rumors and stories of torture, electro-shock therapy, lobotomies and wards full of catatonic patients circulated throughout the community. When anyone was taken to DSH, which stood atop the Wayne Avenue hill, the locals said they were taken to "Wayne Avenue."

The DSH facility had a three-story entrance with a large southern-style white wooden covered porch. White wicker rocking chairs lined the porch. Patients in gowns often sat on the porch and rocked back and forth all day long, rocking away the clock and the calendar. The rest of the facility was red brick construction, three stories tall.

Mr. Kirkbridge specifically designed the Asylum according to treatment methodologies of the 1800s. The un-air conditioned building had numerous wards in the many wings.

Any new patient with little hope of mental recovery or one that presented a danger or a control issue was kept in far-away wards, referred to by staff as "The Back Wards." Patients' distance from the center of the building indicated the seriousness of their behavior or prognosis. Numerous patients spent many years of their lives at Wayne Avenue. Each year, suicide claimed about twenty patients.

Dayton cops and firemen who took people to DSH often passed on rumors and lore about DSH and its horrific and haunted past. When Officers Ballinger and Pysick learned they were taking Neal Bradley Long to DSH, they decided to look around a bit to satisfy their curiosity.

The officers were met at the Admitting Entrance by two male orderlies dressed in all-white uniforms. The cops sized up the orderlies, who looked like they were professional wrestlers on the "ham-and-egg" circuit. It was apparent they could handle people the easy way or the hard way.

The orderlies escorted Neal Bradley Long into the Admitting Office. One orderly, named Joey, returned and handed a receipt to Ballinger. Officer Ballinger patiently waited for the opportunity to ask Joey a few questions about Wayne Avenue rumors. He finally mustered enough nerve and asked, "Hey, Joey, we've heard so much about this place. Can we talk a minute?" Joey smiled and invited the officers to a nearby room and offered them a cup of coffee.

Joey asked, "What ya' wanna' know?"

Ballinger brought up stories he had heard about torture and the tunnels. He nervously asked, "Are there secret tunnels here?"

Joey had been through the routine a few times and he enjoyed perpetuation of the mystery. Joey sipped his coffee and answered in a whispered voice, "Yes. The tunnels are real, but we don't torture that much anymore."

Ballinger and Pysick were drawn all the way into the story line. Both involuntarily swallowed hard and looked wide-eyed at each other, as if they were fourteen-years-old again and about to listen to a ghost story.

Joey said, "You'll have to put your guns in the lockers and come with me; we'll go through the men's wards." Joey led the way. He deliberately took the officers beneath the large central dome and through "near wards." Even close to the dome, patients looked pretty scary, like something out of an old black-and-white movie. They were lined up along the walls in old high-back wicker wheel chairs. Other patients wandered about.

To the discomfort of the two officers, Joey stopped in the middle of the ward to discuss Neal Bradley Long. As they talked, patients stared. Joey said, "Now you take your guy, Long; he'll go to Classification first. If he is cool and takes his medicine like he is supposed to, he will be in one of the wards up front. If he is not cooperative, he will be in a back ward. You can always tell when a guy is really crazy—he doesn't know or care where he is."

They walked deeper into the old Asylum and headed to the back wards. Ballinger and Pysick noticed security became more pronounced as they sank deeper into Wayne Avenue. They went through heavy doors that supported more locks. Bars were on the windows. Every ward held thirty to forty patients on each of its three floors. There were locked office areas with heavy reinforced glass that housed medication, charts and tools of the trade. Orderlies looked older and less congenial than Joey.

Even in daylight, the back wards were gloomy and drab. Some patients were restrained in bed with their arms and feet tied down. The foul odor grew more oppressive, and the officers were glad it was springtime. Barred windows were open on both sides of the wing to catch a breeze and flush out the stench.

As Joey lead the way, Ballenger and Pysick noticed the loud click of their solid heel shoes on the wooden floors. They felt self-conscious in their blue uniforms in the eerie place where everyone else, employees and patients, wore all white. Most patients ignored the visitors' presence; however, a handful of patients stared and gestured at the two "blue men" as they passed by.

Finally, the trio reached Ward D. It was the worst sight of all. People wore dirty gowns soiled with food and body fluids. They paced, mumbled, sat and lay on the floor. Some were catatonic; some cried or laughed in shrieking or guttural tones and others rocked back and forth. Joey blandly said, "Here we are, what do ya' think?"

Neither officer answered. They only wanted to get out of there ASAP. Joey recognized their squeamishness and said, "We'll go back another way, after we see the tunnel."

Ballenger looked at his partner and muttered, "Holy shit, the tunnel!" and then swallowed hard.

They exited the ward and Joey led the police officers down two flights of stairs to a steel door in a dark and dank stairwell. Joey fumbled with the key, and then proudly opened the door as if a portal to a garden. He switched on the light bulbs that lined the center of the old ten-foot high passageway built with rough stone walls and an old brick floor. Every word and noise echoed through the long dungeon-style tunnel that intersected with other tunnels from all wings of the old facility.

Joey resumed his role as the tour guide, "Rumor has it, people referred to as idiots, the dangerous criminally insane and those possessed with the devil, were kept here in the late 1800s. They say a bunch of them died here, right where you're standing. Some people believe that their ghosts live on." Ballinger and Pysick looked at the brick floor; their imaginations ran wild as they envisioned miserable deaths on the bricks beneath their shiny black police issue shoes.

Joey stopped along the way and pointed to steel rings in the wall, about five feet up from the floor. A half-dozen rings were about ten feet apart. Ballinger and Pysick had seen enough. They wanted to leave. Joey droned on, "Rumor has it, men who could not be controlled were tied to the rings. They lived down here, some for a long time. I guess they must have died down here, too."

Joey looked at the police officers and said, "Now I personally don't believe there are any such things as ghosts. Do you?"

Pysick said, "Uh, er, no. Hey Joey, I just realized our sergeant must be lookin' for us. We better go, ok? Can you take us back to Admitting?"

"Sure thing," Joey said, with a slight smile. Joey led them back to the gun lockers to retrieve their service revolvers on their way out.

Ballinger and Pysick rushed past several drowsy patients on the large porch near the Admitting entrance. A few feeble hands waved as they went by. The officers could not wait to get back to their police cruiser. It never looked so damn good to them before. As Ballinger shut his car door, he immediately started the car and said, "Let's get the hell outta' here!"

Pysick agreed, "The faster the better."

Their long drive through the main gate and down Wayne Avenue hill toward downtown felt better with each block they passed. The partners quietly mulled over what they saw. The fresh spring air streamed into the windows of the cruiser and never smelled so good.

———◦———

Neal Bradley Long was in Wayne Avenue, out of sight and alongside other troubled souls. DSH had a checkered past when it came to helping sick minds cope or heal. Chances of a significant recovery were low in that large, bureaucratic human warehouse.

TWENTY-ONE

RX: Kick Some Stones

During the intake process at DSH, Long was guarded and evasive in his communication and demeanor. He stated he had been drinking a lot in the past weeks and heard voices about religion and God. Long was photographed and subjected to a series of evaluations; he underwent psychiatric therapy and was given a host of medications to manage his symptoms.

Within a few weeks of admittance, Long was placed in group therapy in an effort to break his cycle of personal isolation and mistrust of others. He outwardly exhibited small signs of improvement in individual therapy and group sessions, mainly due to his heavy medication that masked his dangerous symptoms.

Grace visited Long and began to advocate for her husband's release. She believed that he was better, and his absence was a hardship since she could not read or write. She worked nights at a factory and tended to their six children, ages three to nineteen years old.

After two months, Grace asked that her husband be granted permission to leave DSH for home visits. Weekend home visits were granted and transitioned to longer conditional extended in-home trial visits. The doctor agreed that Long demonstrated mild improvement. His home visits began May 15, 1967, and a social worker took over Long's case.

Long's plan required follow-up sessions at the hospital. His doctor also prescribed medication to help him manage his symptoms: Trilafon 8 mg., Valium 10 mg. and Akineton 2 mg. He promised to follow his doctor's orders. Shortly after his extended trial visits began, Long returned to his old job at Stolle Company.

Long was required to return to DSH on a periodic basis to evaluate his trial visits, monitor his condition and replenish his medications. Long reported for his first scheduled follow-up visit. He did not see a psychiatrist. He met with a Social Services caseworker named Ms. Leach for thirty minutes. She made a few entries into his case file: "Mr. Long was a little bit more verbal and he enjoyed working and being with his family."

Long told the caseworker, "I don't know how to handle my anger, and I still explode."

Given Long's earlier psychiatric diagnosis that he had an "explosive personality," Long's admission that he "still explodes" was a significant statement made to the caseworker.

The caseworker summarized the session,

> He [Long] doesn't know how to explode or take out anger in small doses. The discussion continued along these veins and he said he understood that he would have to learn to ventilate his feelings in one way or another, even if it meant kicking stones or using non-violent methods.

No other notes were recorded in Long's DSH case file. Nothing indicated any significant effort to address the ominous cry for help from Neal Bradley Long when he expressed his inability to manage explosive anger.

Long was given refills for his medication and scheduled for another routine follow-up appointment September 18, 1967.

TWENTY-TWO

The Jailbird vs. Scientific Evidence

Thursday, May 25, 1967, Dayton prepared for the Memorial Day holiday weekend. Nine months had passed since the riot that followed Lester Mitchell's murder; however, memory of the Ohio Army National Guardsmen on the streets with fixed bayonets was still fresh. The holiday brought an opportunity to focus on family and fun. Summer break for Dayton schools was only days away, and swimming pools opened that weekend.

Days that preceded holiday weekends were usually "slow news" periods. Public officials often used the pre-holiday period to "dump" controversial stories into the public. That was precisely why Dayton Police Detective Captain Grover O'Connor briefed black community leaders in private during the early morning. Afterward, he talked to newspaper reporters about new developments in the Lester Mitchell murder case.

Thursday, May 25, 1967, the evening edition of the *Dayton Daily News* contained the following story, written by Staff Reporter Doug Drake. O'Connor was quoted throughout the story.

Riot-Starting Murder Solved, Police Believe

Police believe they know who killed Lester Mitchell, the 39-year-old Negro whose murder last September 1st, 1966 set off West Side rioting. "We have reason to believe that we now have arrived at an investigative solution to the Lester Mitchell murder," Detective Captain Grover O'Connor said.

"As far as we are concerned," O'Connor said, "a murder is a murder, and the books are never closed until it's solved."

"In the Mitchell case, we are faced with contradictory evidence, which is not unusual in most crimes of violence."

O'Connor says police feel they know who killed Lester Mitchell, but nothing can be done about it at this time. The man who police believe pulled the trigger is dead—killed in a Dayton gun battle.

"The man who we feel killed Les Mitchell was working at McCalls," O'Connor said, "and one of his buddies, who is now in jail, told us he called him and told him not to go into work because he bought a sawed-off shotgun for a dollar and was going to kill someone."

Police quoted a "buddy" of the man who they believe did the shooting as stating "the man wanted to shoot either a police officer or a Negro. Only recently we got information from Cincinnati," O'Connor continued, "that confirmed what we had heard about the Mitchell murder."

"The informant told us that he knew the killer bought a sawed-off shotgun for a dollar and that he planned to kill someone in Dayton," O'Connor said.

"He told us the shotgun was sawed-off right down to the grip and was a single-shot gun," he went on.

"The fact that the weapon was so cut-down meant the pattern of shot would be wide-open," O'Connor emphasized. "The city engineers who showed the shot being fired from an alley across the street from Mitchell were wrong since they did not take into account the fact that a sawed-off gun might have been used," he said.

The fatal shot was fired from a car by two or three white men, according to some half-dozen witnesses to the murder. Later police surmised (referring to the engineering analysis on September 13, 1966) that a car carrying the whites passed at the time the shot was fired from the alley and the blast passed right over the roof of the car.

O'Connor stressed the subsequent information indicated the blast was fired from a speeding vehicle.

"This thing is not dead," said O'Connor, referring to the Mitchell case, "just last month we were back into it." The suspected killer was white—the victim a Negro. Neither knew the other, according to police.

The statement by O'Connor narrowed "the killer" to one person, a white man, for the second time.

———◦———

In an earlier *Dayton Daily News* story dated September 19, 1966 titled "Shots fired from across the street in Mitchell Case, Engineering tests determine location," Lt. Schwartz said, "Based on as much scientific evidence as we can bring to bear on the case, we are 99 percent sure Mitchell was shot from across the street."

The news release of May 25, 1967 totally reversed the previous theory Dayton Police put forth when they published results of an engineering study of shots fired the night Mitchell was killed.

The theory and conclusion that Mitchell was murdered by a drive-by shooter gave DPD a way to claim success. They said, "We reached an investigative solution." Captain O'Connor knew jailbird informants often lied, but he accepted it. The case was "solved." Regardless of the public face Captain O'Connor put on the Lester Mitchell murder case when he used an unofficial classification of "investigative solution," the case was officially closed and labeled "Inactive - Not Cleared."

Dayton Police officials previously blamed black witnesses like Leonard Cantrell for starting the riot when they indicated blacks spread untrue rumors. The September 16, 1966 *Dayton Daily News* story quoted police, "It was the *rumor* of that apparently wanton shooting that spread through the city's West Side and inflamed the rioters."

Captain O'Connor did not apologize for DPD's initial rush to judgment and his erroneous conclusion that the black witnesses were wrong.

———◦———

DPD's significant reversal in theories about Mitchell's murder left the case as clear as mud. There was little public curiosity or outcry for proof of

Captain O'Connor's new claim. Perhaps citizens of Dayton were too exhausted after the riot to care. Journalists at Dayton's two newspapers and those in television and radio media took Captain O'Connor's statements at face value and moved on.

Despite being one of the highest profile homicide cases in Dayton's history, detectives did not seek an independent review of their "investigative solution" to strengthen their credibility. The Montgomery County Prosecutor's Office was never asked to review the case of the murder of Lester Mitchell. There was no evidence that DPD polygraphed the "jailbird" snitch or attempted a photo identification of the alleged killer.

Captain O'Connor's Memorial Day weekend announcement about the Lester Mitchell murder case fell into the dust bin of dead-end stories. His pre-holiday news release strategy was a success.

The Great Miami River continued to symbolize separation of races in the city. Nothing much had been gained since the riot. Much had been lost. Except for handfuls of clergy who worked to achieve racial peace, a tense polarization had set in. Uniformed cops assigned to the West Side traveled back and forth across the bridges each day, in and out of two different worlds. Cops knew it was just a matter of time before the police department would have to change, too. They anticipated a rushed campaign to hire black police officers.

Friday, May 26, 1967 Neal Bradley Long was at home and thumbed through a copy of the *Dayton Journal Herald.* His eyes widened. His pulse quickened. He stared at a headline, "Riot starting murder solved, police believe." Beads of perspiration glistened on his forehead.

He slid his right index finger along the printed page very slowly. He was unsure where the words led. His tension eased when he read quotes by Captain O'Connor that an "investigative solution" had been reached. Long's lips curled into a slight grin. He felt assured that he was not a suspect in the murder of Lester Mitchell. Long tore the article from the newspaper and placed it in his shirt pocket. He went to the basement. He removed a cigar box he kept in a secret place. The box was crammed full of newspaper clippings about the murder of Lester Mitchell and the riots that followed. Long was glad to add the new article to his collection. He fingered a few clippings as he stared into the distance. Long re-lived the excitement of his nighttime hunting trip on the West Side as the ridges of his fingertips tingled while he remembered a hot summer night in the early morning hours of September 1, 1966.

----◄o►----

DPD Homicide Detectives no longer thought about the Lester Mitchell murder case. Any effort to nail down more information was unnecessary. The bosses were satisfied. Many white city officials, police and citizens were glad that "the natives" had calmed down and no longer asked questions about the Mitchell murder.

----◄o►----

Back on the first day of the riot in September 1966, when black leaders had demanded removal of two notorious Vice Detectives from the West Side, Bill Riley and J.R. Walley, also known as 'Batman' and 'Robin,' the Mayor had instantly caved in and agreed, over the strong objections of Police Chief Caylor. But in 1967, Batman and Robin were allowed to return to full citywide duty. They were cleared of all allegations raised by black leaders. Batman continued to crush out cigarettes into an ashtray with Cozy Williams' face taped to the bottom.

TWENTY-THREE

It's Déjà Vu All Over Again

"I say violence is necessary, it is as American as apple pie."
—H. "Rap" Brown, Student Nonviolent Coordination
Committee (SNCC) and the Black Panther Party

Brown was later placed on the FBI Top Ten Most
Wanted List, circa 1967, for Unlawful Interstate Flight,
Arson and Inciting To Riot.

Violence ravaged Dayton's West Side during the September riot. It left behind tremendous damage and deepened the gulf between blacks and whites. The DPD was ninety-five percent white and blamed by black citizens and leaders for being too aggressive. Police were also blamed by white citizens because they did not quickly crush the riot.

The handful of black Dayton Police officers faced a mix of reactions from their neighbors and friends. Nearly all black officers lived in West Dayton. Each day, they looked at damage left in the wake of the riot. They could not erase flashback images of helmeted Ohio National Guard troops on their own streets. They could not escape rumblings and angry voices in their neighborhoods and churches that criticized the police. To some, black cops were courageous due to their decision to work for change inside the white power structure. They visibly changed the face of DPD. To others, they were nothing but "uncle toms" who sold out their black brothers and sisters.

———◦———

White police officers also heard hateful comments. The riots tore off the scab and exposed racism in places that once felt holy and safe. Officer Baker attended Emanuel Baptist Church at East Third and Terry Streets in East Dayton. He was married there in 1963 to his first wife, Judy. However, he left the church abruptly when a senior deacon approached him after services and asked, "You boys have the niggers under control yet?"

Baker had already grown tired of the veiled racist comments he had heard for months in the church where he grew up. He was no longer the quiet shy boy who sang in the choir. He was pissed off that the old man was comfortable asking such a question as parishioners stood nearby. Some looked at Baker, curiously awaiting his answer. Baker shot back, "Are you shitting me? You and your attitude is what is wrong with this city! I'm outta here!" He stormed out of the church and vowed it would be a cold day in hell before he returned. Baker's in-laws also attended the church, and bitter arguments about race followed for weeks and added extreme stress to his fragile marriage.

Despite all the violence Baker saw in the first year he worked on the West Side and the outright hatred of police by many blacks, he also saw many decent black people trapped in segregation, poverty and crime. Subconsciously, it was a turning point in his life when he recognized the plight of blacks. Their unbelievable poverty was compounded by discrimination and outright racist hatred, inside and outside the DPD. It was wrong. Baker realized cops were the thin line between civil order and anarchy, and, fair or not, police would be viewed as the oppressor in the ghetto. The conflict weighed on his mind.

As the summer of 1967 approached, more blacks were outside on the streets. Dayton cops patrolled the streets on the West Side and felt the racial tension escalate. Captain O'Connor expected that the "natives," as he called blacks, would have been calmed by his announcement that police had reached an "investigative solution" in Lester Mitchell's murder. But people in the ghetto knew O'Connor was shoveling bullshit.

————◆————

After the riot in 1966, Dayton Police quietly updated their riot control plans, purchased helmets and weapons and improved their emergency call-in procedures. The plan included an agreement to use Brinks armored money transfer trucks for protection against snipers and as backup paddy wagons.

On June 12, 1967, a major riot broke out in Cincinnati's Avondale area that resulted in activation of 1,500 Ohio National Guardsmen. Dayton Police monitored developments fifty miles south of Dayton.

Timing of Cincinnati's riot could not have been worse. By coincidence, at the invitation of Dayton Civil Rights leader Sumpter McIntosh, the famous black militant, H. "Rap" Brown, National Chairman of the Student Non-Violent Coordinating Committee (SNCC), was invited to speak at a rally billed as an "Equal Employment Rally." Brown's nickname, "Rap" was attributed to his rapping cadence. It was unique and easy to follow; thus audiences said, "Rap on Brother Brown, Rap on. Tell it like it is!"

On the evening Brown was scheduled to speak in West Dayton, Cincinnati's riot raged into its second day. Dayton Police braced for trouble due to Brown's reputation for his fiery and race-hate-filled speech.

By 6:30 p.m. June 14th, the crowd arrived for the rally at Wesley Recreation Center, (Wesley Center), near West Third Street. The hot and sunny daylight lingered as the summer solstice was only a few days away. Wesley Center was filled to capacity of about two hundred. It overflowed by the time H. Rap Brown arrived. A crowd of several hundred people milled about outside and listened to speeches over a loud speaker. Dayton Police established a loose perimeter around the area, and several small reserve forces were deployed in paddy wagons a half dozen blocks away.

When H. Rap Brown and his Minister of Defense, Willie Hicks, arrived, the crowd stirred in anticipation. A *Dayton Daily Newspaper* reporter asked Hicks for a comment as he walked in and Hicks said, "We're here to make white men get on their knees."

Brown was easily recognized by his trademark tall afro, dark glasses and moustache. He wore a black suit and tie. Brown joined Sumpter McIntosh on the platform. The air inside Wesley Center was stifling hot, and open windows offered only a faint breeze.

Sumpter McIntosh spoke briefly, but the riot in Cincinnati was on everyone's mind. The crowd anticipated Brown would speak about it. The agenda broke down quickly as people began chanting "Rap, Rap, Rap!" Brown was introduced to a rousing welcome.

Brown did not waste any time before he angrily blamed whites for the riot underway in Cincinnati. The *Dayton Daily News* quoted Brown as he called the Cincinnati rioting "a warning to the honkies."

Brown charged that "Racist white people control radio, television, newspapers and public education as it is today." He escalated, "Anything in your community you don't control is a weapon against black people. The grievances of black people do have a remedy. The people of Cincinnati are setting a good guideline."

Brown tied his message of suppression of black people to the U.S. Government. "President Johnson is the biggest outlaw Texas ever produced. The reason we are in Vietnam is for natural resources. That's why black people are over there, to make the honkies rich." Brown told the audience, "Be non-violent against each other, but non-violence is not the way to deal with whites."

Brown was a skilled speaker. He paused often to let his message sink in. The crowd's mood darkened as anger rose in Brown's voice. The crowd outside became more restless. Some sipped alcohol from bottles in brown paper sacks.

Rap Brown intensified his rhetoric and quoted a new song in the South: "Too much love, too much love. Nothing killed a nigger like too much love." He added, "Black folk ain't free no place! We got to free them, and Cincinnati is well on its way!" He raised his voice a notch higher and yelled, "Take the pressure off Cincinnati! Take the pressure off Cincinnati!"

Brown dramatically climaxed his rant and screamed fresh incendiary words into the microphone. "There are those who say Negroes should go back to Africa if they're not satisfied here. Before we go back to Africa, we gonna' burn this place down to the ground! Burn this place to the ground!"

By that time, many in the crowd inside the center and those outside were on their feet. They shouted, "Burn it down! Burn it down!"

As the meeting broke up, young men ran outside and joined the crowd in the streets. Their anger, profanity and threats rapidly developed into a mob mentality as small businesses on West Third Street became targets for bottles, rocks and looting. A white tow truck driver who happened by West Third Street at the wrong time was pulled from his truck and badly beaten. Carloads of black males sped away to nearby small business districts that came under attack as looting spread. A wide range of hit-and-run attacks spread down West Third Street.

Dayton Police Chief Caylor immediately authorized call in of seventy-five off-duty Dayton Police officers and concurrently requested mutual aid assistance from Montgomery County Sheriff's Office Road Patrol and the Ohio State Highway Patrol.

Following riots in 1966, the Ohio National Guard had improved its response contingency plans. While the riot surged in Cincinnati, Lieutenant Colonel Edwin Girton, Executive Officer of the 371st Artillery-Air Defense Battalion was dispatched to Dayton as soon as the Guard heard of problems with H. Rap Brown. Colonel Girton told Dayton City Manager Graham Watt that he "could have seven to eight hundred guardsmen in Dayton in two to three hours if deemed necessary."

After an assessment, Dayton leaders determined the situation was not as bad as that in 1966, and the matter was handled locally.

Disorder raged in West Dayton until about midnight. Violence claimed several non-fatal shooting victims. A few City Transit bus drivers were pulled from their buses and robbed. Some white motorists and truck drivers were beaten and robbed. Molotov cocktails were used to start fires in vehicles, garages, lumberyards, vacant buildings and a few occupied houses.

An uneasy calm finally took hold as police arrested about sixty people. Dozens of people arrived at Dayton's four main hospitals for medical treatment. The following night, 150 Dayton Police were deployed in West Dayton. The sheriff's office provided about fifty deputies to control the twelve bridges that isolated West Dayton from the rest of the city.

As if it had been pre-arranged, at about 11:30 p.m., carloads of black youths attacked several areas in West Dayton. They smashed windows and looted stores. Calls flooded into the Dayton Police dispatch center.

In a wild turn of events, Dayton fire engines and police cars raced throughout the West Side as they responded to over thirty untraceable false fire alarm telephone calls. False alarm signals from street corner alarm pull boxes were also set off. These distractions allowed more looting while police responded to alarms. However, not all fire alarms were false. A rash of arson fires cropped up in West Dayton during a two-hour span. One of the worst arson fires involved five houses, garages and a few businesses in one block of Conover Street, only one hundred yards from the West Third Street railroad watch tower. A few white people who lived in what was an old Hungarian neighborhood ran for their lives when fire bombs exploded. Vacant houses and businesses were favorite targets. Molotov cocktails were frequently used by the mob. Kerosene cans were tossed into two lumberyards and warehouse docks and lit. Large bundles of fireworks bound like small bombs were thrown into houses and cars. In one case, a gasoline-soaked mattress was shoved into a broken window of a house that was under repair from the 1966 riot. The house had a large amount of paint and thinner inside. To the joy of rioters, the house exploded with a bright flash and loud boom. Columns of smoke rose into the night sky from over a dozen locations.

Some veteran cops offered their opinion regarding the cause of the riot and they were quoted in the *Dayton Daily News*. Lt. Robert Schwartz said it was "devilment."

Another unnamed veteran said, "To me, it was strictly a case of a group of people using the cover of the civil rights movement for the purpose of pillage and looting."

Mr. Edward King, a black man and Director of the Dayton Human Relations Council blamed the breakout, " . . . on the Brown/ McIntosh rally, I think it triggered it [riot]."

H. Rap Brown remained in Dayton until the morning of June 15th, then announced he was going to Cincinnati to see "his people fight the oppressor."

Before Brown left, he told reporters, "Damn the laws of the United States." Upon his arrival in Cincinnati, he talked to reporters and said, "SNCC has declared war."

It had only been nine months since the September 1, 1966 riot when the H. Rap Brown-inspired riot began June 14, 1967. The West Side suffered a one-two punch and it looked like the city was "going down for the count."

TWENTY-FOUR

Shots Fired!

In the early morning hours of June 28, 1967, Officers Crawford, Baker and Roy Guinn were a three-man team that worked the West Side. They patrolled trouble spots and were dedicated to back up other officers as needed.

The temperature cooled considerably as a result of heavy rain that tapered off around midnight. The trio of officers stopped on Western Avenue at Howard's Cafe located across the street from the City Transit bus barn. About twenty-five bus drivers usually filled Howard's well-worn diner for a meal before they went home. Crawford, Baker and Guinn sat on counter stools, drank black coffee and ate sandwiches while they talked with the owner. As they departed the diner, Guinn took a handful of cheap cigars from a cigar box next to the cash register. He laid a $1.00 bill on the counter. Howard merely nodded. He was used to the routine, cops who only paid half, if at all. Baker cringed. He knew Guinn would light up in the cruiser.

The three cops drove toward the area of St. E. to check on mid-week crowds that lingered outside bars on Cincinnati Street. It was closing time. A light rain and mist hung in the humid night air. Crawford drove while Baker rode shotgun in the right front seat. Guinn, a large portly man with no teeth, rested comfortably in the back seat, cigar smoke and all. Even though light rain fell, two police cruiser windows were rolled part way down so officers could hear outside. Guinn's shotgun lay on the rear seat.

It rained harder as the officers traveled south on Cincinnati Street. They approached the intersection of Albany Street, and suddenly a single loud shot rang out and echoed off the quiet streets. A half-dozen narrow two-story houses lined one side of the street, and Irving Elementary

School stood prominently across the street. The officers were sure the shot was aimed at their police car, and it probably came from the houses. Crawford spun the car around in the intersection, pointed its headlights toward the houses, and stopped.

Baker grabbed the radio microphone and shouted, "Shots fired! Shots fired! Cincinnati and Albany!" All three officers jumped from the cruiser and moved through heavy rain toward the houses while they maintained a position of cover. Baker and Guinn carried 12-gauge shotguns. Crawford drew his service revolver.

Suddenly, a second shot was fired. The officers were certain it came from either between the houses or from a window. The weapon's report and its echo on the street made it hard to distinguish if it was a shot from a rifle or handgun. There was no doubt; the gunshot was fired in their direction. The officers took cover alongside a corner grocery store on the same side of the street as the houses. Baker ran to the alley behind the houses and took cover. He looked for anyone who might have fled the scene to the rear.

In less than one minute, police sirens screamed from all directions. Red lights approached in the distance. Captain O'Connor worked in uniform that night on special assignment as commander of the beefed-up patrol teams. While he was in route, O'Connor took command on the radio and ordered all responding officers to "Shut off the sirens, kill the red lights and stop about seventy-five yards short of the location."

As about twenty officers sealed off the area, a major thunderstorm broke loose with lightening, deafening thunder and sheets of rain so hard and heavy one could barely see ahead.

Undaunted by the heavy rain, Captain O'Conner ordered officers to enter each of the nearby houses and search for a suspect. With the confusion and heavy rain, the search process was complicated by families who had been awakened suddenly by gunshots and the storm. Residents were surprised by cops who barged into their homes as they searched for the shooter. The cops were wet, guns were drawn and bright flashlights darted about in the darkness. The families were poor working-class folk with lots of children. They all huddled together as children cried. Adults were angry and demanded answers for the violent intrusion by police in the middle of the night.

Officers were not able to determine exactly where the shots came from or to recover a weapon or shell casings. All the occupants pled ignorance about the shots. After police searched for about one hour, Captain O'Conner apologized to the families and pulled his officers out of the houses.

Despite the fact the shooter was never found, a potentially deadly message was sent to police, perhaps by a Black Panther or a follower of H. Rap Brown. They signaled that a cop could easily be picked off at the right time and place. DPD sent its own message with their fast and aggressive response. If the police were shot at, DPD responded, fast and hard.

Dayton Daily News reported the shooting incident in a small article buried on the back pages of the newspaper. At DPD, announcements at shift change reminded officers to back up one another on calls. The beefed-up patrols continued for a few more weeks.

Officers Baker and Crawford beefed up their own protection. They carried additional rounds of .38 caliber ammunition and put a bandolier full of '00' buck shotgun shells in the trunk of their cruiser.

TWENTY-FIVE

Mission Impossible

*"Maybe the end doesn't always justify the means, but it
sure as hell gets the desired result most of the time."*
—DPD *Vice Squad Detective Bill Riley,*
AKA "Batman"

Captain O'Connor was back at his desk a few days after shots were fired at Officer Baker and his partners on Cincinnati Street. He was concerned by the apparent sniper attack and frustrated with safety challenges officers faced on the street; however, he refused to let the shooting incident intimidate DPD.

In his unguarded moments, O'Connor told stories of how violence was sometimes used in the "old days." He said when he was a detective, he tried to get a confession or critical information from a reluctant suspect. Sometimes "You'd stand him up in the corner and slap him a few times." His philosophy of rough police work bled over to the troops, literally.

Anyone who worked around Captain O'Connor knew occasional use of violence and "skirting" rules and the law by detectives in pursuit of information was necessary and unofficially sanctioned. Although some informant information was developed about activities of the Black Panthers, it was hard to corroborate. O'Connor desperately wanted more intelligence information about the Panthers and any other militant group that presented a threat to police or the public. However, the mostly-white police department had little hope of penetrating militant black groups to gain information.

Captain O'Connor proposed formation of a secret Intelligence Unit within DPD. He obtained support from Police Chief Caylor and other key command staff. Major Robert Igleburger, heir apparent to be the next

Chief, also supported the proposal. It was obvious to Captain O'Connor that DPD had to employ "non-traditional and some illegal tactics" to develop reliable information about militant groups.

O'Connor's goal was to disrupt, in advance, any planned violence, particularly sniper attacks. He believed it was more important to interrupt plans for violence than to let them mature in order to obtain enough information for arrests. It was just too risky.

A new DPD Intelligence Unit was formed. They acquired all resources needed to conduct covert surveillances, including illegal telephone taps, eavesdropping devices and cameras. O'Connor knew the risks of his decision to approve illegal tactics and wiretaps, but he was defiant. It wasn't the first time he "stepped over the line" and risked his career. "Sure, I want to know what the Black Panthers are up to and I'll risk going to the penitentiary . . . " O'Connor said.

A salty veteran detective sergeant named Nick Black was handpicked to lead the unit. He recruited three trusted veteran detectives named Otis Glass, Bill Campbell and Chris Westmoreland. They were joined by one young black uniformed officer, R.T. Ogletree. The fact was, the unit needed a black officer to develop black snitches and to do covert surveillance on the West Side. Ogletree was happy to be on the team, and he received a dream promotion. After only two years on the street, Ogletree became an undercover detective.

The new Intelligence Unit worked out of a secret office located in the city's warehouse district near Leo Street in North Dayton. They had access to cash from an obscure budget line item to rent automobiles, pay informants, pay for hotel rooms or rent apartments on short notice. In addition, they carried false personal identification and had numerous sets of vehicle license plates. Unit members wore clothing to fit their daily work. The DPD Intelligence Unit did not appear on any organization chart. It simply "did not exist."

Confidential contacts and informants were groomed at a local telephone company. Unofficial training on wiretaps was provided to detectives by telephone company linemen and installers. Detectives received highly sensitive telephone numbers to call for closely guarded subscriber information. They were given codes to use when they acted as telephone repairmen who called in to request "pairings and posts" for a specific telephone number that belonged to a target telephone. It was critical to accomplish surreptitious wiretaps.

It took patience and manipulation of informants to acquire the latest phone equipment. The equipment was gathered in three ways to diversify sources. Basic equipment was purchased with cash at local stores. More sophisticated equipment was purchased with cash in other cities near Dayton to reduce traceability. Third, and most valuable, Detective Glass had an informant who was a telephone installer for Ohio Bell Telephone Company. In exchange for "working off" a personally embarrassing prostitution case, the installer was eager to cooperate. The white man knew detectives had a Polaroid photo of him with a black prostitute that they promised to destroy if he did as he was told.

The phone man was given a list of telephone-related equipment detectives needed. Over a period of a week, the installer had to load extra supplies on his truck without his foreman's knowledge.

The installer was instructed to stop at a telephone booth on a specific day and time and call a member of the Intelligence Unit to coordinate a drop-off spot. He was sent to a small restaurant outside the city on North Dixie Drive. He was instructed to back into a parking space at Maggie's in the far corner of the lot, next to a white unmarked delivery truck.

The phone man followed instructions and went inside the restaurant for one hour. While he had lunch, DPD Intelligence Unit unloaded equipment and supplies from his truck and placed them in the rear of their unmarked delivery truck. Spools of wire, hand tools, company shirts with logos, hard hats, gloves, telephone butt-sets, headphones, phone blocks, wiring panels, voltage meters, crampons for climbing wooden poles and a heavy leather climbing belt filled the order. All of this was done under the watchful eyes of a detective who parked nearby to ensure no one else observed the activity.

The Intelligence Unit spent a week going over the new equipment. They practiced installations at home and in an apartment building where one detective lived. They also practiced climbing telephone poles and found it to be physically challenging, and, to no one's surprise, they always looked for an easier way to do a hook-up. It took nerves of steel to risk discovery.

They tried to look official as they climbed a telephone pole or worked in a dark basement of an apartment building where illegal wiretap equipment was attached and hidden. Operations in broad daylight often required them to wear official telephone company uniform shirts. They also used legitimate looking vehicles, tools and equipment. God forbid they would run into a real telephone company employee. As a precaution, a detective always provided surveillance while they worked, just in case the backup crew needed to create a diversion so a fake installer could escape.

Captain O'Connor had a tenuous but necessary relationship with the FBI Assistant Special Agent In Charge (ASAC), in Dayton. O'Connor told the ASAC of his plans to gather intelligence on the Black Panthers. He used cryptic terms and told of DPD's new intelligence capability to know in advance if something involving the Panthers was about to "jump off."

The FBI ASAC was glad to hear it. He agreed the need was real and they needed fast and agile action to respond to threats, not a lot of red tape.

Over the following months, hand-picked FBI agents were kept in the loop. The FBI was glad to reduce a number of their own "black bag jobs." The agents "looked the other way" while DPD did its work. Agents followed up days later and joined detectives at a covert location. They listened to replay of taped reel-to-reel conversations. Agents made notes and used the valuable information to their own advantage.

Once illegal wiretaps and other jobs began, their technical capability improved, and it was rumored that police began to stretch the limits of the law on cases that involved armed robbery gangs, major sports betting operations and some narcotics cases. It was simply too tempting. Cops learned one hundred times more information on a wiretap in a week than in six months of "shoe-leather" surveillance.

Rumors surfaced that Montgomery County Sheriff's Office had also developed its own covert wiretap capability. A well-known businessman became a part-time member of the Sheriff's Department, and it paid off handsomely. The owner of a large electronics warehouse operation was given the status of detective. He gave county detectives full access to everything they needed for illegal surveillance. Like DPD, county detectives could not resist the wealth of information gleaned from surveillances. The elite Intelligence Units mimicked the concept of a new television show aired in 1966, *Mission Impossible*. Opening scenes always warned the main character about discovery of his team, "... if any of them are caught or killed, knowledge of their actions will be disavowed." The DPD Intelligence Unit had cover from O'Connor, unless they were caught red-handed.

The DPD Intelligence Unit gathered actionable intelligence, identified militant ringleaders and disrupted plans for crimes. They funneled information to detective squads who raided locations for weapons, drugs or stolen property. Uniform cops were often directed to make specific traffic stops and detailed searches of suspected militants and their associates that often resulted in arrests. The targeted harassment worked. It enabled the Intelligence Unit to stay beneath the radar while militants wondered who snitched on them.

While DPD conducted its own covert operations, the FBI went full steam ahead, too, but on a different level. The FBI's intelligence-gathering activities increased as "Negro Riots," as the FBI called them, spread across America. The frequency of "black bag jobs" across the country grew as the FBI gathered intelligence on prominent black leaders, known militants and some who affiliated with the Communist Party and anti-war protesters.

———◄○►———

Montgomery County Prosecutor Lee Falke filed a felony violation of Ohio Law 2923.12, *Criminal Syndicalism*, against H. Rap Brown on July 28, 1967. Authorities knew Brown planned a return visit to the Dayton area. On August 1st, Brown was arrested without incident. The Affidavit charged that during his visit to Dayton June 14 and 15, Brown "... advocated crime, sabotage, injury or destruction of property of another, or unlawful methods of terrorism as a means of accomplishing... political reform that preceded a riot." Brown posted bond. When his case was heard by a Grand Jury, no indictment was returned due to a conflict with Brown's First Amendment right to free speech. Charges were dismissed and H. Rap Brown accused Dayton police and the prosecutor of being racists.

TWENTY-SIX
A "Throw-down Gun"

The Montgomery County Fair finished its run on Labor Day and Dayton Public Schools resumed classes without any racial incidents.

Saturday, September 16, 1967, Dayton was blessed with warm weather and a mild evening. Thousands of people in the Dayton metropolitan area looked forward to a well-publicized parade scheduled to kick off in downtown Dayton at 8:00 p.m. Rivaled only by the annual Christmas Parade that commonly drew over thirty thousand onlookers, Dayton Antioch Shrine Temple hosted a major convention that brought thousands of Shriners and visitors into Dayton for three days. Shriner conventions historically included a major parade in the host city. They displayed well-organized bands, motor units, marchers, floats and classic cars from around the country. Their colorful parades were geared to all ages and offered citizens of Dayton a refreshing change of pace. Blacks and whites planned to attend.

By 6:00 p.m., many people staked out spots along a one-mile-long parade route on Main Street. Hotels, shops, restaurants and bars along the route were open to cash in on the event. Street food and trinket vendors hawked their goods.

The most popular souvenir for sale was a replica Shriner Fez, a burgundy color cylinder-shaped hat, six inches tall without a brim. It was made of felt and had a long black tassel. Children and adults bought hundreds of faux Fezzes. Shriners from other cities wore their authentic Fezzes with a different temple or city name spelled out in shiny stones on the front.

Pickpocket thieves from Dayton and elsewhere mixed in with heavy crowds and took advantage of jostling and tight movement of people. Unsuspecting victims did not notice that a bump in the crowd was their wallet or cash being lifted. Prostitutes were also in the crowd and worked hotels and bars. Dayton Police assigned about thirty plain-clothes Dicks who mingled in the crowds and watched for thieves, hookers and other undesirables.

Dayton Police Vice Detectives Robert Collier and David Michael were part of the security detail. Collier was the senior officer with eight years service and Michael had five years.

The Dicks wore dress slacks, casual shirts and sport coats that hid their handcuffs, badges and guns. They borrowed two genuine Fezzes adorned with rhinestone Shriner logos from the Columbus, Ohio Temple. Indeed, the two detectives looked like authentic out-of-towners as they walked among the crowd.

The loud glitzy parade started from Dayton Antioch Shrine Temple at 140 West First Street. As the evening sun dissolved into the horizon, a watermelon sunset comingled with the glow of streetlights as the day melted into a delightful evening. Soft breezes caressed tanned summer faces. Major buildings along the parade route lit every office on each floor, which added a glamorous feel to the city skyline. Rike's Department Store, The Biltmore Hotel, Lowes Movie Theater, The Historic Victoria Theatre, Winters Bank and the Old County Courthouse were all aglow.

Officer Baker worked overtime in uniform on foot patrol in advance of his regular 11:00 p.m. shift. The Shriner Flag Corps and Legion of Honor led the parade, followed by groups of musicians, including the pipe and drum corps. Children and adults alike applauded the Mounted Patrol as it passed by on their well-groomed horses. Cheers and laughter blended into a constant buzz as "Funster Clowns" came by in their colorful costumes and rode miniature red vehicles. Clowns stopped often and played tricks on children and one another along the route. The Shriner Marching Patrol, Troubadours and faux Bobbies wore their London Police helmets and looked smart as they performed synchronized drills every fifty yards along the route. Classic cars from the 1920s and 1930s weaved their way down the streets. The Shrine Motorcycle Corps paused along the way and demonstrated precision riding and figure eight movements. Harley Davidson motorcycles were fully decked out in bright Shrine colors and lights. A Four Wheel Midget Motor Car team showed off their skills and garnered huge laughs and giggles from the crowd.

By 9:30 p.m., the last of the parade made its way past the main viewing stand in front of the Montgomery County Court House. Many viewers were so enchanted by the mild night and one-of-a-kind parade that they lingered on the streets and some remained in their lawn chairs and on blankets and chatted with newfound acquaintances.

After midnight, hundreds of people still roamed downtown. Detectives Collier and Michael were in and out of a half dozen bars, including the King Cole restaurant at East Second and Ludlow Streets. They drove an unmarked police car. Around 1:00 a.m. they stopped at a traffic light. The detectives observed a man near the corner at West Second and Ludlow Streets. They could not determine the man's race due to dim lights, but his movements caught their attention. They believed his actions were suspicious.

The man was Robert Barbee, a light-complected black man in his early 40s from Findlay, Ohio. He was a Social Security Administration employee in town visiting friends. Barbee was on his way to his parked car. Barbee saw the two white men as they got out of their unmarked car and walked toward him. He turned as they approached him. The two men still wore their Fezzes. Detective Collier believed he saw the butt of a gun tucked in Barbee's trouser waistband when Barbee's jacket opened. Collier ordered Barbee to stop but Barbee quickened his pace to get away from the two men. Detective Collier yelled, "Police!"

When Barbee turned his body to look back, he again exposed what looked like the butt of a handgun. Collier believed Barbee was armed and about to draw a weapon. Collier suddenly drew and fired his weapon. He struck Barbee twice, once in the side and once in the back as he spun around. Robert Barbee crumpled to the sidewalk, mortally wounded.

Both detectives rushed to Barbee. Detective Collier got to him first. He immediately opened Barbee's jacket to retrieve his weapon. Collier was shaken to his core when he discovered the object he thought was a gun was instead, a common tobacco pipe tucked in Barbee's trousers. The bowl protruded above his waistband.

In a split second of sheer panic, Collier grabbed the pipe, put it in his jacket pocket and told his partner, Michael, that he got the gun. Collier was visibly upset. Suddenly Collier said he had to go home immediately. He ran to the detective car and sped away as his portable red light flashed and the siren screamed. Detective Michael was puzzled by Collier's bizarre departure as he knelt down to help Barbee.

A crowd formed, and a black female friend of Barbee screamed that police shot Barbee for no reason at all. Word of the shooting spread like wildfire among blacks in the area and soon throughout the West Side. Barbee was removed by ambulance and later died at the hospital.

Detective Robert Collier raced about four miles to his home on Dayton's East Side. He ran inside and frantically looked through his personal belongings and retrieved a cheap off-brand small-caliber pistol. Collier never said a word to his wife who was awakened at about 1:30 a.m. and startled by his sudden appearance. Collier rushed back to his car, made another emergency run, and returned to the crime scene. He was visibly nervous when he turned over a pistol to Homicide and said it was the gun he removed from Barbee's waistband. Detectives were suspicious of Collier's conduct and told their supervisors that Collier's story and actions were highly unusual.

There was no late night news coverage in Dayton, save two radio stations, WING and WDAO. Station WDAO was in West Dayton and broadcasted with a black music and talk format. The disc jockey interrupted programming with news of the shooting. Initial news coverage reported the incident as a legitimate shooting of an armed man by Dayton Police. However, Barbee's friends were shocked to hear police claimed they found a gun on Barbee. They told detectives he never carried a gun. Barbee commonly tucked his wooden smoking pipe stem down inside his waistband. His friends called radio station WDAO and said Barbee was unarmed and WDAO broadcasted the allegation. Rumors spread quickly.

By 8:00 a.m., Detective Collier broke down under questioning and admitted he panicked when he found Barbee's pipe in his waistband instead of a handgun. Collier said he rushed home and got a gun. The small handgun was stolen months earlier by Collier during a raid of an illegal bootleg joint. Collier decided to keep the gun rather than turn it in to the Police Property Room. Detectives Collier and Michael both insisted they feared for their lives. They believed, under the circumstances, that Barbee was armed and turned toward them to draw a gun. Collier admitted he falsified his story that he recovered the gun from Barbee; however, Collier insisted he had to fire his weapon in his own self defense. Collier immediately retained a lawyer and invoked his Fifth Amendment rights.

Percy Vera, a Professor of Economics at Sinclair Community College, was a black man with strong opinions about Barbee's death and his mistrust of cops. His personal opinion was shared by others. "They planted a gun. I guess all cops have that extra gun inside their socks. One of them pulled out his extra gun and stuck it in Barbee's hand."

This incident unearthed a secret practice known to quite a few police at all levels. Some law enforcement officers often talked confidentially about an extra handgun they carried in their duty box or hid in the trunk of a cruiser. Their throw-down guns were cheap handguns found or stolen by police during an arrest or raid and never turned into the agency property room. The serial number was usually ground off and therefore difficult to trace, just in case there was a shooting of an unarmed man.

Detective Collier was suspended from police duty that afternoon, pending further investigation. City Manager Graham Watt and Police Chief Caylor huddled to plan how to notify black leaders and the press about Collier's lie. They knew the news could trigger demonstrations and police quickly increased the number of officers on the street in anticipation of problems.

City Manager Watt called a special meeting of the Dayton Human Relations Council the next day. Out of "concern for complete candor," Watt detailed Collier's false story to the *Dayton Daily News*. He hoped sharing information with the Council would deter demonstrations and violence. He pledged to "pursue an effective and aggressive prosecution" of Collier.

Although Collier insisted he fired his weapon in self-defense because he believed Barbee had a gun and turned to draw "the weapon," he was charged with one count of manslaughter. Collier remained free on his Own Recognizance Bond. He was never physically arrested, which infuriated the black community.

By afternoon, news of Barbee's death and the lie told by Detective Collier grew into a firestorm on the streets of West Dayton. Crowds formed on street corners. Blacks were shocked that a man of Barbee's reputation was gunned down by a cop who planted a gun when he tried to cover up his mistake. Anger grew like a pot that boiled over.

After the Barbee shooting, cops who had a throw-down gun realized how stupid it was. They saw the perils of planted evidence and all the lies that followed. The practice faded but it did not totally disappear. However, a few cheap handguns were thrown into the river.

----◄○►----

"Black Power! Black Power!" Angry voices broadcasted over loudspeakers and reverberated off buildings and parking lots in the heart of West Dayton. Even though it was a Tuesday night, a large crowd converged in the parking lot at the corner of West Third and North Conover Streets and attended a rally to protest police shooting Robert Barbee. Ironically, it was only two blocks from the former home of Paul Lawrence Dunbar, a famous peace-loving black poet born in 1872.

The angry crowd of all age groups included many young black men. It also attracted a large number of rowdy people who spent most of their days on the street corners, in dope houses and bootleg joints.

The rally was planned by the Non-Violent Direct Action Committee, Dayton Alliance for Racial Equality (DARE), Moving Ahead Together (MAT) and the Ohio Freedom Movement. The first speakers did little to calm the mood of the crowd that continued to grow. Nearly six hundred people attended and demanded action. Many cars were parked in the lot. Young men sat on car roofs and fenders, consumed alcohol and gained false courage as they drank. Charles Tate, Chairman of DARE, enraged the crowd when he yelled, "The cracker cop who shot your brother was freed and there was no bail! We want justice! We want justice!"

Lawrence Nelson of MAT yelled, "We . . . need to organize against the honkies!" Nelson went on to urge coming together to fight the police and he described how " . . . the Indians were wiped out because the tribes stayed apart."

As the violence-tainted-rhetoric continued with other speakers, the crowd rocked back and forth and chanted, "Let's burn! Let's go downtown. Let's burn whitey out!"

The crowd reached a fever pitch, and speakers could no longer be heard. Motorists stopped along West Third Street and blocked all four lanes and drivers got out, listened and watched. The streets became a parking lot. Officers Crawford and Baker stood outside their police cruiser in front of Winters National Bank at West Third and Broadway. The roar of the crowd was easily heard by the officers.

Baker reflected on how he enjoyed the Shriner parade a few hours before Barbee was shot. As he stood and watched a mighty hate-filled black storm form just two blocks away, the memory of a mild summer night and thousands of happy people at a parade, black and white, seemed like a world away.

A handful of young black men at the rally grew tired of the talk. They climbed atop hoods of cars so they could be seen by hundreds of people. At that point, they drowned out the rally as cheers rose louder to encourage them. One of the young men took his shirt off and waved it in circles over his head. He yelled, "Black Power! Let's go! Let's go downtown," and he pointed east toward the business district around Third and Broadway and downtown Dayton, just across the Great Miami River. Suddenly, many in the crowd responded to his call, "Let's go!" The mob ran out of the parking lot onto West Third Street and weaved their way through cars parked in the street. Hundreds of people, mostly young men in the lead, smashed every store window in sight. They carried clubs, bottles, rocks and anything they could throw.

Baker and Crawford had not worn their new riot helmets. Officers were told to wear soft uniform hats only, so as not to look too aggressive. They both thought that was just plain stupid, but there they stood, as ordered. Every street cop knew there would be trouble that night, but DPD commanders pretended that the wild crowd up the street would just say a prayer and go home.

The roar of the crowd grew louder as the mob charged toward the intersection where Baker and Crawford stood alongside their cruiser. "Holy shit!" Baker said. "They are headed right for us!"

Crawford reached inside his police cruiser, grabbed the microphone, and yelled to the police dispatcher, "The crowd has broken up and is running toward our position at Third and Broadway. They're throwing everything and smashing windows!"

Suddenly shots were heard from the area of the mob. Crawford urgently added, "Shots were just fired, too!" Just then, their police cruiser was hit with rocks. Without permission from the brass, the officers grabbed their helmets from the trunk.

The mob moved toward them and grew in size. Their advance was slowed because they looted as they moved east toward the river. The officers got into their cruiser, pulled around the corner, and moved a block away. At that point, police commanders directed officers to assembly points that allowed for a few minutes of coordination. The officers then moved back into the main trouble zone.

For the next eight hours, blacks rioted and looted through West Third Street and other pockets of West Dayton. Police were in pitched battles with crowds that threw rocks. During the first two hours of trouble, Governor James Rhodes was so concerned about Dayton's situation, he called Mayor Dave Hall around 9:45 p.m. and offered Ohio National Guard troops, if needed. The Governor placed 250 soldiers on active stand-by at the Troy, Ohio Armory, about twenty-five miles north of Dayton. Mayor Hall expressed his appreciation to Governor Rhodes for his offer but declined after consultation with Police Chief Igleburger.

Over one hundred arrests were made that night. The paddy wagons and Brinks armored trucks transported maximum capacity loads of rioters to the City Jail.

At West Third and Summit Streets, a crowd gathered in front of Accountant David Jones' office around 10:30 p.m. Jones, a thirty-four-year-old well-known black man, wore a suit and tie and stood on the top steps that led into his office. He yelled at police and waived his fists as he incited about fifty people who stood on the sidewalk. There was a mixture of men and women in the crowd. Some men in suits and women in dresses joined with intoxicated street thugs. All yelled threats and obscenities at the police as they worked to disperse another larger crowd in the middle of the street. Baker was one of a dozen uniformed officers who pushed people up the street while he ducked bottles and rocks. When a few glass bottles were thrown from Jones' crowd into the left flank of the police team in the street, the sergeant in charge decided to break up the Jones mob. He took Baker and three officers over to the crowd on the corner and ordered the group to disperse. Instead, Jones' crowd became more defiant and the sergeant radi-oed for additional officers to assist. Two detective cars with about six men in plain clothes responded, but they were about two blocks away.

Baker wore a helmet with a hard plastic face shield and he carried a thirty-inch-long wooden riot baton with leather straps. Suddenly, a rock came from Jones' crowd and hit the sergeant in his chest. Baker and other officers immediately pushed into the middle of the disorderly group. It was a bad move.

The crowd suddenly opened up like the parting of the Red Sea and swallowed up Baker. One of the mob members grabbed the end of Baker's riot baton while other members of the mob got behind him and pushed him up the steps. Baker was unable to get free of the leather straps wrapped around his left wrist. He felt himself being pushed and pulled up to the top step where Jones stood in an open doorway to his office. Jones leaned forward, arms outstretched and incited the crowd and yelled, "Bring him in! Bring him in!" Baker heard someone yell, "Get his gun!" Baker grabbed his pistol grip and held it tight with his right hand as he felt others' hands pulling on his weapon. The crush of the crowd was so tight and violent the gun did not come loose.

The crowd pushed harder. "Bring him in and close the door!" Jones commanded.

Baker could not overcome the mob's momentum. He felt punches to his ribs, back and stomach. Baker saw a very dark black man with a three-inch scar on his left cheek reach up under his face shield and try to poke his eyes. The man screamed, "Dirty Pig!" Baker closed his eyes tight and turned his face but not before he was scratched.

Baker heard screams of pain from the mob just behind him as other police officers moved in to rescue him. Jones and a half-dozen men backed into the office as Baker was pulled and pushed inside.

The tide suddenly turned as detectives fought their way into the office. Four detectives got inside and Baker felt the push-pull momentum subside as he was freed from the mob's grip. Jones ran behind his desk and sat down. He sat up straight in his chair and yelled to the top of his voice, "I'm a black man in my own office!" as if it somehow created a force field to protect him.

Jones was placed under arrest, but he refused to comply with police orders to get up from his desk. He yelled, "I'm a black man . . . CRACK! "I'm a . . ." CRACK! Baker did not have to look to know what had happened to Jones' head. A detective in a riot helmet tapped Jones' head with a club every time he resisted and opened his mouth. Jones was dragged from his chair, across the floor and out the front door.

Accountant Jones rode in a Brinks armored truck to City Jail. As he was unloaded from the truck, he saw Mayor Hall. Jones immediately tried to pull political strings. It was obvious Jones had sustained a head injury, so the Mayor had his handcuffs removed.

Jones was sure the Mayor showed deference to him when he had the cuffs removed so he boldly complained about police brutality and demanded to know why he was arrested. Jones' confidence and arrogance rose even more when the Mayor left to check out Jones' complaint.

According to the *Dayton Daily News*, when Mayor Hall returned to address Jones' complaint he curtly informed Jones, "You were raising hell, inciting the riot and resisting orders. That is why you are under arrest!" The "hot-shot" got even hotter. Jones was pissed. He eventually contacted Judge Arthur Fisher and was released for medical treatment. Jones received five stitches in his head. Upon release from the hospital, he returned to DPD Headquarters and complained to Police Chief Igleburger. Although Jones had his audience with Chief Igleburger, he was unable to identify who hit him. Chief Igleburger was not sympathetic.

After the Black Power rally, Chief Igleburger responded to numerous complaints of police brutality. News accounts alleged " . . . unnecessary unruly tactics employed by Dayton Police." The next day, Igleburger was quoted in the *Dayton Daily Newspaper*. "I didn't see any bad conduct on the part of officers, but I wasn't able to see everything. I can tell you one thing, I don't think any officers acted any different than their normal police instincts called for anywhere Tuesday night." Baker and a hundred other Dayton Police officers and detectives could not have agreed more.

———◁◦▷———

News of Robert Barbee's death at the hands of a white police detective was elevated to the national level. The fact that a gun was planted on Barbee made headline reports. It was picked up by *AP* and *UPI* wire services and reported across America.

———◦———

In late September 1967, Ms. Leach, the caseworker assigned to Neal Bradley Long's follow-up sessions, sat at her desk in a crowded office at Dayton State Hospital (DSH). Her in-basket was crammed full of paper. She gathered energy with a strong cup of coffee and started to work.

After an hour and a second cup of coffee, she came across her reminder file for "Neal Bradley Long Follow-up Session—September 18, 1967." She reviewed the notes. "Mr. Long failed to appear for his Conditional Home Trial Visit update as scheduled. No call was received for re-schedule." The caseworker paused and mulled, *We had him on a lot of medication and his prescriptions have expired.*

The caseworker decided not to make an effort to contact Long or his wife. No other entries were made in Long's file. Dayton Police were not notified that Long had dangerous symptoms and failed to return. The "conditional" release had no penalty clause.

Neal Bradley Long was in the city without medication to help control his distorted thinking. He self-medicated with alcohol and marijuana. Advice from DSH that he "kick some stones" when his anger felt out of control was a distant and confused memory.

———◦———

As if racial tensions were not high enough, Dayton Police learned of another rally with racial overtones. Alabama Governor George C. Wallace planned a visit to Dayton just two months after Barbee's death.

Wallace was most famous for his gubernatorial inauguration quote in January 1963: " ... I say, segregation now, segregation tomorrow, segregation forever." Wallace was building name recognition to declare himself a third party candidate for President of the United States.

Governor Wallace, a fervent supporter of states' rights, resisted federal interventions to achieve desegregation. On June 11, 1963, in a scene of defiant discrimination, he blocked the door to Foster Auditorium at the University of Alabama to halt enrollment of black students. Wallace was confronted by U.S. Federal Marshalls and then he stepped aside, but only after his brief speech.

Governor Wallace, a World War II Veteran with the United States Marine Corps and an attorney, was pleased to learn that his Dayton rally would be held at Memorial Hall in downtown. Dayton Police prepared for Wallace's November 14, 1967 visit and anticipated protestors.

The weather was mild for November, and Memorial Hall was filled to capacity with an all-white crowd of men, women and children. Outside, it was a different story. An organized protest involved several hundred blacks and a handful of whites who marched in front of Memorial Hall. As whites passed blacks on their way inside, heated words were exchanged. Police, dressed in riot gear, formed a single line between marchers and Wallace rally attendees that precluded fights.

Thirteen DPD Harley Davidson motorcycles lined up in the middle of the street in front of Memorial Hall. They were positioned to respond as needed on a moment's notice.

Baker spent most of three hours as part of a fifty-man reserve force. DPD deployed five police paddy wagons one block away from Memorial Hall. Each wagon carried one sergeant and nine officers equipped with helmets and riot batons.

Even though tension was high, Wallace's visit went off without a major incident. However, the visit sent a chilling message to blacks in Dayton that racism was alive and well. Many whites were glad to see Wallace and the outpouring of white support, including some police officers who opposed the push to integrate the races.

———◄○►———

Neal Bradley Long attended the Wallace rally. He did not like that he had to walk past black protesters at the entrance. He was sick of their chants and protests. He sat by himself at the rear of the crowded auditorium. Although he agreed with Wallace's core beliefs about separation of the races, he believed that control was slipping away from whites.

A few weeks after George Wallace's rally, Officer Baker was surprised when he received a personal letter from Governor Wallace, as did all members of the DPD security detail. It was handed out at Shift Change

Roll Call like it was an award. On Wallace Campaign letterhead, dated November 29, 1967, George Wallace wrote a personal thank-you. It said in part,

> "... In every speech I make, I tell my listeners that
> I stand with the police in this country. If you are
> allowed to do your job, the problem of law and order
> will be solved."
>
> Signed,
> George C. Wallace

Officer Baker bristled that Wallace made the solution to racism and riots sound so simple: "Just let the cops do their job."

George Wallace came in a distant third in the 1968 Presidential election that was won by Richard Millhouse Nixon. Wallace won only five states, all in the south.

TWENTY-SEVEN
Street Justice

Street patrol. The paddy wagon cruised along West Third Street. Thank God it was quiet. Baker and Crawford talked over a wide range of topics as cops do when on patrol. Officer Baker and many other cops were idealistic when they joined the DPD. Baker knew the job and its trying times would not be perfect or free of ethical conflict. During the riots and months that followed, Baker got a crash course in dealing with violent people. Crawford said, "Things are still tense out here; it's going to be a long while before things cool off on the street. Remember, if we get into a tough arrest situation that starts to get out of hand, you better be a couple of seconds quicker to hit some bastard with your stick if you have to."

Baker didn't offer a word. Thoughts tumbled through his head as a tug of war was underway in his mind. He rationalized that "street justice" has its place in policing.

"Now Baker, you can do what you want, but I'm still looking for a couple of those ass-holes who tried to hurt me or one of you guys during the riots. If it takes a year, I'm gonna even some scores. You can do what you want. If you have a few to settle too, I'll back you."

"Ditto," Baker said without hesitation as he remembered a few rioters who were particularly vicious or interfered when officers made arrests. In the confusion, quite a few escaped into the crowds. Baker learned how the old timers saw the situation. The "bad guys" thought they had gotten away without paying the price. Not so. A check had been written—payable to street justice. Some cops waited for the right time to cash in.

Baker had one more score to settle. For months, he tried to identify a dark-skinned black male with a three-inch scar on his left cheek. He looked through random mug shots and talked with snitches with no luck.

One afternoon, before going on duty, Baker stopped by Dick Section to see Detective Beu-tell. Baker was a little nervous about approaching Beu-tell with such a minor issue. He waited outside the Homicide Office until Beu-tell called him in.

"Ye, ye, yeah, Officer Baker, wh,what you ne, need?"

"Well sir," Baker said, "I'm looking for a guy from the Barbee riot that reached under my riot face shield and tried to poke my eyes out. It happened during the big mess outside accountant Jones' office. I want to find this guy, if you know what I mean. The son-of-a-bitch got away."

Beu-tell looked at the young officer over his reading glasses and grinned. "Okay, wh, what does he look like?"

"Black, dark, very dark, in his 30s. Six foot tall, a scar on his left cheek about three inches long."

Beu-tell opened his desk drawer and removed a shoebox full of Polaroid pictures bound together with rubber bands. Stacks were separated by race and characteristics. There were whites, blacks, light skinned, dark skinned, visible scars, gold teeth and teeth with diamonds. "This is how I keep 'em. These are ro, rogues I kn, know. Look 'em over, I gotta go." As Beu-tell walked out, he said, "Good hun, hunting, Baker."

Baker found the photo he was looking for. He turned it over; Beu-tell's notes indicated a nickname and labeled him a small-time thief and an addict. It was also noted that he drove a faded green two-door Chevrolet with no rear bumper. Baker made a copy and put it in his shirt pocket. The hunt was on for a man with the nickname "Crawdad."

———◦———

It was 3:30 a.m. when Baker was on patrol with a fill-in partner. Baker saw a car parked along the curb that matched the description of Crawdad's car. The hood was up and a man was bent over the car with what appeared to be car trouble. Baker drove the paddy wagon past the car and went another block and turned around in the street. "I'm going back to the broken down car. I think it's a guy I need to talk to," Baker said. As they pulled up behind the car, Baker said to his partner, "Why don't you have a cigarette. I'll be back in a minute." The other officer did not have to be told what the stop was all about. He lit up and waited patiently.

Baker offered, "Can I help you, sir?"

"Well, yeah," said the thirty-year-old black man with a three-inch scar as he slowly raised his head up. Crawdad's expression tightened when he looked at Baker's face. "Now wait a minute, Baker," Crawdad said as he backed up against the fender of his car.

"Wait for what? You want to talk now? You didn't want to talk when you tried to dig my eyes out under my face mask during the riot," Baker said.

Baker removed his battle-scarred hickory billy club from the ring on his belt and pressed it hard into Crawdad's solar plexus. He said, "I'm sorry man, I was high . . . " Crawdad gasped for air as Baker held the billy club for about 30 seconds without saying a word before he released the pressure. Crawdad's knees buckled, and he fell to the ground as he labored to catch his breath. Baker walked away and said, "We're even, Crawdad. See ya' around."

Baker and most other cops, black and white, rationalized 'payback' in simplistic terms. Baker believed rogues and thugs, who took cheap-shot attacks on cops needed to know someday they would have to pay a price. Thus, the practice of targeted 'payback' persisted. Regardless of race, cops closed ranks on this issue. Cop logic held that without 'payback,' the destructive criminal element would know no bounds.

TWENTY-EIGHT

A Near Miss

The Christmas holidays of 1967 helped mask racial tension in the city. Downtown was in full holiday mode with decorated department store windows that enticed pedestrians to stop and gaze at festive scenes. Rike's huge downtown department store at Second and Main Streets had mechanical Christmas displays in six windows. Scenes depicted elves hard at work as they built toys. Families crowded the windows and held children up to see. They laughed and pointed as puppets moved. Shoppers crowded sidewalks, and the black and yellow trolley buses were filled to capacity with passengers.

At DPD Central Police Station, the atmosphere was a bit more relaxed on Christmas Eve. Food trays and potluck dishes were spread around on tables. A Christmas tree with bright red blinking lights stood duty in a corner of the Assembly Room.

Shift changes came and went and officers knew working during holidays was one of the uncomfortable requirements of a cop. Everyone wanted to get on duty, stay safe and go home. Officers Baker and Crawford worked the 3:00 p.m. shift, and they hoped for a quiet night on the West Side. Crawford knew from experience that Christmas Eve was unpredictable. A lot of lonely people mired in poverty mixed with alcohol and drug use did not handle holidays very well. It was a dangerous and unpredictable area of the city for cops.

A thin layer of snowfall masked ugly parts of the West Side destroyed or vacated during the riots. As soon as Patrol Crew 336 hit the street, Baker and Crawford knew it would be a tough shift. Family trouble calls and disturbances at a handful of bars and bootleg joints dominated the call load. Within the first six hours, Crew 336 also responded to a shooting that turned out to be a homicide, and detectives were called in.

As the night sped by, there was no time to have more than a cup of coffee and a Christmas snack shared with nurses at the St. E. Emergency Room. By 10:00 p.m., Crew 336 responded to a dozen calls and the grind continued until 10:45 p.m. when Crawford pointed their police cruiser toward the West Third Street Bridge and headed into downtown and off duty.

"Car 336! Car 336!" The dispatcher's voice sounded urgent. Crawford looked at Baker as if to say, *Should we answer?*

"Car 336!" Crawford reluctantly answered the radio call.

The dispatcher said, "Go to 317 South Summit Street, a disturbance. The time is 10:50 p.m."

Crawford threw the microphone at the dash board and said, "That rotten bastard. A routine disturbance call! That's it? It couldn't wait?"

Crew 336 pulled up in front of the house and noticed it was completely dark. A narrow concrete walk-up porch led to a door. The partners were pissed and anxious to dispose of the call quickly as they walked up the steps. Since the porch was narrow, they could not stand to the side of the door, which cops always did if they could, just in case someone shot through the door.

No light was seen inside and no noise was heard. The officers decided to check and make sure nothing was wrong inside. Baker stood in front of the screen door and noticed a heavy wooden door behind the screen. He used his left hand, rapped on the door frame, and announced, "Police!" There was no answer.

Crawford said, "Do it one more time and then let's get the hell outta' here."

Baker elevated his voice and announced again; "Police!" No answer. Just as the officers turned to leave, they heard a squeak as the old door knob turned. Baker spun around as the heavy door opened suddenly and a revolver was thrust toward him. The barrel pushed against the screen near Baker's face. In a split second, he barely saw the black man in the darkened house as he pointed the handgun straight at Baker. His gun was unsteady as the man tried to squeeze the trigger. Time seemed to slow to the pace of a scene from a motion picture that advanced ever so slowly, one frame at a time. Baker's eyes and his brain struggled to comprehend the imminent danger as the man attempted to shoot the officers.

Illumination from a streetlight in front of the house allowed Baker to glimpse tips of bullets in the revolver pointed at his face. Instinctively and without hesitation, both Baker and Crawford ducked and moved fast. Baker snatched the screen door open and lunged inside, low and from the side of the man. Baker grabbed the man's gun just as he was taught to do in the Academy. He placed his left hand in a death grip over top of the cylinder of the cheap revolver. Baker felt the cylinder rotate a bit as the man squeezed the trigger.

Crawford entered right behind Baker and grabbed the man from behind. He drew his gun and pressed it against the back of the man's head. Simultaneously, Baker drew his revolver with his right hand and jammed it against the man's ribs. In the darkened room, both officers yelled at the man who mumbled incoherently and did not let go of his weapon. After a few seconds that felt like minutes, Crawford yelled, "Shoot him if he don't let go!"

The man relinquished his grip on the gun and the officers gained control. Baker shoved the man's gun down to his side, and Crawford pulled it free. Baker smashed his fist into the man's face and knocked him to the floor where they handcuffed him in the darkened room.

The partners breathed heavily and looked at each other. They realized how close they had come to death. The officers dragged the handcuffed intoxicated man outside to the cruiser and shoved him into the back seat. The drunken man mumbled that he had mistaken the officers for people he had thrown out of his house earlier that evening.

During the ride to jail, Baker rode in the back seat behind Crawford and next to the prisoner who continued his incoherent cursing and rambling. Baker replayed the scene over and over in his mind. He doubted himself. Baker wondered if he had hesitated too long to decide if he should shoot the armed man. The guy was "paid for," as cops said in legitimate shootings. Baker wondered, *Were we just lucky? My partner or I could have been killed tonight, on Christmas Eve, for christsake.*

Baker concealed his delayed reaction that suddenly surged through his mind that he and his partner were somehow spared from being shot. For a few seconds, his hands trembled but he snapped back to reality when the prisoner spat on him and yelled, "You dirty mother fuckers!"

Baker instinctively slapped the man in the mouth with the back of his hand and he was surprised that he hit the man, but it eased his tension, and his hands did not shake anymore. The prisoner continued to be difficult when he was booked in the city jail. He resisted fingerprinting. The DPD jailer, a cantankerous man, grew impatient and yelled at Baker, "Control your prisoner! Why did you guys bring me this asshole?"

Baker twisted the man's wrist so hard, the man fell to his knees and begged in pain to be allowed to get up and finish fingerprinting. As Baker and Crawford walked out of the jail, the jailer yelled angrily, "And don't come back. Its fucking Christmas Eve!"

Crawford and Baker could not wait to get out of that miserable place.

The officers finished their reports around 12:30 a.m. Christmas morning. The partners walked to the parking lot. Crawford turned to Baker and said, "I'm glad you didn't shoot the son-of-a-bitch. We'd be doing reports for days and miss Christmas."

He laughed as he said it, and Baker saw that the incident bothered his partner, too. Crawford added, "You did good by jumping him so fast and grabbing that piece of shit gun like you did."

Crawford's confidence was extremely important to Baker. He felt a deep respect and trust for his partner that night. They wished each other Merry Christmas and got in their snow-covered cars.

The peaceful snow-covered scene of Christmas morning in the city was in dramatic contrast to his episode of life-threatening violence a few hours earlier. Baker was preoccupied and he paid little attention as he drove by the scenes in Rike's department store windows that he loved to see as a young child. He drove in silence to his small nine-hundred-square-foot house that he and his wife rented on the north side of Dayton.

A week before Christmas, Baker and his wife bought a small scrawny live Christmas tree at a cut-your-own tree farm near Tipp City, Ohio. The tree was tucked in a corner of the living room, decorated with blinking lights.

His wife of three years, Judy, waited up for him. Fresh warm brownies and a cold glass of milk rested on a nearby table. Baker was welcomed home with a hug as he shook snow from his shoes and took off his police issue black leather jacket and gun belt. He did his best to hide his troubled thoughts and flashbacks of scenes on the porch and inside the gunman's house.

At about 2:00 a.m., Baker told his wife to go on to bed and that he would be in soon. He still felt mentally numb as he relived the scene when the drunk man pushed his gun against the screen door, inches from his face.

Baker laid on the sofa in the tiny living room. Sleep finally came. Baker's wife came out to the sofa a few hours later and placed a soft afghan blanket over her husband and looked down into his young face. Deep down, she knew the man she called Danny was changing very rapidly, in so many ways. His once-simple aspirations and views of life were more complex. His personality was not as soft. His day-to-day work on the West Side, the riot duty, a few on-the-job injuries and his passion for the job all turned him into a different man. She feared for his safety when he worked on the black side of town, but she knew he thrived on police work. He told a lot of stories about criminals he dealt with. He also talked about many decent black people he met, food they ate, music they listened to, all introductory exposure to a culture that he was coming to respect and trying to understand.

Baker began to drink for the first time in his life, and he enjoyed off-duty time when he hung out with other cops. His vocabulary became rough and foul. He grew impatient and restless when he was off duty for a few days. He perked up when it was time to get back on the street. When he talked to his cop friends at parties or on the phone, Judy overheard stories about rough arrests and danger. Baker occasionally came home with a torn uniform. He was "juiced" on the action. He bitched about Internal Affairs complaints and "candy-ass" supervisors who crimped his work. His wife tried desperately to hold back the change but those quiet and predictable days were gone. As his wife returned to bed, she knew the "Danny" she dated since high school and married at Emmanuel Baptist Church had slipped away. She knew down deep that their marriage would end someday, like so many other cop marriages she knew about. She could not compete with his other love, the action on the street.

As the gentle glow of Christmas tree lights reflected softly on his face, Baker slept all night on the sofa, still in his police uniform. He needed to sleep. He was scheduled to be back on duty on the West Side at 3:00 p.m. Christmas Day.

TWENTY-NINE

Foreman, You May Read The Verdict

The Montgomery County Common Pleas Courtroom No. 3 was filled with news reporters, citizens and off-duty police officers. It was 4:30 p.m. January 23, 1968. Extra sheriff's deputies were on duty. A group of fifty people, mostly black, were unable to get into the courtroom and they maintained a vigil in the hallway. Another crowd of seventy-five blacks marched in a circle on the sidewalk in front of the courthouse. They carried signs and chanted, "Justice, justice, we want justice."

A handful of attendees included well-dressed black ministers; some wore white clerical collars, Homberg dress hats and crosses that dangled from long chains. Other black men and women wore bright colors and traditional African-print clothing. Women dressed in flowing brocade outfits or dashiki's and hausu kufi hats sat quietly on benches while men paced in their colorful agbada clothing and Malo kufi hats.

Many whites were unaccustomed to seeing African garb. Some felt uncomfortable by the appearance. They did not understand the desire of blacks to reconnect with their roots and proudly claim their African heritage amid turmoil in America.

The jury deliberated for only four hours and surprised everyone when they signaled that a verdict had been reached. Television cameramen were poised in the hallway to film interviews.

Judge Robert McBride entered the courtroom and settled into his chair. He gave the gallery time to settle down before he instructed his Bailiff to bring in the jury. Six men and six women quietly filed into the jury box following their short deliberation. The trial lasted five days, and court-watchers were taken aback at how quickly the jury reached a decision.

The foreman of the all-white jury gave a written verdict to the clerk, who handed it to the judge. The judge opened the note and silently read it. He then returned it to the foreman. Tension in the courtroom peaked. The jury foreman paused and stared at the paper in his hand.

People seated on benches in the gallery struck a variety of poses. Some had bowed heads, others leaned forward, a few covered their mouths or faces and there were those who sat stiffly. Some people, including family members of Robert Barbee, sobbed quietly and wiped their eyes. Detective Robert Collier stood next to his attorney and braced for the verdict. At the adjacent table, Prosecutor Herbert Jacobson stood ramrod straight.

Judge McBride opened with a very strong voice, "Foreman, have you reached a verdict?"

The foreman replied, "Yes, your honor."

"You may read the verdict," Judge McBride commanded.

The foreman cleared his throat and began, "Regarding the single charge of Manslaughter in the First Degree, we the jury, find the Defendant, Robert Collier, 'Not Guilty.'"

Gasps and screams of disbelief echoed in the courtroom as four deputies moved to form a line in front of the gallery. Detective Collier slumped down in his chair, his head bowed; he was limp with relief. The judge struck his gavel several times and ordered all in the courtroom to quiet or he would clear the courtroom.

News of the verdict flooded into the hallway. Groans and cheers filled the air. After he regained order in the courtroom, Judge McBride thanked the jury, read final instructions and dismissed them. The judge then declared the case completed and told Detective Collier, "Your bond is released and you are free to go." The judge heard the clamor outside his courtroom and hastily said, "Court is dismissed," and he disappeared from the bench. Collier was quickly ushered from the courtroom through a rear door.

Many blacks were shocked but most were not surprised at the verdict. They believed the case was rigged from the beginning.

The jury rejected the prosecutor's claim that the shooting of Barbee was reckless and wanton and that Collier made up the story that he believed he was in danger for his life. Instead, the jury focused on Detective

Collier's state of mind and believed that he had acted reasonably and in self-defense when he believed Barbee was armed and about to draw a gun.

The fact that a stolen gun was planted on Barbee was an event after the fact. Collier had not been charged with tampering with evidence or any other criminal act. The planted gun and subsequent lie told by Collier did not sway the jury from their primary focus on Collier's state of mind when he fired his gun. Detective Collier immediately left the courthouse and went into seclusion.

Major Harry Book, Acting Police Chief, was informed of the verdict. He immediately ordered the head of Patrol Operations to implement a riot response posture with additional officers placed on duty in the downtown area and the West Side. News of the "Not Guilty" verdict spread through the city and hit *AP* and *UPI* wire services. The story of a cop found "not guilty" for killing an unarmed black man spread across the United States. The planted gun inflamed the story. Many viewed the Collier decision as one more example in a long legacy of injustices by white cops who "walked away" after killing blacks.

Dayton Police officers had mixed feelings about the shooting of Barbee. They knew what it was like to be in a situation when a suspected armed man did not cooperate. Most, but not all cops deplored the fact that Collier planted a gun on Barbee.

It wasn't long before officers were reminded of Collier's "throw-down gun" move when they made arrests on the street. For a long time, whenever police made arrests, onlookers ran to the scene and watched the police "just in case they tried to plant a gun."

In wake of the Collier verdict, community activists and clergy tried mightily to hold the line and prevent reactionary street violence. Hard lessons of the past two years made it clear that self-destruction of the West Side was not the answer to real or perceived police misconduct. Hundreds of blacks had been arrested in previous separate riots. Three black men had been killed by whites in less than two years: the man killed by Dayton Police in McCabe Park in August 1966 that resulted in Baker's transfer to the West Side; the death of Lester Mitchell in a drive-by shotgun shooting September 1, 1966; and Robert Barbee's death in September 1967.

Following Detective Collier's "Not Guilty" verdict, Dayton's black leadership channeled their anger to demonstrations, and they marched to protest the court decision.

————◄○►————

Out of public view, several black groups rejected the non-violent approach. They secretly planned for retaliation against the 'honkeys' at DPD. In fact, Dayton Police Captain O'Conner was told by DPD's Intelligence Unit that threats by black militants had been uncovered to "get a police officer in a vulnerable position", to get even.

————◄○►————

A large rally was held at the vacant parking lot at West Third and North Conover Streets on Friday, January 26, 1968. Over five hundred people marched and protested the acquittal of Detective Collier. Before the rally, a flyer was distributed that gave an ultimatum to the City of Dayton Police. Although billed as a non-violent protest, the flyer threatened violence in retaliation if more blacks were shot by police.

"This is the last rally. This is our final warning. This racist city must decide whether it wants to treat black human beings with dignity or whether it wants to be destroyed. We want to put this town on notice that we will not see another black man barbarously gunned down in the streets without retaliation in kind."

Charles Tate, Chairman of the Dayton Alliance for Racial Equality, called for a boycott of downtown stores and said, "For black people there will be no Easter and Christmas in 1968." He added, "We are no longer afraid. We shall boycott, we shall strike and we shall shoot when we're threatened by white racists."

Civil Rights leader Sumpter McIntosh joined Tate and others as the march made its way east on West Third Street to the bridge that spanned the Great Miami River. As they reached midpoint of the bridge, the march stopped in silence to reflect on the hated symbolism of the bridge and its line of demarcation between blacks and whites. The group then continued into downtown where it ended at West Second and Ludlow Streets, the exact location where Barbee was shot. After prayers, marchers broke up and a few hundred walked back across the Great Miami River to West

Third Street. Each step on the bridge took demonstrators deeper into the forsaken part of the city where poverty, discrimination and violence lived on.

———◄○►———

Within a few days after acquittal, former Vice Detective Collier resigned from the DPD. The *Dayton Daily News* reported,

> ... Collier issued a statement saying he hoped his resignation would assist efforts to maintain peace and tranquility in the City of Dayton. Collier further stated, "... I personally felt that further efforts to remain in the department would only contribute to an atmosphere of unrest."

Acting Police Chief Major Book was also quoted as he accepted Collier's resignation and dropped all departmental charges including "false reports to a superior officer, failure to deposit with the Property Room a gun seized in a gambling raid and altering a crime scene." Book was curt in his explanation and said Collier's resignation "rendered the matter moot." When Book addressed the subject of the gun Collier kept for himself, Book said, "Collier would not face legal action regarding his failure to turn in property." Book defended his decision not to pursue the matter further when he said the owner of the stolen gun had been shot dead in a gambling house argument. "Who's your complaining witness?" he asked rhetorically.

To many blacks, the "we can't do anything because the witness is dead" story used by Dayton Police had worn thin. It sounded like the other story Detective Captain Grover O'Connor told the *Dayton Daily News* in May, 1967 when a "jailbird snitch" told police he knew a guy who may have shot Lester Mitchell in 1966 and started the major riot; but alas, the alleged killer had himself been shot dead.

Robert Collier collected his severance pay of $2,266.35 and left town. Within weeks, he was hired to be a State Liquor Agent by the Ohio Department of Liquor Control in Columbus, Ohio. State Liquor Agent Robert Collier's new job required him to carry a gun.

———◄○►———

January 26, 1968, Caseworker Leach at DSH processed paper and reviewed Neal Bradley Long's file. Four months had passed since his "no-show" appointment in September 1967. She annotated the file as follows:

> Mr. Long didn't come in for his last appointment, (September 18, 1967) and apparently is not interested in the Trial Visit Program. The social worker has waited a length of time for him to come in or his wife to call, neither has done so, therefore, the social worker recommends "discharged."
>
> Signed,
Ms. Leach, Caseworker

————◦►————

A firearm is an inanimate object, but in a man's hands, it can stir the dark corners of his soul. Feeling its weight, the cold metal, a wood stock or a knurled grip, tantalizes the senses. It may even stir a tingling sexual sensation as the heart beats faster and endorphins drip into the nervous system. Eyes widen. When most men hold a weapon, they instinctively raise and extend their arm and hand as they point the weapon. Some see nothing at the end of the gun sights while others have visions of something or someone. With each pull and click of the trigger and each imaginary round, a troubled mind can gain courage for an unthinkable act.

A few blocks from Emmanuel Baptist Church on East Third Street, Neal Bradley Long sat in his rented half-double house at 39 South Torrence Street. He was alone in a dark room, except for the glow of his nineteen-inch black and white portable RCA television set that rested atop a rickety TV cart. As the Channel 7 anchor read news of the day, he led with protests by blacks about Detective Collier's acquittal for the death of Robert Barbee.

As Long sipped from a Tupperware cup half full of Old Grand Dad Whiskey, he was unmoved by the anger of black men and women dressed in their African garb. As he watched, he cradled a sawed off 12-gauge shotgun on his lap. After another swig of whiskey, he placed the cup on the floor beside his chair. The weight of the shotgun offered comfort and strength to a weak mind. Long stroked the shotgun, opened the empty breech then closed it with a flourish. A parade of black faces in African garb moved across his TV. Homicidal ideation had become common for Long as he visualized cold blooded murder. Long raised his shotgun, pointed it at the people and tracked them across his screen. "Click." A feeling of satisfaction welled up inside him as he took aim again and again. Long "shot" at as many coloreds as he could.

Long had his own long list of grievances about Negroes in Dayton. He was pissed off when rioters burned the Kuntz Lumber yard in a riot in 1967. He once worked at the lumberyard and could not understand why "the coloreds" burned down places just for the hell of it.

Long heard stories of whites attacked on the streets on the West Side and rumors of white women raped by coloreds. He also believed Dayton Police were afraid to do their job on the West Side. Long accepted rumors and stories as truth. He swallowed his hate and it came to rest in his churning gut.

Long continued to stare at his TV. While his eyes were transfixed on the television screen, he reached for his bottle of Old Grand Dad. Since living alone, Long had adopted a new habit. He placed the bottle of whiskey and a small new testament under his pillow and lay down.

THIRTY

Three Famous Men

The news flashes shocked America. Hundreds of radio and television stations blared loudly with the a news bulletins:

April 4, 1968, shortly after 6:00 p.m., "Dr. Martin Luther King, Jr. has been assassinated in Memphis, Tennessee while standing on the outdoor balcony of the Lorraine Hotel. City braces for trouble. National Guard Troops have been ordered to Memphis."

As the tragic story spread across the United States, it sparked riots in over one hundred cities, including Dayton and Cincinnati. Dayton police handled a small riot and did not call in the Ohio National Guard. However, Cincinnati was forced to call in troops for the second time in less than a year.

Eventually, violence gave way to overwhelming sadness of Dr. King's sudden death and cooler heads prevailed. Memorial and religious services were planned. The impact of King's death affected all races. In Dayton, many blacks and whites joined ranks in the time of grief. Dayton's clergy, black and white, worked more closely for a while, but many blacks remained suspicious about whites' motives. Decades of discrimination could not be quickly washed away by a few tears that flowed down the cheeks of white faces.

A few days after Dr. King's death, Dayton joined hundreds of cities around America and held vigils and solemn marches in his memory. Approximately one thousand blacks, joined by white clergy and white citizens, gathered at the rally parking lot on West Third Street and organized a prayerful procession. The crowd slowly walked down the middle of the street and headed downtown. They crossed the West Third Street Bridge and continued into the core of the city for a service at the Old County

Courthouse. Churches on both sides of the Great Miami River held special services in honor of Dr. King, and they prayed for a peaceful end to racial violence.

Suspicion and mistrust of Dayton Police continued following the riots of 1966 and 1967 and the violent death of Robert Barbee. Some marchers believed Dayton Police posted marksmen with high-powered rifles on a dozen building rooftops along the route. One man told his wife as they pushed their child in a stroller, "Honey, I think we are in the middle of something. Look up. They will shoot us if somebody gets out of place."

Dayton Police did not have marksmen on roofs to shoot at marchers. Instead, they wanted to keep a low profile on the street so they used high vantage points to observe, as well as protect marchers from anyone else who tried to harm them. When the Chief was told of the rumor, he lamented, "No good deed goes unpunished."

The death of Dr. Martin Luther King, Jr. (MLK) left an immediate vacuum in the Civil Rights Movement. Militant leaders rose to fill the gap. The new angry leaders openly challenged King's followers who continued to embrace non-violent civil disobedience. Stokely Carmichael saw King's death as a sign that blacks needed to aggressively fight for their rights and shed techniques of non-violence and passive resistance. That was echoed by growth of the Black Panther Party with its leader, Huey Newton, and his mantra of an aggressive self defense. The Panthers flaunted their constitutional right to keep and bear arms.

Members of the Black Panthers were seen more often in black jumpsuits, black berets and combat boots. Huey Newton's picture often appeared with H. Rap Brown on posters that proclaimed, "Power to the People!" fists and guns raised defiantly.

———◦———

Another senseless assassination shook America once again, and the black community in particular. Presidential candidate Robert F. Kennedy (RFK) was in the Ambassador Hotel in Los Angeles for a rally with supporters of his primary race. As a primary candidate, he was not afforded Secret Service protection, and he relied on a handful of private bodyguards. At the conclusion of his rally, RFK took a shortcut through the kitchen area of the hotel to attend a press conference.

At about 12:30 a.m., (PDT) and 3:30 a.m. (EDT) June 5, 1968, the pathway to the conference room was cramped and crowded with supporters who cheered as RFK walked by.

In the crowd, just within feet of RFK, Sirhan-Sirhan, a Palestinian, waited with his handgun. All of a sudden, gun shots rang out. The cheers and exuberance were replaced with horror stricken pandemonium. Sirhan-Sirhan shot RFK three times before he was subdued. RFK was hit once behind the left ear, and two bullets entered under his armpit. Five other people were wounded by stray bullets. With six people shot, there was utter chaos at the scene and in the hotel.

RFK was removed to a hospital where he was pronounced dead. Sirhan-Sirhan plotted to murder RFK because of his support of Israel. Sirhan-Sirhan purposely selected that very day to kill him. It was the one-year anniversary of the first day of Israel's famous Six Day War with Palestine that reclaimed territory for Israel in a decisive victory.

Most Americans did not immediately learn of RFK's murder due to the late hour and lack of nighttime television programming. Greeted by bulletins on the early morning radio and television shows, the nation awoke to yet another terrible Kennedy tragedy. His brother, President John F. Kennedy, (JFK), had been assassinated in Dallas, Texas, in 1963 by a Communist named Lee Harvey Oswald.

Black people across America had a strong bond with JFK and RFK and supported their ideals. With RFK's death, many blacks believed whites would never support a president who embraced blacks as equal citizens. Assassination of the three men, Martin Luther King, Jr., John F. Kennedy and Robert F. Kennedy, over a period of five years, fed wild conspiracy theories and undermined hopes and prayers of many blacks for an end to segregation.

The initials of all three famous men were fodder for psychics and prophets. All of their last names began with the letter "K," as in *KKK.*

THIRTY-ONE

New Blood

November 1, 1968, Crew 336, Officers Baker and Crawford ended their joint crew assignment and were individually reassigned. An influx of new hires since early 1968 broke up a lot of good crews so experienced officers could serve as training officers for new probationary officers. DPD conducted two recruit classes per year and added about fifty officers. With an infusion of new blood and a mildly successful effort to recruit minorities, about fifteen percent of the new hires were black, mostly men.

Baker and Crawford had forged a good relationship, and they were known as one of the best teams of uniformed officers in the city. They accepted the change and moved on, both wiser and glad to have survived some rough times.

Crawford enrolled at the University of Dayton. He took advantage of a brand new free tuition opportunity offered in the University of Dayton's new Criminal Justice Program. The Federal Omnibus Crime Control Act of June 1968 recognized a need to provide more education for law enforcement officers and established the Law Enforcement Assistance Administration (LEAA).

Baker was so caught up working the street, he did not see the need for college. He stayed on C Platoon.

Officer Baker was selected by his newly promoted sergeant, Bill Riley, former Vice Dick known as "Batman," to take on a new partner, a black officer named Tony B. Spells. Spells and Baker had worked together for a week a few months earlier when Spells was on Academy Field Duty. Their week together had gone well.

Spells was a handsome dark-skinned black man who stood six feet tall and weighed about 220 pounds. His quiet demeanor and quick smile were trademarks of his personality. He was a native Daytonian and attended school on the West Side.

Sergeant Riley was supportive of minority hiring and believed Baker was receptive to work with a black partner more than some other officers. Sergeant Riley took a personal interest in the two men and he expected success. DPD command staff was slow to assign two black officers together. They were not ready for that much change.

Baker knew he and Spells were scrutinized as if under a microscope. A lot of white officers did little to support black hiring and believed hiring and performance standards were lowered to reach quotas. There were white officers who were hyper-vigilant about the new blacks and highlighted every petty difference. Distrust of black officers seemed automatic. Some white officers watched to see if new black cops would be tough on black citizens who broke the law.

———◦———

Baker and Spells worked the 3:00 p.m. to 11:00 p.m. shift on Beat 336 in the West Side. Baker had over two years of West Side experience under his belt. He learned pretty fast through the riots and under Crawford's critical eye. Baker was knowledgeable of gambling, prostitution and narcotics activity and key locations. He enjoyed an aggressive style of policing and established a solid reputation for high activity.

A few black officers cautioned Tony Spells about his new partner. Baker was known to have a high numbers of felony arrests and more frequent use-of-force incidents than other cops. Spells remembered an active and enjoyable week during his Academy Field Duty with Baker, and he took the talk in stride and made his own decisions. Spells knew good cops had high arrest numbers and they were more physical on the job. He was ready for action.

When Baker worked with Spells, it was the first time in Baker's life that he worked full-time with a black man. He looked forward to it, but his family expressed concern that if he worked with a black on the West Side, it would lead to problems since "blacks always stuck together." Baker was also a man who listened to his internal voice, much like Spells did, and he ignored the negative concerns.

At the beginning of their first day, Baker and Spells sat in their cruiser in the parking lot. Baker told Spells he was glad to work with him, and added, "Relax, just take it slow for awhile, Tony." Then Baker started through the same routine he got from Crawford on his own "day one." "Tony, don't touch the radio, I'll answer. Don't unlock the shotgun unless I tell you to. Don't plan on driving for awhile. If the sergeant comes around or calls, I'll do the talking."

Spells gave Baker a glancing look and broke into a smile, "Okay, I got it."

Baker started to tell Spells to remove his nametag, just as he had been told as a rookie, then he stopped before the words came out. "I was going to tell you to take your name tag off," Baker said. Then he held up his hand and rubbed his white skin on the back of his hand, looked at Spells and said, "Hell, if anybody wants to complain about us, it will be real easy to I.D. us. We stick out like a sore thumb!"

Baker and Spells both laughed, and it broke the ice. They were one of the few "salt-n-pepper" teams in the police department.

Baker silently wondered about Spells and what his thoughts were as they crossed the West Third Street Bridge into part of the city where Spells' family lived every day. Baker could not imagine what it was like for Spells when he answered police calls near his home, his parent's home, his old schools and playgrounds. A new black cop was on patrol in the West Side with a young white partner. It was new ground for both men.

The chemistry was right. The partners bonded as they shared experiences and their backgrounds. Most occurred during gaps in work while they rode on patrol, on coffee breaks and in the Hospital Security Office at St. E., shooting the breeze. They talked about their families, hobbies, sports, food and life. Those things became the glue for their partnership. The unspoken outcome of these interactions was realized when the two officers worked together long enough to anticipate the other officer's thoughts or actions. Both talked about how much they wanted to become a homicide detective some day.

When Baker and Spells got out on foot to deal with something on the street or in crowded bars or clubs, they capitalized on things said about them. "Here comes them 'salt-n-pepper' cops. They'll get you if you be black or you be white!"

While on patrol, Spells and Baker discussed racial issues in the city and in the police department. It took a while, but Baker shared some of his own personal opinions and experiences. Baker confided, "Tony, you're the first black guy I've ever worked with."

Spells challenged him, "Oh, you silly bastard, the first black guy? What about the black girls, you leavin' them out?"

"Seriously," Baker said. "You're pretty much it, ok?"

"Well, I worked at the GM Plant," Spells said, "and most of the guys there were white, okay? So I been around guys like you, so what? I've even seen you guys eat chicken and watermelon!"

"Well, for me," Baker said, "it doesn't make any difference, you're my partner."

Spells changed the course of the conversation and replied, "Well Bake," calling Baker by a short name for the first time, "I see you've noticed the black girls when we go in some clubs like Peyton Place or the Inn Crowd." He rolled his eyes at Baker and said, "I think they notice you, too."

Baker was not sure how to respond. "I got to admit, I never really noticed black women before working the West Side, but I gotta' say, some of them look pretty good to me. Man, the big afros, dark skin and the way they rap to me is pretty damn interesting. I love the music and atmosphere in the bootleg joints."

Spells burst into laughter, "Aw shit, now Bake, you better slow down, those girls are more than you're used to! This is the fast lane out here, boy."

"What about you?" Baker asked Tony.

"You mean white girls?" Spells asked.

"Yeah."

Spells smiled, "I've known a few."

The police dispatcher suddenly interrupted their conversation. "Car 336, respond to the Palace Bowling Lanes on West Third Street, a shooting in progress."

The siren screamed and red light flashed as the two officers headed toward trouble. Their closeness was evident as they changed their focus back to the job. The glue between partners began to harden.

———◄○►———

Spells and Baker eventually ended their uniform assignment together. Spells became a training officer and worked a full-time uniformed patrol beat on the West Side. Both Spells and Baker knew they had a special chemistry and believed they would team up again someday. Their off-duty friendship continued to blossom.

Baker was elated when he was notified he had been transferred to Detective Section. His high quality felony arrests and knowledge of rouges on the West Side paid off. It was an honor to be selected so early in his career. He went shopping and bought two dark blue blazers, two pair of grey slacks and black wing-tip shoes. Baker was determined to "look the part" on day one.

THIRTY-TWO

"Officer Down! Officer Down!"

"The wicked flee when no man pursueth: but the
righteous are bold as a lion."

—*Proverbs 28:1, KJV*
(Inscription at the National Law Enforcement Memorial
Washington D.C.)

It was not long before Officer Spells was an experienced patrolman.
Even though he was well-known on the West Side before he became a
cop, Spells' name recognition grew rapidly when he became one of the new
waves of blacks who joined DPD after the riots. His time with Officer Baker
helped his job skills evolve quickly, and he desired to do more than answer
radio calls. In late 1969, new police officers were hired, and Spells continued his assignment as a field training officer assigned to patrol #336.

In early December, Officer Spells was introduced to his new rookie
partner, James Lee Mobley, a twenty-one-year-old white man fresh out
of the Academy. Spells shook hands with Mobley and told him to meet
in the parking lot after roll call. Spells was delayed as he had been given a
note to see Shift Lieutenant Robert Stevens.

Lieutenant Stevens was gray at his temples and looked crisp in his white
uniform shirt, black tie, gold bars and badge. He was a "no-nonsense" man,
but he always treated his men fairly.

"Officer Spells, I want you to look after the Mobley kid. As you know,
his dad was with DPD for a good long while, but he got sick and had to
leave the job."

"Yes sir," said Spells. "I'll look after him."

"His dad, Lee, called me today and asked where his son would be working and in which district," the Lieutenant said as he rose from his desk and

walked around to face Spells. Spells began to feel uneasy, not sure where the conversation was headed. "I told his dad about you, that I trust you with his kid, and he'd be working the West Side. Spells, you gotta' know, his dad was more than okay with it; he ain't asking for favors."

Officer Spells thanked the Lieutenant. As he prepared to leave, Spells started to salute but was interrupted by Stevens. "Tony," he said, as he extended his right hand, "be safe."

Officer James Mobley was the second member of his family to serve with DPD. He grew up on Dayton's north side. His father, Lee Mobley, was forced to retire on disability after sixteen years when he had major surgery to remove a brain tumor that impaired his vision and caused paralysis on his right side. Lee and his family were full of joy when James graduated from the Academy. Lee knew the risks of the job, and he always had a nagging feeling of apprehension when his son James was on duty.

Officer Spells met Officer Mobley at their police cruiser and checked their equipment. Spells turned in his seat and looked at Mobley who was wide-eyed. He looked a bit nervous as he sat stiffly in his seat. He knew the speech was coming. His dad had prepared him well for the "don't touch anything or say anything" speech all rookies had to listen to. Spells began, "If the dispatcher calls, I'll answer. Don't touch the radio until I say you can. Don't unlock the shotgun unless I say so. If the sergeant calls or stops to talk to us, I'll do all the talking. Got it? One more thing," Spells said. "I'll do all the drivin' for a while, too."

Spells had to look away when he finished the old-time cop rundown. He tried to conceal his grin as he thought back to when his partner, Baker, put him through the same drill on his first day on patrol.

Mobley felt good as their police car left the station and arched over the bridge that spanned the Great Miami River into the West Side. Lee asked his son to call each day and just let him know how his shift went and to say "hi" when he got off duty, no matter what time of day or night. Each time he hung up the telephone, Lee counted one more safe tour of duty for his son.

———◦———

The first few weeks on patrol passed quickly as Spells and Mobley learned each other's habits and quirks. The cold January weather and slow call load allowed more time to talk as they prowled city streets. When Spells and Mobley reported for duty Saturday, January 24th at 3:00 p.m., Mobley talked non-stop about his plans to be married February 7, 1970. Mobley was excited as he shared details about his fiancé, Chris Hunter.

Spells listened patiently and occasionally flashed his smile as he watched the young man wave his arms as he talked. Mobley told how he spent "this very Saturday morning" with his younger brother Mike and others as they were fitted for tuxedos. He and Mike were very close brothers. They shared the same bedroom at their parents' home. Mobley talked about dozens of gifts his fiancé expected to receive at two upcoming bridal showers. Mobley invited Spells and his wife to attend the wedding ceremony.

The cold weather and light snow produced a slow night for crew #336. Spells and Mobley stopped at St. E. Emergency for coffee in the security office. Before they finished, the police dispatcher interrupted.

"Car 336! Car 336!" The high pitched emergency tone followed.

Spells reached for his radio microphone clipped near his left shirt pocket. "336, St. E., go ahead."

"Car 336, good, you're close," the dispatcher said. "A stabbing at 540 Bolander, 9:40 p.m." The emergency tone sounded again. "The suspect is a black male, wearing a long shirt, no coat. He left the scene on foot."

Both officers dumped their coffee and hurried out to their car. The red emergency lights flashed overhead and their siren yelped as they left St. E. and turned onto Cincinnati Street. The dispatcher also sent a second crew to the scene as backup.

They approached the address within three to four minutes. Spells and Mobley slowed when they saw a black man as he walked on the sidewalk near the scene. It was cold and light snow fell. They noticed the man was not wearing a coat. He wore a long shirt, not tucked in his trousers, and carried a six pack of beer bottles.

The pedestrian appeared intoxicated, and the officers believed he could be the suspect. They stopped the man who identified himself as Albert Payne, age fifty-six, with an address on Dakota Street, approximately twenty blocks away.

The officers got out of their cruiser and gave Payne a quick pat down. No weapon was found, and Payne was placed in the rear seat of the cruiser, directly behind Mobley. Payne was not handcuffed. Payne mumbled and cursed. Spells got behind the steering wheel of the cruiser and was ready to drive another block to the victim's location to meet the backup crew. Officer Spells shifted the cruiser into drive. Before the car moved, Payne began cursing louder. Payne suddenly leaned toward the front seat. He pulled a handgun from beneath his shirt. The handgun was missed by officers during their pat down. Without warning, Payne fired the weapon.

Bang! . . . Bang! . . . Bang! Bang!

The first three shots were fired in rapid succession. All three bullets hit Mobley.

The first bullet entered the left side of his neck. The second into his chest. The third bullet hit him in his left side. Mortally wounded, Mobley screamed in pain and opened his car door. At the same time, the cruiser lurched forward as Spells turned in the seat with his gun drawn. Payne then shot Spells once in the right shoulder. Payne jumped from the back seat and ran. Spells opened his car door, ran around the cruiser and chased Payne.

Spells yelled at the top of his voice, "You dirty mother fucker!" Spells held his service revolver in his left hand and shot Payne once in the side. The bullet exited his groin. Payne instantly fell to the ground. The shooting was over.

Spells grabbed Payne's gun and ran back to the cruiser and found Mobley critically wounded and bleeding heavily.

Snow glistened on the street under a streetlight. The white snow rapidly turned red as Mobley's warm blood spread over the ground.

Spells screamed into his radio, *"OFFICER DOWN!! OFFICER DOWN!!"*

Spells fell to his knees beside his partner. He tried to prop Mobley up, but Spells grew weak from his own wound and loss of blood.

As other police officers arrived on the scene, they found Spells and Mobley as they lay together on the red bed of snow. Spells desperately clung to his young dying partner, as if he could somehow save his life. Spells pleaded, "Oh no, oh no . . . God no!"

Dayton Police Officer James Lee Mobley died in surgery January 25, 1970, a few months after he joined the force, just fourteen days before his wedding was scheduled to take place. Mobley's family was devastated. His fiancé and his eighteen-year-old brother were in deep shock. His mother, and most of all, his proud but seriously-ill father, suffered unimaginable grief. Their faith, family and the brotherhood of police officers helped sustain them.

James Lee Mobley was among 218 law enforcement officers who died in the line of duty in the U. S. in 1970.

———◦———

On a very cold and sunny January morning, hundreds of uniformed police officers from all over Ohio and from many other states across the country stood at attention as the Police Bag Pipe Corps finished playing "Amazing Grace."

"Attention!" DPD Sergeant J.R. Hopkins barked out the order as he had done at other police funerals. Officers braced to his order. He choked back his own emotions and his recollection, since he was one of the first to arrive at the scene of the shooting. Sergeant Hopkins methodically led the procession through its duties. In silence, troops stood patiently. The hearse moved slowly to the burial ground as "Taps" was played.

Tears streamed down Officer Spells' face as he and his family stood with Mobley's family. They bore the unbelievable burden of their loss. Spells remembered the fresh and excited face of the young policeman. He painfully recalled words Lieutenant Stevens said to him when he discussed Mobley, his new rookie partner on day one of their time together. "Tony, be safe."

Officer Spells was surrounded by friends and fellow officers, including Baker, but no one could carry his burden. Spells replayed the scene over and over in his mind. As the senior officer, Spells second-guessed himself. He relived their steps. Payne was not thoroughly searched for a weapon. He was not handcuffed before they placed him in the rear seat of their cruiser, behind his partner.

Spells dreaded Payne's trial. He knew he had to relive that horrible night in the cold and bloody snow on Bolander Avenue.

———◦———

Neal Bradley Long saw news coverage of Officer Mobley's murder and follow-up stories about his funeral. Long was unmoved. He felt no emotion as the sad story unfolded about Mobley's family. Long was focused on his belief that "the coloreds" were still out of control. They assaulted whites for years and got away with it. Now a white cop was killed by a "colored." Long could not understand why Dayton Police were afraid to do their job and stop the "coloreds."

———◄○►———

Lieutenant Riley, who originally paired Spells with Officer Baker a year earlier, worked hard to help Spells return to duty. Riley pulled strings behind the scenes and landed a position for Spells as a detective, assigned to the Intelligence Unit. Spells accepted the new assignment and returned to work after two months off. He slipped away from view of most people in the police department and became immersed in the unit's clandestine operations.

Officer Tony Spells was able to heal physically, but the mental anguish and scars seared into his memory remained forever. He lost his partner. Survivor guilt plagued him. He lay awake at night and questioned God as to why he did not die instead of his young partner.

Days that led up to January 24th of each year that followed Officer Mobley's murder were misery for Detective Spells. He did not work on January 24th ever again, no matter what. Spells traveled alone to the cemetery and stood by Mobley's graveside. Time at the graveside was made far worse when it snowed.

Albert Payne was tried and convicted of the murder of Officer James Lee Mobley. Payne was found guilty and sentenced to death; however, he died of natural causes while on death row.

Neal Bradley Long. Dayton Daily
News Archive. Wright State
University.

Rookie DPD officer Dan Baker.
Authors' collection.

Dayton, Ohio Police HQ. Authors' collection.

DPD shift change, 1967. Gem City Saver Magazine.

DPD dispatchers, circa 1966. Authors' collection.

Sumpter McIntosh leads Demonstration. Authors' collection.

Mayor and black leaders argue as riot rages, 1966. Dayton Daily News Archive. Wright State University.

Officers with shotguns clear streets. Authors' collection.

Fixed bayonets. Officers in riot zone. 1966. Dayton Daily News Archive. Wright State University.

National Guard with .30 caliber machine gun. 1966. Dayton Daily News Archive. Wright State University.

Shotguns loaned by pawn shops. 1966. Authors' collection.

Narcotics detectives Dan Baker and Tony Spells. Authors' collection.

DPD Captain ponders riot deployment decision. 1966. Dayton Daily News Archive. Wright State University.

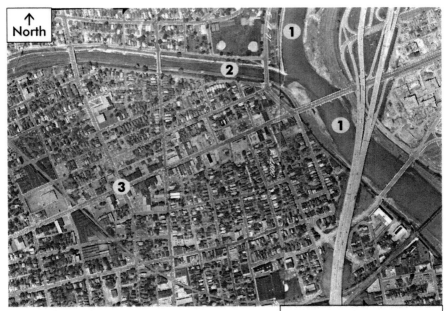

West Side ghetto where riot started. Aerial
view, Miami Conservancy District.

LEGEND
❶ Great Miami River
❷ Wolf Creek
❸ Intersection: West Third
& Broadway Streets

Anonymous threat letter to Frank White by Neal Long. Authors' collection.

Dr. Glatt. Desegregation expert. Dayton Daily News Archive. Wright State University.

Detective Baker (left) and DPD Chief O'Connor. Authors' collection.

US Post Office, Federal Building. Dayton, Ohio. Authors' collection.

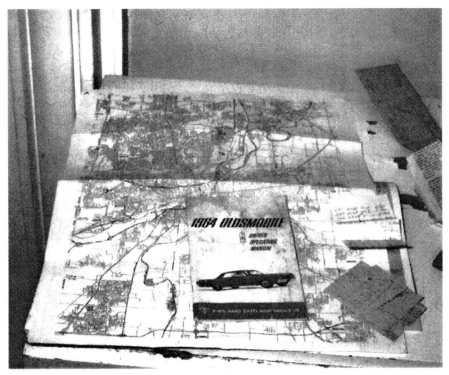

Dayton street map and clippings used by killer. Montgomery County Prosecutors Office.

Baby Blue 1968 Ford Fairlane 500. Shotgun was fired from windows. Montgomery County Prosecutors Office.

PAY FROM THIS INVOICE NO.

F 16869

TERMS	CASH ☒	MASTER CHARGE	BANK-AMERICARD	LAY-A-WAY EQUAL PAYMENT REQUIRED EACH MONTH	BUDGET PLAN	☐ CONTRACT ☐ POLICE SALE	CREDIT TO ACCOUNT ☐ MERCHANDISE

QTY.	CATALOG NO.	DESCRIPTION	USED LOG. NO.	✓	SERIAL NO.	UNIT PRICE	AMOUNT
1	190262	Charles Daly Auto			Y-44976		144.29
1	415024	Cleaning Kit					5.80
							150.09
						TAX	6 75
						TOTAL → $	156.84

TRANSFEREE'S (CUSTOMER'S) SIGNATURE WHICH APPEARS ON FORM 4473 PART 1 BELOW AUTHORIZES CUSTOMER'S ACCEPTANCE OF TERMS AND CONDITIONS SPECIFIED ON THIS INVOICE.

Form 4473 Part 1
(Rev. June 1970)
Department of the Treasury
Internal Revenue Service
Alcohol, Tobacco and
Firearms Division

Firearms Transaction Record
Intra-State Over-the-Counter

Transferor transaction number

F 16869

Section A—Statement of Transferee or Buyer

1. Transferee's (buyer's) name (last, first, middle) (Mr., Mrs., Miss) LONG NEAL B	2. Height 5' 10'	3. Weight 175	4. Race CAUC
5. Address (number, street, city, state, ZIP code) 622 Cosley St. Dayton, Ohio 45403	6. Date of birth 9-11-27	7. Place of birth Campton, Ky.	

8. Certification of Transferee (Buyer)—an untruthful answer may subject you to criminal prosecution. Each question must be answered with a yes or no.

a. Are you under indictment in any court for a crime punishable by imprisonment for a term exceeding one year? no

b. Have you been convicted in any court of a crime punishable by imprisonment for a term exceeding one year? (Note: The actual sentence given by the judge does not matter—a yes answer is necessary if the judge could have given a sentence of more than one year.) no

c. Are you a fugitive from justice? no
d. Are you an unlawful user of, or addicted to, marihuana or a depressant, stimulant, or narcotic drug? no
e. Have you been adjudicated mentally defective or have you ever been committed to a mental institution? no
f. Have you been discharged from the Armed Forces under dishonorable conditions? no
g. Are you an alien illegally in the United States? no
h. Are you a person who, having been a citizen of the United States, has renounced his citizenship? no

I hereby certify that the answers to the above are true and correct. I understand that a person who answers any of the above questions in the affirmative is prohibited by Federal law from purchasing and/or possessing a firearm. I also understand that the making of

any false oral or written statement or the exhibiting of any false or misrepresented identification with respect to this transaction is a crime punishable as a felony.

Transferee's (buyer's) signature Neal Long.	Date 22 MAY 75

Section B—Statement of Transferor or Seller

The person described in Section A, is known to me ☐, or has identified himself to me ☒ in the following manner:

9. Type of identification (driver's license, etc.) Ohio Drivers License	10. Number on identification HH 717206

On the basis of: (1) the statements in Section A; (2) the verification of identity noted in Section B; and (3) the information in the current list of Published Ordinances, it is my belief that it is not unlawful for me to sell, deliver, or otherwise dispose of the firearm described below to the person identified in Section A.

11. Type (pistol, rifle, etc.) Shotgun	12. Model Auto-pointer	13. Caliber or gauge 12 gauge	14. Serial number Y-44976
15. Manufacturer (and/importer, if any) Charles Daly			
16. Transferor's (seller's) signature Greg Myers	17. Transferor's title Sales	18. Transaction date 22 May 75	

Federal form for shotgun purchased by Long and used to shoot victims within 24 hours.

Victim killed in random drive-by shooting, 1975. Montgomery County Prosecutors Office.

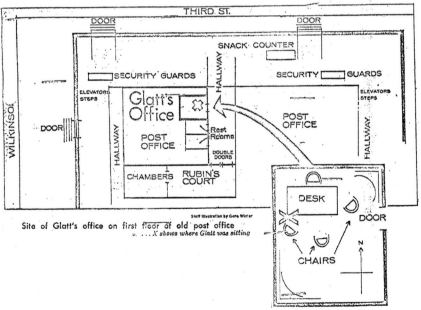

Murder scene sketch, Federal Building, 1975. Dayton Daily News.

Long and US Marshal on way to court, 1975. Dayton Daily News Archive. Wright State University.

Lt. Riley, with Long's murder weapon, 1975. Authors' collection.

Police line-up. Long is No.3. The others are police officers. Authors' collection.

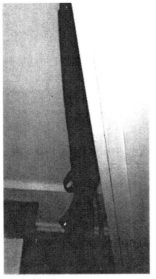

West Third Street Bridge. Renamed "The Peace Bridge." Authors' collection.

The murder weapon, a sawed-off shotgun. 1975. Montgomery County Prosecutors Office.

Neal Bradley Long's grave, Tipp City, Ohio. Authors' collection.

THIRTY-THREE

Keepin' Tabs On The Black Panthers

"Off the Pigs!" was spray-painted on boarded up store fronts on the West Side. It was early August 1970, and abandoned structures and vacant lots provided glaring reminders of the riots. Many businesses never reopened. Crime and drug traffic spread like a cancer.

The Dayton Black Panther Party and alliances with other local and national militant groups represented a new and sophisticated threat to cops. They openly waved their flag, strutted about in their all-black uniforms and spewed hate-filled rhetoric in confrontation with police on the street. Tension increased to a hair-trigger level. In an effort to head off violent attacks, the DPD Intelligence Unit secretly gathered information about the Black Panthers and other militant groups.

———◦———

One warm summer morning, two scruffy-looking white men donned soiled, well-worn work clothes and headed out to their maintenance assignment. They carried a stepladder and a box of tools from their faded and dented old pick-up truck to a twelve-unit apartment building on North Western Avenue on Dayton's West Side. They walked past an old car in front of the building where a young black man leaned over under the hood of a car and attended to what appeared to be engine trouble. The black man nodded as the two workers walked by.

The two men entered the front lobby door and walked directly to the basement. One man removed a small black pouch that contained a fourteen-piece lock pick set. It took less than fifteen seconds for him to use stainless steel picks, and he opened a cheap lock to the telephone room. A single light bulb in the room provided sufficient light as they got to work.

They opened a black duffle bag and removed the tools of their trade: needle nose pliers, an adjustable wrench, screwdriver, thin insulated copper wires in various lengths that were pre-stripped on both ends, and a roll of black electrical tape.

One man retrieved a scrap of paper from his shirt pocket and read off "Post and Pairing" numbers that identified a specific telephone number of 275-3673 for a specific apartment. They examined the telephone panel mounted on the wall where all lines in the building connected for service. Each incoming set of wires for a specific telephone line was secured by a threaded screw and a nut tightened down on each wire. The "technician" counted down the number of posts until he found Post 6 and Pair 8.

A blue color telephone "butt set," the same kind that was carried by official telephone linemen, was removed from the bag. One undercover detective stepped outside the door to act as a lookout while the wire technician of the Intelligence Unit used the red and black wires with alligator clips of the butt set and connected specific posts. He used a rotary dial on one end of the butt set to confirm a dial tone. The detective dialed a non-published confidential telephone number at the Dayton Police Intelligence Unit office. After two rings a man answered, "Butts Auto Repair." The wire technician smiled slightly and quickly disconnected the clips; he had located the right line.

One more step remained. Two wires were connected to the target telephone line and then carefully concealed among other wires. The two new wires were routed across the phone panel and connected to another set of Post and Pairs for a telephone line in a vacant apartment in the same building. A week earlier, a black undercover detective rented the apartment using false I.D. and paid the rent in cash.

The illegal wiretap job that was approved by the police command was done. Every time the "target" telephone was taken off the hook, it silently activated a Sonora reel-to-reel tape recorder in the rented vacant apartment unit.

The two detectives left the apartment. They walked by the black man out front of the apartment building as they departed. He closed the hood on his car indicating his "repairs" were done. Another nod was exchanged. Both vehicles drove away, in different directions.

During the following two weeks, an undercover detective drove an old truck and stopped by the rented vacant apartment to do a little work inside. The middle-aged white man had a few days of stubble on his face and his dirty paint-stained clothes drew little attention. He carried a bulky folded drop cloth, a paint can and brushes. He worked inside for an hour or two, then left.

The worker entered the apartment with paint and left with fresh intelligence information on reel-to-reel tapes in his bag about plans and priorities of militant groups. The recorded discussions gave police an edge they desperately needed that prevented violence and saved lives. Based in part on the intelligence information learned on the wiretap, police stepped up their use of search warrants, vehicle stops and stop-and-frisk confrontations. Allegations of harassment were made, but DPD did not back down. Numerous arrests were made for carrying concealed weapons and other violations. The Black Panther Party and a few other rogue elements were disrupted by the effective use of information by DPD.

——◄◦►——

Friday, August 28, 1970, Dayton Police Chief Robert Igleburger was angry, and he told the *Dayton Daily News* of "persistent rumors that black militants had plans to kill a Dayton Police Officer." In an ironic twist, the rumors and intelligence information indicated that a black "uncle tom" cop was the prime target. Some black officers had reported being harassed by threatening phone calls at their homes, and a few believed they were followed home by strangers. In a private morning meeting, the Chief met with a dozen black patrolmen and reassured them of their right to use deadly force when threatened.

Chief Igleburger insisted the rumors of plans to kill an officer were true and he was quoted in the *Dayton Daily News*: "Two national militant leaders are in the city expressly for the purpose of instigating a shoot out." He added, "Police intelligence reports confirm it." Although the Chief refused to identify the out-of-town militants by name or organization, he said he believed " . . . one of our police officers could be sacrificed for their crazy ambition."

Saturday, August 29, 1970 about seven hundred people attended a

Black Panther rally. The rally took place at the Old Courthouse in the heart of downtown Dayton on the very steps where Abraham Lincoln once stood.

John Taylor represented The Black Liberation Coalition that included The Republic of New Africa, Black Panthers, Black Guard and The Black Liberation Movement. In a *Dayton Daily News* story, he denied national permission to "... stage a shootout... we need no charter!" He blamed police for "... building up pre-planned excuses to kill and brutalize black people."

Richard Lasley wore his black uniform and beret and stepped to the microphone. The Black Party Defense Captain yelled his message to the crowd as riot police looked on from a distance. Lasley claimed, "Police were setting up a story of self defense if they shoot a black man," as he recalled the 1967 incident when a detective killed Robert Barbee and planted a gun.

The demonstration finally broke up, and the crowd had grown to nearly one thousand. They did not have a permit to march on the streets but they defiantly walked past City Hall and Police Headquarters. Police anticipated the unauthorized march and avoided being baited into a confrontation. Once again, information from a wire tap gave them an edge. After crossing the West Third Street Bridge, the crowd broke up.

The following month, black militant groups moved underground. Their leaders could not figure out how DPD was so effective at knowing their plans and making specific arrests. Their suspicions turned inward. A few members of the groups suspected an informant working for police. Accusations and internal struggles grew as the groups were marginalized.

Since the first riot in September 1966, through the rise of black militant groups, not much changed for the average black citizen who lived in West Dayton. Segregation was pervasive, and the Great Miami River continued to preserve the dubious reputation Dayton had earned: "one of America's most segregated cities."

———◦———

Neal Bradley Long left work and stopped at a beer and wine carryout, about six blocks from his rented half-double house in Dayton's East Side.

While he waited in line to pay for a quart bottle of Burger beer, the clerk and another customer talked about the Black Panther rally downtown. The clerk said, "Them niggers never get tired of beggin' & threatenin'. Somebody ought to put some bird-shot in their asses!"

"Bird-shot? You mean 00-buck shot don't ya?" said another young man that stood in line.

Long kept his head down and listened. He thought about how he hated "them coloreds." He paid for his beer and headed back to his dingy home.

THIRTY-FOUR

Detective '101'

"The police officer carries a heavy responsibility when called to investigate a sudden or violent death, for he stands in the dead man's shoes to protect his interests against those of everyone else in the world."
—*Lemoyne Snyder.* "Homicide Investigation,"
First Edition, Ninth revision. 1959. Chapter 1, p.1.

Rookie Detective Baker's first assignment was in Dick Section to the Auto Theft Squad. In the pecking order, it was known as a "paper squad." Lots of reports and it was a less- prestigious "break-in" squad. His core work schedule was 8:45 a.m. to 4:45 p.m., Monday through Friday, and he wore a suit and tie every day. It did not matter how hot the temperature, not to mention police cars were not air-conditioned. Detectives were not permitted to have their gun or handcuffs exposed in public. Like the FBI, image was a big thing for Dicks.

Baker joined the thirty-five detectives who worked in an office arranged in a large bullpen-type configuration. It was a busy and noisy place. Telephones rang constantly. Cigarette and cigar smoke hung in the air. Complainants, witnesses and prisoners in handcuffs paraded through the office as detectives worked their cases. Another fifteen detectives assigned to homicide, armed robbery and rape squads had private offices. Detective Baker gained experience quickly. He often volunteered to help other squads on surveillances and arrests. Whenever possible, he spent time with Robbery and Homicide Dicks to learn from the best.

————◦————

The Homicide Squad was always busy during the summer, particularly on the West Side. One day, numerous shootings occurred within a few hours, and about ten detectives were tied up at the scenes. Baker sat at his desk and prepared to go off duty. Lieutenant Schwartz came out of his office and tapped Baker on the shoulder with an order that he had hoped would come one day.

"Baker, Homicide's swamped today," Schwartz said. "Another shooting just came in. I want you to help out. Detective Beu-tell is on his way to the Thirsty Eye Bar at 1822 West Third Street. One is dead at the scene and one about to die at the hospital. Musta' been a robbery gone bad and the owner shot both suspects."

Baker could hardly believe it. As a rookie detective, he was asked to go to a homicide scene and work with Mr. Beu-tell! "Holy shit!" he said to himself as he left the bullpen and went to the parking lot to pick up a reserve detective car.

As Baker drove across the West Third Street Bridge, he slapped the magnetic portable flashing red light atop the car. Baker thought about how he could not screw up his first big chance as a detective out on a homicide! "Just be cool, slow down, walk in and act like you belong on the scene," he told himself.

Detective Baker rolled up at the crime scene and he experienced something he never forgot. As he stepped from his unmarked car, two uniformed officers on the scene cleared a pathway for him to walk through dozens of onlookers. Baker saw expressions on faces of people gathered outside the scene as if they waited for Mr. Beu-tell and Baker to do something very important.

As Baker stepped to the door of the bar someone yelled, "It's Baker, man! Hey Baker, you homicide now?"

Baker turned to see John-John and nodded. "What's happenin' John-John?" Baker asked. Baker felt his ego swell from attention afforded detectives.

When he walked inside, Baker stood still for a moment to get an overall impression before he took another step. The crime scene was inside a long narrow building with a bar, pool table and about a dozen tables. A black man lay dead on his back across a pool table with a handgun beside his right forearm. He had a massive wound from a shotgun blast that removed the front of his skull. His right eyeball was missing. Blood and grey brain matter dripped from the large light shade that hung above the pool table.

A uniformed officer stood at the rear door and protected the crime scene where a second suspect fell after he was shot. A pool of coagulated blood and flesh marked the spot. Another officer stood by a half-dozen people who sat in one corner of the bar. They were inside when the shooting happened, and each of them gave statements of what they witnessed. A few were intoxicated and talked loudly. The bar owner had already been taken to Dick Section for questioning. His pump shotgun lay on the floor.

Baker knelt beside the gun when he felt a tap on his shoulder and turned to see Detective Beu-tell, who was the "god of gods" in Homicide. Beu-tell had just arrived and said, "Ba...Ba...Bake, I'm sur...sure glad to see ya. Can you d...d...do the scene for me?" Beu-tell did not wait for an answer. Baker knew he was going to get his feet wet, real fast. "Man, we're swa...swamped. I'm workin' one mo...more case, but now I got...gotta go to St. E. to ch, ch, check on the number-two guy and try to get a sta...statement before he di, dies."

Beu-tell turned and left as Baker stood there by himself with a whole scene to take care of. Fortunately for Baker, he had been on many shooting scenes as a patrolman, and he had watched Homicide Dicks work. Before he left, Beu-tell gave Baker his Polaroid camera. "Do the ba..ba.. best you ca...ca...can, Bake."

Baker worked the crime scene for two hours. He asked some of the uniform officers to help. Their willingness to get involved reminded him of how he felt just a few short years ago as a uniformed rookie. A lot of veteran detectives hated to sketch a crime scene. They relied on a sole on-duty photographer from the lab to take photos and sketch the scene, but he wasn't available. Veteran detectives liked action. They wanted to hit the street, talk to people and hunt for suspects, not try to draw. Baker did not mind sketching a crime scene.

He used a clipboard and outlined the crime scene in about thirty minutes. He included general measurements of the victims' pools of blood and recovered weapons. He also collected evidence in large paper sacks he found under the bar. A shotgun, handgun, shotgun shells, bloody clothing and a wallet were marked with the date and Baker's initials.

Detective Baker arrived at Dick Section around 7:30 p.m. and found the office full of witnesses, uniformed officers and detectives from several shooting cases. As Baker walked into the office, he carried bags of evidence. Beu-tell saw him and headed his way.

Beu-tell said, "Hey Bake, man I...I...I'm sorry I lef...left you. Yu, you ok?"

Baker, still pumped up, responded, "Yes, I'm good. I need to talk to the bar owner and get written statements from witnesses. It looks like it was self defense."

Beu-tell said, "Le me see, wha, whatchu got?" Baker showed him a dozen Polaroid photos and said the photographer never showed up.

"You got...gotta a sketch of the sce...scene?" Baker handed him an 8.5 x 11 inch sketch of the scene and Beu-tell studied it for a minute without a word. Beu-tell asked, "You did thi, this?"

Beu-tell did not wait for Baker to answer. He walked away with the sketch and showed it to Homicide Sergeant Bill Mortimer. Mortimer glanced at it, then looked at Baker while the two of them continued to talk.

Beu-tell walked back to Baker and said, "Bake, I'd like to ha..ha...have you co...co...come along on a few call outs. You d...d...do good work, kid. Sarge will put you on the backup list, maybe even get you a ca...ca...car later on, too, okay?"

Baker tried to suppress his elation. It was hard to believe that "*The* Mr. Beu-tell" would ask for him to be a backup on homicide. Baker shook hands with Beu-tell, thanked him for the complement and opportunity and then returned to his work. It was the break Baker wanted.

Over the course of the next few months, Baker was the backup homicide detective on call-outs, mostly after regular hours and on weekends. The veterans liked having a rookie detective with a lot of energy to do basic grunt work at crime scenes, including most sketches. DPD Homicide trained new detectives on-the-job. Only a few men went to any special schools or seminars. Baker gained experience whenever possible, and he sat in on interviews and confessions. He also witnessed autopsies. Baker watched, listened and learned from the experts. He volunteered to take a detective car home on some weekends when the squad was short of men. The workload continued to outpace the small squad of four detectives, and homicides reached over sixty in 1970.

Baker hung out in the homicide office in his spare time, and he volunteered for any task. He constantly looked for wanted suspects or key witnesses and conducted interviews and interrogations on his own. Baker was slowly absorbed into the regular call-out rotation, and his primary assignment on Auto Theft Squad faded as he was groomed by Mr. Beu-tell.

———◦———

In April 1971, Homicide Sergeant Bill Mortimer called Baker at home on a Sunday morning and told him he had been assigned to homicide call-outs for a week. Mortimer told Baker he would pick him up for a ride into work Monday morning so Baker could get a car to drive home that evening. Mortimer and Baker lived in the same neighborhood along with another rider, Detective Larry Kincaid.

Monday morning, they headed into the city. As they approached downtown, the police radio crackled with a crime-in-progress call. The dispatcher sent uniformed crews to the Winters National Bank at the corner of West Third and Broadway Streets on a silent bank robbery alarm signal. It was 8:20 a.m., forty minutes before the bank was scheduled to open. Detectives suspected the silent alarm was set off manually by an employee inside and a crime was in progress.

Winters Bank was a traditional old-style three story bank building adorned by large limestone columns at the front entrance with a foyer and two sets of doors. The entire city block of three and four story buildings was among the oldest in the city and was connected by a series of stairways and catwalks in the rear. Several buildings had abandoned attic and basement doorways that connected tenement apartments, bars and stores together.

Sergeant Mortimer loved the action on the streets, and it was not unusual for him to pick up the microphone and call the dispatcher. Sergeant Mortimer radioed, "Car 710 to dispatch."

"Go ahead," the dispatcher replied.

"Car 710, I have two detectives with me; we are about ten blocks away; we'll fall in on the call."

The dispatcher cleared the air and broadcasted, "Dispatch to all crews responding to Winters Bank, plain clothes detectives are responding; use caution."

"710. We'll come in on Broadway and approach on foot," Mortimer stated.

"Dispatch to all crews, plain clothes detectives will be on foot."

Another detective joined the radio traffic. "714 to … Di … Dis … Dispatch," said Detective Beu-tell. "I'll b … be coming up fr, fr, from the other side and meet up wi..with sev … sev 710."

Detective Beu-tell was already on the scene near the front door. He leaned his back against the wall when Mortimer, Baker and Kincaid arrived. Beu-tell was armed with a 12-gauge police riot shotgun.

"710 to dispatch, this looks legit," said Mortimer over his portable radio. "Send crews to cover the rear and alleys. Also seal traffic for at least two blocks in all directions. We still got people drivin' by for christsake!"

A dozen officers and detectives responded with shotguns and surrounded the bank. Mortimer noticed the front door to the bank lobby and inner foyer doors were ajar. No one was visible. Sergeant Mortimer crouched down and entered the foyer. He stayed low and slowly rose up slightly but saw no one. He then motioned for Beu-tell, Baker and Kincaid to ease into the foyer as he slowly opened the inner glass doors. The interior of the bank was U-shaped with counters along both sides and in the rear. When the four men moved to the right at the end of the long teller counter, they heard muffled voices that sounded like grunting noises and attempts to speak. They looked around the counter and saw a uniformed bank guard, the manager and two female tellers tied up and gagged with strips of cloth. They all lay on the floor. The manager saw the detectives and he rose to a sitting position. He frantically glanced to his right and nodded his head in the direction of the rear of the bank to warn detectives.

Detective Kincaid loosened the gag on the guard and he whispered, "In the back, there's a colored man and white woman, both have guns. They came in on us as we opened up."

The detectives crept low halfway down the counter and stopped. Sergeant Mortimer yelled, "Police. Drop your weapons, come out with your hands up!" There was no response.

After a few seconds, a person's head rose above the counter of the teller cage in the rear of the bank. As the person rose up to eye level, a handgun also came into view pointed toward the front of the bank. The rest of the face came into view up to the nose. It was a white female with black hair. She wore round "Jackie-O"-style black sunglasses.

"Drop the gun!" Mortimer shouted again. The woman immediately ducked down and running footsteps were heard. The detectives used cover and quickly moved to the rear of the bank, and they found an open door that led to an outside staircase.

Baker radioed, "Dispatch, two suspects, one black male and a white female, both armed. They may be trying to get out the rear!"

The bank robbers fled through old connections between century old buildings. They hid in a vacant tenement apartment. A half-dozen FBI agents arrived and joined in the search and investigation. The robbers were arrested two hours later and were wanted for a string of bank robberies from New York City to the mid-west. Their M.O. was to rob banks when employees arrived for work before opening time.

As work at the crime scene wrapped up, Sergeant Mortimer gave Beu-tell, Kincaid and Baker a pat on the back for their teamwork. He then turned to the two most junior men and said, "Fellas, let me know when the reports are done. Beu-tell and I are going to the Pancake House for breakfast." Mortimer and Beu-tell hopped into Mortimer's car and sped away. They left Baker and Kincaid with clipboards in hand and a mountain of work to do. Somebody had to pick up evidence, tag & bag, arrange witness interviews, transport prisoners and type reports. Baker shrugged his shoulders and said, "Let's get busy. Shit rolls down hill and more is coming."

———◦———

November 1971, Detective Baker was in Dick Section as he prepared to go off duty at 4:45 p.m. He finished typing his daily report when he received a call. "Baker, this is Lieutenant Riley. Hey, I hear you're doing a bang-up job. I'm not surprised."

"Thanks, boss," Baker responded. Baker had seldom seen or talked with Riley since he was promoted to lieutenant in early 1971. Riley worked nights in charge of Uniformed Field Operations and he hoped his nickname, "Batman" had faded into a distant memory.

"Remember I told you we may be forming a special unit someday? I've been working on a federal grant to form the Organized Crime Control Unit, the OCCU. Today we got the green light. It's going to happen. I'm tellin' you and a few others. You'd be a good fit."

Baker was hesitant to leave Dick Section, but he told Riley he wanted to be a part of the Unit. Riley elaborated, "The OCCU will have about a dozen guys working Intelligence, narcotics, gambling and major surveillances, the whole nine yards. We'll have a lot of special training, money and the 'toys' we've never been able to afford. I'll want to start with at least one black and white 'salt-n-pepper' team on narcotics right away and that will involve you. How's it sound?"

"I'm ready boss," Baker said.

Baker placed the telephone in the cradle and sat quietly for a moment. He thought of the path his career had taken to get to this point. He thoroughly enjoyed Homicide, but now he had a chance to be a charter member of the department's brand new specialized Investigative Unit. He knew the OCCU meant he had to work nights and weekends and undercover sometimes, but he could not resist the pull it had on him. In the meantime, Baker kept the future opportunity to himself and continued to respond to dozens of scenes of violent crimes until something final was announced.

THIRTY-FIVE

Getting Even

Alcohol took its toll on Neal Bradley Long. The stress in his life was unrelenting. He was often late for work and called off on sick leave. His manager at the Stolle plant, Frank "Red" White gave warning after warning and heard many promises from Long. The situation did not improve. Long had been off his medication for years, and alcohol no longer dulled his internal conflicts. He increased his use of marijuana. Long left his family again and moved to a sleeping room at 70 Fountain Avenue in North Dayton. The troubled man withdrew even more.

On March 26, 1971 Frank White decided he had to terminate Neal Bradley Long from his job as a chrome plater helper at Stolle. White and another supervisor were fearful of Long's reaction, so they planned his exit carefully. When Long reported for work at 3:00 p.m., White softened the blow and told Long he was technically "laid off" and he would receive unemployment benefits.

Neal Bradley Long was numb as he heard the news. He moved like a robot and showed no overt reaction, only a flat depressed affect. He placed his belongings in a cardboard box and walked to his car. Long drove to the Moraine Carryout and bought two quarts of beer before he headed to his rundown apartment.

Frank White told co-workers that he thought Long "could be trouble." For weeks, White used more care when he walked to his car at the end of his shift and on his drive south on I-75 to his home on Elberon Court in Cincinnati.

White's fears were correct. Long often watched White on the highway when he drove to Cincinnati on I-75. He took note of White's arrival and departure times. Long frequently drove past the Stolle entrance and fought the urge to stop, go inside and get even with White. He always had his sawed-off shotgun on the front seat, covered by a blanket. Long decided to wait for the right opportunity when his prey was most vulnerable.

————◦————

In early October, 1971, Long was served with a subpoena to appear in Domestic Relations Court for a final hearing in the divorce case filed by his wife, Grace. Long asked the Process Server to wait a few minutes while he hand wrote a message on the court's copy. Long's message to the judge underscored his dismay and feelings of inadequacy. He wrote,

> When I worked, I always paid my family and I helped them any way I could. I gave my children money every week, and during the week. My wife and I tried to live together, but doesn't seem to work out. I love my family but fate has worked against us. You can give her a divorce if you want to and if I find work, I'll help her pay for it. So I hope my family the very best and am sorry I haven't been able to do more for them.

November 3, 1971, Grace Long's divorce from Neal Bradley Long was granted. Although her previous filings in 1968 and 1969 were withdrawn, it was final. She still loved her husband, but he was too hard to live with. His sullen and brooding moods coupled with his drinking reached the breaking point for Grace. The couple agreed that he would see his children regularly and have meals with the family. Long would help Grace read and understand her papers and help her get back and forth to her factory job.

Grey skies of early winter hung low over the city. Long's dark and lonely moods pressed down as he dwelled on the divorce and loss of his job at the Stolle Company.

————◦————

New Year's Eve was a time of reflection and anticipation for most people. It was also a difficult time for souls who carried heavy burdens and troubled thoughts. On December 31, 1971, an hour before midnight, the temperature hovered around freezing when an Oldsmobile sedan turned from South Broadway Street onto West River Road on Dayton's West Side. Neal Bradley Long fussed with the defroster, which was on the fritz. He drove past the main gate of the Stolle plant. He knew a skeleton crew worked over the holidays to keep 24/7 watch on the boiler room and chemicals used in plating.

Frank White's 1969 Chevrolet and two other cars that belonged to maintenance men were in the lot. Long drove beyond the plant and parked on a gravel lane about one hundred yards to the south. He got out of his car and carried a Marlin Model 55 sawed-off shotgun. He purchased the shotgun six years earlier for $25.00 at a second hand store near the corner of Filth and Wine Avenues in East Dayton.

Long was familiar with the layout of the Stolle plant. He crept up to the large air intake vent and fan in the outer wall. Long knew Frank White often spent time in the break area. Long's presence was concealed and he was able to see through the vent. After Long waited for about fifteen minutes, Frank White entered the break room alone and prepared a cup of coffee.

Like a hunter in the steep hills of Campton, Kentucky, Long knew the habits of his prey. He felt powerful as he was in full control of White's life or death. His aim did not have to be perfect; the spray of the blast was wide enough to hit its target.

As Frank White turned to his left to leave the room, the sound of the blast and the pain was simultaneous. The number two shot traveled forty feet and ripped into White's left arm and knocked him to the floor. Long ran to his car and sped away, satisfied he had gotten even with White for laying him off. Within minutes, Long was south bound on I-75, headed to Campton, Kentucky, his refuge in times of trouble.

The boiler room operator found Frank White on the floor and called Dayton Police. White survived his wounds because a portion of the blast was deflected by fan blades in the air vent. White did not name Long as a suspect in the shooting because he was not sure who shot him. Frank White terminated a half-dozen other men since Long was laid off and White did not want to falsely accuse anyone.

White returned to work a month later. In the absence of leads, on

January 21, 1972, Homicide Detectives closed the "Shooting to Kill" investigation as Inactive - Not Cleared.

One month after the shooting, curiosity got the best of Long. He wanted to know if White had died, as he intended. He called the Stolle Company office from a pay phone. Long did not identify himself and he asked if Mr. White was scheduled to work. The receptionist said White would be in on the afternoon shift. Long hung up.

The obsession to kill Frank "Red" White flooded back and added another layer of problems to Long's frustrations. Long barely existed on odd jobs in Campton and only occasionally sent a few dollars to his ex-wife, Grace. Long was also disturbed by his obsession about black people and stories he heard from Grace. She told him about problems in Dayton schools his children attended. Neal Bradley Long vowed to return to Dayton and finish what voices urged him to do, kill Frank "Red" White and more importantly, stop the coloreds from taking over everything.

THIRTY-SIX

The Return Of "Salt-n-Pepper"

D uring the first week of December 1971, the DPD announced it had received funding from the U.S. Department of Justice to establish DPD's new Organized Crime Control Unit (OCCU). The grant consolidated all of DPD's specialized investigative squads and targeted major narcotics operators, career criminals, gambling and major prostitution cases. An Intelligence and Surveillance Unit was also included. Even though Dayton was not a major city, it was home to local and regional crime gangs, some with ties to major crime organizations in the United States, Canada and Mexico.

The fight against major criminal organizations required a highly trained and focused group of detectives who had time to conduct long-term major investigations. Formation of the OCCU was supported by the FBI, the Drug Enforcement Administration (DEA), Alcohol Tobacco and Firearms (ATF) and the IRS Criminal Investigation Division.

Lieutenant Riley, the commanding officer, advertised two slots for sergeants and ten positions for detectives. Even though the selection process was touted as "open to all" with at least five years experience, in reality Riley had about a half-dozen names of people he personally recruited.

———◆———

Lieutenant Riley invited Baker and Spells to an early Sunday morning breakfast at the Pancake House on Keowee Street in North Dayton. Riley had always wanted the two detectives to pair up again because he liked their chemistry and track record when they served in uniform.

Riley waited in a corner booth in the back of the restaurant. He sifted through a stack of papers while he smoked a cigarette. A pot of coffee and three cups were on the table. Baker and Spells met outside and walked in together. Riley rose from his seat and walked toward the men and smiled broadly as he quickened his step. "What a pair," Riley said to himself as the men approached. "You boys look good together," he said as he extended his hand.

Over breakfast, Riley laid out his plan for the two detectives. "I want you two to be the lead narcotics team in the OCCU. You've worked together before. Both of you have developed into good detectives and have snitches all over town. Working together as Narcs,' you bastards will be dyn-o-mite!"

Spells took a drag off his cigarette and did not respond; neither did Baker. After a pregnant pause, Riley could not wait any longer. "Well?" Riley said.

"Look boss," Baker said. "Tony and I have talked and we want to have a free hand on what we work on. No limits. No roadblocks. We both know you, and we like working for you, but we need your word."

"Holy Christ, you guys gotta ask me that? You know the answer—hell yeah!" Riley added. This city hasn't had a black and white team of cops ever work narcotics together and you guys will be the first and, I believe, the best ever, okay?"

That was good enough for 'Salt-n-Pepper'. The "meet" was over an hour later. Baker and Spells were more than ready to hit the streets.

———◇———

Training for the new OCCU was paid for by a federal grant and was unlike any training ever sponsored by DPD. The initial two weeks at the Dayton Police Academy covered a wide range of topics on all major forms of organized criminal activity. There was heavy emphasis on surveillance techniques that included following someone on foot, in autos, malls, airports and the like. Actual case studies of major crimes were reviewed for lessons learned.

The OCCU was funded to acquire everything it needed to operate as a high-functioning unit. There was plenty of "buy money," rental cars, pagers, surveillance equipment and almost any new "toy" detectives desired. Detectives dressed any way they pleased and wore long hair and beards if it fit their assignment. The technical surveillance guys on the OCCU found a vendor in Miami, Florida who sold vehicle-tracking devices. A Cuban-American salesman spent a week in Dayton and trained everyone how to use the equipment. The device was secretly hooked on the rear undercarriage of a vehicle then tracked by its signal on a dashboard receiver in one or more surveillance vehicles. The tracker was popular, and the detectives had wet dreams as they made their own list of suspects they wanted to put under intense surveillance. Within a few months, most members of the unit attended a confidential training program in Atlanta, Georgia. At the conclusion of the two weeks of training, no certificates were handed out and no one expected one. Each member of the OCCU who attended was exposed to the full range of surveillance techniques and tools available. Due to the sensitive topics covered, each detective's training record only reflected, "Intelligence Seminar, Atlanta, Georgia 2 weeks." DPD and the city administration did not want to document the fact that the training topics covered wire tapping and eavesdropping.

———◄○►———

The heady days of the new OCCU and the hustle of the dozen handpicked detectives dramatically changed how DPD attacked narcotics, gambling, vice and career criminals in the region. The federal grant provided training that was unprecedented and only exceeded by their access to new resources. Detectives used a wide range of leased vehicles, a special cash fund for expenses, money to pay informants and cash totaling up to $5,000 for drug buy-bust operations.

The OCCU was able to commit resources for long term investigations often culminating in dramatic raids. Detectives became well known for simultaneous raids and their use of sledgehammers and battering rams to smash open doors at dope houses. Detectives Baker and Spells contributed to the success of the OCCU. Their bust of a major international marihuana smuggling ring near Greenville, Ohio was one of their biggest cases. The arrests netted them Police Officers of the Year Award from the Ohio Prosecuting Attorneys Association.

———◄○►———

Lieutenant Riley's OCCU also supported major investigations in Dick Section on an ad hoc basis. Detective Baker served as liaison with Homicide on significant cases. Spells was often tapped as well for his extensive network of snitches on the West Side. Riley made Baker and Spells available for extended undercover surveillances of suspects whenever requested by the Robbery or Homicide squads. Baker and Spells were involved in surveillance of career criminals, armed robbery and burglary gangs and developed new leads that assisted detectives.

THIRTY-SEVEN

The Hunter Returns

"White people are leaving the city. It has become a
warehouse for the poor, black and needy."
—*James H. McGee, circa 1966*
In 1970, he became Dayton's first black Mayor

The 190-mile drive from Campton, Kentucky, to Dayton, Ohio, was slowed by heavy winter weather. The Appalachian Mountains were covered by a blanket of snow and the roads were treacherous. It was January 25, 1972 as Neal Bradley Long coaxed his 1964 Oldsmobile north across the Mountain Parkway, Kentucky route 15, toward Lexington. The snow gave way to spotty icy conditions on I-75 as Long made his way through Covington, Kentucky and across the double-deck Brent Spence Bridge that spanned the Ohio River into Cincinnati. The trip had taken twice as much time as he navigated bad roads, skirted accidents on the highway and paused for delays for ash and gravel trucks as they spread their loads. Long was very tired, and he stopped for a quick meal at a Frisch's Restaurant. He gobbled down a Big Boy hamburger, fries and strong black coffee before he covered the last fifty miles north to Dayton.

Long was glad to be in Ohio again. He hid in Kentucky after he shot Frank "Red" White at the Stolle plant in West Dayton on New Year's Eve. As far as he knew, Long did not think he was a wanted man. Even though Long still wanted to kill "Red", he decided he had to take his time before a second try.

It was nearly dark at about 5:15 p.m. Long pulled a scrap of paper from his shirt pocket with a telephone number scribbled in pencil. He used a pay telephone in the lobby of the restaurant and deposited three quarters for three minutes of long distance service. He called "Cap" Collins, owner of Collins' SOHIO gasoline station at 4030 Marshall Road in Kettering, Ohio, a bedroom community on Dayton's south edge. After a few rings, a man answered, "Cap Collins' Service Station."

"Mr. Collins, this is Neal Long. Is that job still available? You know, the one I called about last week."

"Well, yes it is." Collins replied. "Just pumpin' gas and changing tires. That's all it is. Pays $2.20 an hour, mostly the three to eleven shift. Do you want it?"

Without hesitation, Long responded, "I sure would like it, Mr. Collins." Collins told Long to stop by, sign a few papers, and plan to start work February 1st.

Neal Bradley Long drove into Dayton and headed to a rooming house he knew had rooms to rent by the week or month. He made enough money at odd jobs in Campton to rent a sparsely furnished sleeping room in a large old, rundown two-story house at 238 West Grand Avenue. The house was just a few blocks from the Riverview Avenue Bridge that crossed into the West Side at the Great Miami River. The closer to the West Side, the better, he thought.

Long paid the rent and got a key from the landlord who lived on the first floor. He unlocked the padlock and hasp on his room on the second floor. He replaced the landlord's lock with his own. There was also a hasp inside, and Long locked the door when inside the room.

It was about 10:30 p.m. as Long looked around his room and reflected on how little he had to show for forty-four years on earth. He looked at a single electric wire with one light bulb that hung from the ceiling. It was a dirty, musty-smelling room. A hot plate sat on a small sink in the corner. The boarding house was full of weekly renters, mostly single men, and everyone shared a bathroom down the hall. It was a noisy place that smelled of beer, hard times and hard people.

Long brought a few possessions back from Kentucky. The first thing he hauled upstairs was his bulky portable RCA TV. He immediately plugged it into a wall outlet. The old black-and-white television had seen better days. It took a minute or two for the half-dozen tubes to warm up. It finally illuminated the picture tube with a snowy picture. He sat on the edge of his small bed as a newscaster recapped stories of the day. The picture cleared a bit, and a newsman showed film as he reported a story of a Dayton School Board meeting. Board Chairman, Mr. Maxwell, a staunch conservative, argued with School Superintendent Dr. Wayne Caryle. Dr. Caryle, a progressive man, supported a proposed plan to have black and white students attend a small number of classes together in a few Dayton Public School buildings.

He turned the TV off and retrieved a bottle of cheap bourbon from his old Army duffle bag. Long finished unpacking and removed a sawed-off 12-gauge shotgun and two handguns, .22 and .32 caliber revolvers. He hid them in a storage area behind a dirty curtain beneath the sink. He then pulled two books from his bag. Long had been deprived of a good education and dropped out of the seventh grade at Pomeroyton School in Campton, Kentucky. Even so, he liked to read. Occasionally he bought paperback books at secondhand stores.

As he sat on the bed, he thumbed through a paperback and looked for passages in John Keel's book, *Our Haunted Planet,* about extraterrestrials, men in black visiting earth, glass mountains, and ancient maps left by visitors from space.

Long sipped from the bottle and reached for his other book, *The Brotherhood of Strange* by John Macklin. Long read slowly and followed along with his fingertip. He liked books about paranormal phenomena, and stories "stranger than fiction." He enjoyed reading about flying saucers and those that described conversations with the dead. He was drawn to two passages in Macklin's book that discussed murder and man's ability to justify it, perhaps something we share with the biblical Cain.

"Yes, I did my part," he said, as he remembered when he met with DPD Homicide Detective Krisher on Halloween night in 1966. "I told the detectives what I had done and where they could find me."

The other Macklin passage that Long fixated on involved death after midnight and dreams foretelling the future and warning of deaths, including one's own. The passages registered in Long's subconscious as he often thought about and planned the death of others, and perhaps even his own suicide someday.

The bourbon had the desired effect as Long finally slumped backward on the bed. Hours later, the bright morning sun streamed into his room through a narrow opening in the ragged curtains. A laser-like stream of light came to rest on his face. He squinted as he awoke. Long knew right then. It was a sign. He wasn't exactly sure what it meant, but he believed it was a sign.

———◇———

Long reported for work at Cap Collins' SOHIO February 1st. on the 3 p.m. to 11 p.m. shift. He had rotating days off. Cap's was a busy full-service gasoline station, open 24/7, in a white, middle class suburban neighborhood. Long had the most menial job there. He pumped gas and changed tires. Repetitive tasks suited him well, and he worked alone. He barely mixed with his co-workers, and he was known as a loner. Long was required to wear a uniform that consisted of a light blue shirt with an oval SOHIO logo patch on the left breast, dark blue work pants and black shoes. Since the company provided and cleaned his uniforms, Long wore the outfit every day, even when off duty. He also wore black plastic framed glasses.

———◇———

April 17, 1972, was a momentous day in Dayton's history. The Dayton Chapter of the NAACP filed a lawsuit in U. S. Federal District Court in Columbus, Ohio that charged Dayton Public Schools operated and maintained a racially segregated school system. The case was initially filed on behalf of a half-dozen black families in Dayton, one of which was named Brinkman; thus, it became known as the "Brinkman Case" and was commonly referred to as the "busing case." Unlike other school desegregation cases filed in the United States that sought a regional or metro plan for multiple school districts, the Dayton case focused only on the City of Dayton Public School District. It was a major strategic decision with long term and unforeseen implications.

Had the NAACP sought a regional solution, it would have encompassed a dozen or more suburban school districts. Nearly all-white school districts outside the City of Dayton were not affected at all by any court action. However, the "Dayton only" filing unwittingly accelerated decay of Dayton's school system and neighborhoods as white flight to suburban cities and towns and school districts had already begun. Residential housing values plummeted when "block-busting" realtors used the prospect of white children bused across the river to the black side of town as a scare tactic. White flight prompted a firestorm of real estate transactions at rock bottom dollar prices. Thousands of white families fled the city.

The NAACP was prepared to fight the case all the way to the United States Supreme Court. In 1972, approximately 31,300 white students and 22,600 black students were enrolled in Dayton Public Schools. The Dayton School Board Advisory Committee held public meetings to discuss alternatives to "reduce racial isolation," but their talks were stymied by many white citizens, including a group known as Save Our Schools (SOS) that vehemently opposed busing to achieve integration. Black citizens wanted the opposite. They insisted on immediate improvement in black education and if it took busing, so be it.

Neal Bradley Long watched the news stories. While at work, Long read the *Dayton Daily News* about efforts to integrate the schools. He heard negative racial comments from fellow workers and customers at Cap's station. He despised talk of school busing and mixing of races. Long hated the U.S. Supreme Court and he believed they would roll over and give coloreds everything. Welling up inside, Long had an uncontrollable urge to make it all stop, make it all go away, any way he could.

———◦———

As if the filing of the busing case was not enough to trigger fear and emotion among whites in Dayton, another series of events added dramatically to racial tension. Three violent attacks on whites by blacks on the West Side blanketed the news.

On July 3, 1972, at 12:25 a.m., a white man, Harold Borchers, age thirty-two, was shot as he drove west in the 3800 block of West Third Street. A shotgun blast struck the driver door and his left arm. He did not see the shooter and sped away and called police. His wound was not serious. He was unable to pinpoint the shooter, but he did notice a group of black males gathered on the sidewalk. "Shooting to Wound Report 361050" was filed with police.

July 8, 1972, at 12:35 a.m., Liberty Cab driver Charles Wells, a white man, age twenty-five, was driving in the vicinity of Broadway and Grand

Avenue when a shotgun blast hit the left side of his car and the back of his head. Fortunately, only a few pellets struck him. The shooter was not identified, but a group of black males was seen seconds before. "Shooting to Wound Report 361541" was filed.

July 8, 1972 10:45 p.m., violence against whites escalated. Joseph O. Baker, a white man, age thirty-eight, returned home from a visit with friends. His wife, Phyllis, and their two children, five-year-old Mark and twenty-three-month-old Lynn, were in the automobile with him. They were headed home to Nathaniel Street, a rural area west of Dayton's city limits. They reached the intersection of Hoover and Whitmore Avenues and stopped in a long line of traffic. Hoover Skating Rink closed early due to large disorderly crowds and several fights amongst hundreds of black youths. Three local gangs, Chains of Rap-Brown, Dayton Panthers and Vanguard were involved. Some gang members were armed, and a few roamed the street clogged with traffic. They had been drinking, smoking marijuana, yelling and cursing, particularly if they saw a white person. One black male, age seventeen, nicknamed "Mister," carried a sawed-off shotgun and waved it around gangster style and approached Baker's car. Without warning, Mister fired at Joseph Baker, a total stranger, and killed him instantly as his wife and children screamed. The blast tore into Baker's face, neck and throat. Additional pellets struck his wife, Phyllis, and their infant daughter but were not life-threatening. Blood and tissue spattered all over the inside of their car. Another black male in the gang jerked open the right passenger door, grabbed Joseph Baker's arm and yanked him across his wife, who lay wounded in the front seat. Baker's body was pulled out onto the pavement while scores of startled motorists looked on in horror. "You got him man!" he yelled, and the gang took off.

Mister was identified and arrested a few days later. Elliott Brown, age seventeen, was charged with murder on "Homicide Complaint 361623."

Days after the shooting of the Joseph Baker family, many whites spoke out on the radio, on the television and in the newspapers. Whites who traveled through, worked on or lived in small enclaves on the West Side began to travel in groups. Some visibly armed themselves and openly carried weapons. That led to police responding to numerous disturbance calls, including hair-trigger arguments and gun complaints. Police made a handful of gun-related arrests of whites that further intensified criticism that they could not or would not protect white people on the West Side. Whites seldom picketed about social issues or crime, but a few dozen openly picketed at City Hall and demanded arrests and crackdowns on black criminals.

Some whites decided they would not go to the police for help. They vowed to protect themselves. Rumors sprang up of a few underground groups that had armed themselves. Detectives Baker and Spells were ordered to gather information on the individuals and groups that could be a threat. Surveillances were initiated and relevant information provided to uniformed patrol officers and detectives for their own protection and to set up "stop-and-frisk" checks that yielded weapons and arrests. Two search warrants were executed that resulted in nearly one hundred weapons, including high power semi-auto rifles, shotguns, handguns and silencers seized from a white bar owner who dealt in guns.

———◄○►———

Neal Bradley Long watched television news coverage of the shootings of whites, particularly the murder of Joseph Baker and wounding of his family. He was convinced whites were not safe at all on the West Side, and Dayton Police were afraid to clean up the West Side. When he coupled crimes with the recent news about the busing case filed to force black and white children together, it was more than his mind could handle. His troubled life was again spinning out of control, and he projected his problems on others. His boss laid him off, and his failed murder attempt of Frank White had to be finished. Busing of school children had to be stopped. Murders of whites by "niggers" had to stop. Long believed no one was doing anything to correct the mounting problems.

Neal Bradley Long continued to hear voices in his head. Words came through as thoughts and gave him a plan. The thoughts morphed into commands, as if from God. Long began to sense he was on a mission for good, that he could fix a lot of the problems in his life and in Dayton. He just needed to eliminate the troublemakers. It reminded him of the KKK and their goal to preserve white America. He would protect whites and their white schoolchildren. Long believed in the "code of the mountains" from Eastern Kentucky. Generations of shootin' and killin' by the Hatfields, McCoys and Sizemores were the most glaring examples and the lore of the hills. Violent revenge was part of life.

Sipping whiskey, Long accepted the challenge of being a vigilante. He prepared for his new role.

———◄o►———

Long's irregular days off work were mostly spent alone in his room. When he ventured out, he randomly tailed his former boss, Frank White, who survived Long's first murder attempt on New Year's Eve.

On one occasion, as White left the Stolle plant at the end of his afternoon shift, Long followed him down I-75 toward Cincinnati. His shotgun lay on the front seat, under a blanket. He hoped White would stop at an exit for fuel or some other reason that would give him a chance for a clear shot. Luckily for Frank, he never stopped on his way to or from work. During one commute, Long pulled beside White on the interstate and startled the man. White was not sure who it was, but he believed it was Long. Because he was unsure, White passed it off as a coincidence. Neal Bradley Long's hatred for Frank White was an obsession, and he decided to taunt White. Long hand printed a menacing anonymous letter to White and let him know that he was being hunted. Long enjoyed the sadistic feeling as he printed the sentences, folded the letter and stuffed it into an envelope. He spent days relishing in the knowledge that he had power over Frank White. In fact, Long felt he could decide if and when White would die.

July 22, 1972, Long mailed the threatening letter from Miamisburg, Ohio, a small town where his father lived, just a few miles south of Dayton. The letter was addressed to "Frank White (Red) Stolle Corp. Dayton, 1525 W. River road." The jerky writing on the envelope was hard to read, and the address was incomplete, so delivery was delayed until the post office could determine the postal zone.

———◄o►———

Long was settled on his path forward. He would avenge those who mistreated him personally and launch a wave of terror against the coloreds the likes of which Dayton and America had seldom seen.

THIRTY-EIGHT

The Midnight Slayer

The air was muggy and damp from a light rain. Neal Bradley Long drove past Deeds Carillon Park with its 150-foot tall bell tower at Dayton's southern city limits. He worked an extra hour, until midnight, and he headed to his rented room at 238 West Grand Avenue. On the way, Long took a few sips of cheap whiskey. His lips still yearned for the sting of alcohol. Once inside his room, he twisted the cap off a new "shorty" of whiskey and took a long swig, wiped his mouth with the back of his hand and prepared for a "hunting" trip on the West Side.

The black-haired man wore his light blue work shirt and black plastic framed glasses as he knelt down in front of the sink in his room. He pulled back the tattered curtain that covered the storage area and reached inside for his Model 55, 12-gauge bolt-action shotgun. It was capable of firing three rounds with a detachable two-round magazine box. The cool metal and wooden stock of the sawed-off shotgun felt good in his hands. He paused as he sat on the floor. He checked it over and loaded it with #2 shot Remington shells. He wrapped the shotgun in a piece of bed sheet and stuffed a small bottle of whiskey in his back pocket as he left the room.

The hunter aimed his car toward the West Side, to the killing fields. "Nigger-town." Long believed God had shown him signs and directed him to act and to teach the "coloreds" a lesson.

It was 12:30 a.m., Monday, July 31, 1972. Long lowered the windows of his Oldsmobile and laid the shotgun on the front bench seat. He moved the safety switch to the "off" position. The hunter was ready to find his target. Long drove onto Riverview Avenue and headed a short distance to the bridge at Sunrise Avenue that crossed Wolf Creek directly into the West Side at the Great Miami River. He carried a dozen other shotgun shells, a mixture of 00 buck and #2 shot. He was determined to send a message to the "niggers." He felt immense power over the life and death of his soon-to-be victims.

———◄◦►———

At 1:30 a.m., Long trolled streets on the West Side. Like an experienced hunter, he watched for people who strayed from the pack and made themselves more vulnerable. Two black men, who appeared to be in their twenties, walked across the street at Germantown and Summit Streets, and Long honed in. Long was headed in the opposite direction, so he slowed his vehicle and moved into the center lane. He nearly came to a complete stop. The men did not pay attention to Long's vehicle as it crept along. In the same manner Lester Mitchell was shot, Long rested the sawed-off shotgun on the windowsill of the driver's side of the Olds. BOOM! The weapon's report echoed off the streets and buildings. The two men instantly crumpled to the sidewalk. They suffered minor wounds to their arms and legs. Long sped away and disappeared as he turned north on Summit Street. By the time a passerby called police from a pay phone booth and reported the shooting, Long had driven about ten blocks north on Summit Street, crossed Wolf Creek and back to West Riverview Avenue.

At about 2:10 a.m., Long intensified his hunt. He looked for a pedestrian; any black man would do. As Long approached the intersection of Meredith and West Riverview, he saw a man alone on the sidewalk. Long readied his weapon and slowly crossed the center line and drove up behind the pedestrian, who had his back toward Long's car. Neal Bradley Long's focus was intense as he pointed the shotgun out the driver's window and slowed to a near stop. The twenty-year-old black man, Raymond Malcomb, saw headlights illuminate him and he turned and saw Long's shotgun pointed at him. Malcomb ran, but Long sped up and pulled alongside Malcomb, who tripped and fell. As Malcomb tried to get up, Long stopped, sharpened his aim and fired a single shot that tore into Malcomb's right side, thigh and under his right armpit. He slumped down onto the sidewalk, critically wounded. Long sped away.

The emergency tone blasted loudly over the police radio frequency. "Car 551, report of shots fired in the street, Meredith and Riverview, 2:24 a.m." There was no mention of a victim as the caller only reported that they heard the shot.

Patrolman D.E. Vanzant was the first officer on the scene. He found Malcomb and called for an ambulance. Despite his wounds, Malcomb provided a description of the shooting suspect as a white male, blue shirt, black hair and black framed glasses. He was clean-shaven with ear length sideburns, possibly in his forties. He drove a blue or brown 1964 Oldsmobile. Officer Vanzant broadcasted the suspect's information as patrol cars searched the area for the suspect's car. Homicide Detectives were dispatched to the scene.

———◄�‣———

Within minutes, and eight blocks from where Raymond Malcomb was shot, another victim was wounded. "Crew 331, 331!" The police dispatcher sounded the emergency tone. Bleeeeeeeep! "Crew 331, go to West Third and Conover, a man shot in the street. No description of the suspect yet, not sure if it is connected to the Meredith and Riverview shooting. The call came in from the railroad tower watchman who heard a shot but did not see a suspect vehicle. The time is 2:50 a.m."

A twenty-six-year-old black man, Alfred Heath, was shot and wounded in the thigh and buttocks. He told officers he was shot by a man as he drove slowly in the westbound curb lane on Third Street. Heath turned and looked at the car and saw a shotgun barrel protrude from the right front passenger window as the driver leaned over. A single shotgun blast hit his left leg, and he fell as the car sped away. The victim told police the shooter was a white man, dark hair and glasses. He drove a General Motors car, probably an Oldsmobile.

Police cars flooded the area and stopped any car with a white driver, particularly since quite a few had been in the area in the market for street prostitutes. However, Long was not seen or stopped by police.

———◄�‣———

The emergency tone sounded again. "Crew 336! Shots fired, possibly a man down on the sidewalk, corner of Cincinnati and Stewart Street. 3:15 a.m." Police sped to the scene and found another young black man had been wounded by a spray of shotgun pellets. His wounds were relatively minor. He had been struck in his hand and thigh. The victim described the shooter as a white man who drove an older GM car.

———◦———

The news media provided blanket coverage of the shootings. A *Dayton Daily News* reporter mistakenly believed that Raymond Malcomb had died from his shotgun wounds and quickly dubbed the white drive-by shooter the "Midnight Slayer." The moniker was a catchy tagline and it stuck. Neal Bradley Long liked the title, too.

———◦———

Chief Igleburger and Major O'Connor were notified of the shootings around 4:00 a.m., and they quickly headed into headquarters. They knew the series of new random shootings of blacks by a white man was very bad news for the City of Dayton.

At 7:00 a.m., July 31st, several detective sergeants and a half-dozen of their men sat in the conference room as O'Connor, cigarette in hand, paced back and forth as he talked. "Listen up men, the shootings this morning were all related. All the victims are alive, but Raymond Malcomb was seriously wounded. The suspect is a white male, possibly late thirties, dark hair, wearing dark framed glasses. One victim said the shooter wore a blue shirt. He drove a GM car, possibly a 1964 Oldsmobile sedan, blue, tan or brown. The suspect didn't say anything, and he surprised his victims. He fired a sawed-off shotgun from a seated position in his car and drove away."

Grover O'Connor paused and used the stub of his burning cigarette to light a fresh one. "The shooter is probably using a 12-gauge shotgun. Quite a few lead pellets of #2 shot have been recovered from the first shooting victim. The suspect was within fifty feet or less of each victim." The Major stood silently and scanned the room. "Does anybody have any good leads or snitch information?"

Detective Beu-tell spoke for the group and said they had checked some tips, but nothing panned out. No one else responded and their silence bothered the impatient O'Connor.

"Surely somebody saw something! There had to be whores and drug dealers out on the street that saw something," O'Connor demanded. "Start shakin' the bushes, get me some leads, damn-it! Start looking at all shotgun cases, cleared or un-cleared cases in the West Side for the past year. Get with the Organized Crime Control Unit (OCCU) Intelligence Squad, Vice and Narcotics folks. Get 'em up to speed. Put pressure on the white snitches. Somebody's got to know this son-of-a-bitch! The Patrol Division will be stopping anything that moves on the street. Anybody that looks out of place. I want all white men driving at night on the West Side stopped and identified."

Mild laughter interrupted O'Connor when a detective piped up, "This will put a crimp in the take-home pay of the ladies of the night."

O'Connor angrily seized on the light humor. "Hell yes it will! And that's the point! Those whores and pimps will want things back to normal, and until they tells us everything they know, it ain't happenin.' Put the pressure on 'em. Who the hell knows, this could even be a "trick" getting revenge for being ripped off by a whore or robbed by a pimp."

"Men," O'Connor said with his stained coffee cup in hand, "this ain't going to be easy. This is *not* our normal kind of case. We've never had a white guy drive through the West Side shooting blacks."

O'Connor and the detectives either forgot or ignored that Lester Mitchell was killed with the same M.O. in 1966 by a white man who drove by in a car. The Mitchell case remained officially "Unsolved. Inactive - Not Cleared." O'Connor said it was cleared by the jailbird snitch information.

"We've got to stop this bastard, and soon." He clapped his hands loudly. "Let's hit the street!"

Detectives relied on their memories and pulled six one-year-old shotgun shooting cases excluding the Mitchell case, from the files. Aside from the Mitchell case, none involved a white shooter. However, no one pulled the white-on-white shotgun shooting files, including Frank White's unsolved shotgun shooting case.

Within hours, detectives contacted snitches all over town. Patrol crews stopped and questioned white men who drove through the West Side after dark.

Detective Beu-tell met with Lieutenant Riley, head of the OCCU and Narcotics Detectives Baker and Spells and briefed them on the shootings. Baker and Spells promised to press their snitches for information and conduct extensive surveillances, if needed.

Black community leaders and neighborhood and civil rights leaders amped up their speeches and demanded police action. Black ministers urged vigilance and calm. Many young black men who were regulars on the street took particular notice that two of the shooting victims were black men in their twenties. Words of calm from black leaders and ministers did not reach the ears of angry young men. Their desire for revenge simmered.

The shootings that targeted black men caused widespread fear of being on the street after dark. The random shootings threatened the safety of innocent women and children, too. Many blacks risked being arrested and illegally carried concealed weapons in the belief that it was "better to be judged by twelve than carried by six."

While DPD did not yet understand a motive for the shootings, the violence was clear in Neal Bradley Long's irrational mind. He was a "lone wolf" who had to do his part to stop all the bullshit about civil rights, race mixin' and shootings of white motorists. He believed other vigilantes would follow his lead.

In his dirty dim room, Neal Bradley Long sipped a cup of whiskey and watched TV news coverage of the shotgun shootings. He was sure he killed the man on Meredith Street and was disappointed that he had not. Long was satisfied he scared the hell outta' the "coloreds." The Midnight Slayer was not done, not by a long shot.

Frank White received the anonymous threat letter written by Neal Bradley Long around noon July 31, 1972. He was startled by the scrawled handwritten message inside. The poorly printed message read:

Look Frank, I'm sorry I missed you last new years. I've really

had a hard time trying to contact you. Be speaking to you soon.
It's hard to speak during the day. I've seen you. I stop along 75
and try to see you. I'll try like hell not to miss the next time and
it don't have to be on Rt. 75.

Frank White's memory jogged and he suddenly recalled an incident on
I-75 southbound to Cincinnati. Upon reflection, he was certain he had
seen former employee Neal Bradley Long as he drove an Oldsmobile
alongside him on the highway. White remembered Long's face, dark hair
and black plastic frame glasses that he always wore. He immediately dialed the Dayton Police dispatcher.

About an hour later, Detective Sergeant Gene Melson stopped by
White's office and took custody of the letter and wrote his initials "G.M."
and date, July 31, 1972, on the back of the envelope. Sergeant Melson was
edgy and tired as he talked with Mr. White. Melson had been at work
since about 3:00 a.m. when he was called in along with a half-dozen other
detectives to work on the drive-by shotgun shootings.

Melson told Frank White, "We are looking for some white guy who
had shot several black men with a shotgun on the streets in the West Side
early this morning."

Frank White told Sergeant Melson about being wounded by a shotgun
blast at work last New Year's Eve. White described Long and said he was
laid off work March 27, 1971 due to his excessive absenteeism and drinking problems. White also told Melson he saw Long on I-75 months later
and believed Long followed him.

Sergeant Melson did not spend much time with Mr. White's complaint.
He wanted to get back to Dick Section and help on the shotgun shooting
cases on the West Side. Frank White gave the sergeant a copy of Long's job
application for employment at Stolle, dated 10-18-65. It included Long's
personal information, employment history, family names, addresses and
past medical history. Information about Long's admission to DSH in
November 1967 was also included. It did not dawn on Sergeant Melson
that Neal Bradley Long, the suspect in the sniper shotgun shooting attack
and death threat against Frank White, was a close match to the suspect in
drive-by shotgun shootings on the West Side.

The letter that threatened Frank White and Long's job application were turned over to Detective Bob Keen for follow-up. He sent them to the Miami Valley Regional Crime Lab on August 2, 1972 and requested a "Document Examination for comparison of handwriting." A new crime report was made for the threatening letter, a misdemeanor violation of "Menacing," and listed Neal Bradley Long as a suspect.

————◦————

August 7th, Crime Lab Document Examiner, Roy Mantle, evaluated the samples of Neal Bradley Long's handwriting with the unsigned hand-printed threat letter sent to Frank White. Mantle used traditional analytical techniques. His examination followed two steps. First, he looked at samples with the naked eye. Second, he used magnifying lens. In both cases, Mantle studied the size, direction, slant and connections between letters. Observations about vocabulary, phrasing, spelling, punctuation and grammar were studied as well. The handwriting samples were hard to reconcile with the threatening letter because the threat letter was hand-printed and scrawled across the paper while samples from Neal Bradley Long's personnel file at Stolle plant were all in cursive handwriting. The two styles of writing could not be compared with any degree of certainty.

Friday, August 11th, Document Examiner Mantle wrote the following to Sergeant Melson:

> Although comparisons of samples of hand printing were very limited, no conclusive determinations could be made from it, there were sufficient comparative characteristics of innate hand printing pattern and form to merit further collection and examination from the same suspect.

Detective Keen spent most of his time on the Midnight Slayer shootings but he finally broke free to follow up on Frank White's case. Keen went to Long's last known address listed in the Stolle plant personnel records, 60 Fountain Avenue. He found that Long had moved in late 1971 and gave no forwarding address. The detective persisted and checked the Dayton

Police Records Section and found Long received a speeding ticket August 10, 1972, at 7:09 a.m. in the city of Oakwood on Dayton's south border. Oakwood Police Officer D. McClanahan cited Long for speeding while driving an Oldsmobile, Ohio License tag 1410QQ. The officer recorded basic data on the traffic ticket: Long's date of birth, SS number and driver's license number. Detective Keen noted Long's address of 238 West Grand Avenue, Dayton.

Detective Keen and a uniformed police officer met at Long's West Grand address August 17th at about 1:00 p.m. They did not know they were about to approach a dangerous, well-armed man who gunned down men at random two weeks earlier.

Detective Keen and the officer went to Long's second floor room and noticed the unlocked hasp and padlock on the outside of the door. After repeated knocks, police heard sounds of a padlock being unlocked from inside. Both officers instinctively placed their hands on their guns. Long finally freed the lock and opened the door only a few inches. Long saw the police uniform and the detective, and his throat tightened. For a split second, he wished he had one of his handguns.

"Mr. Long?, I'm Detective Keen, Dayton Police and this is Officer Williams from the Fifth District," said Keen as he held up his Detective badge. "Can we come in? I'd like to ask you a few questions." Long had been drinking the night before, and he felt the effects of a colossal hangover.

Long was subdued and could hardly be heard when he answered, "About what?" Long peered from the partially opened door.

"About Frank White at Stolle. You know him don't you?"

"Yeah," said Long. "I got laid off there a long time ago and I got another job. You can come in for a few minutes, but I got to get ready to go to work soon." Long's mind raced as he thought about his shotgun under the sink.

Detective Keen and Officer Williams glanced around as they walked into the small dirty room, but they did not see anything unusual or illegal in plain view. "You've moved around a bit haven't you, Mr. Long?" Detective Keen asked. "You been here awhile?"

Long replied, "Oh, 'bout a month."

"Where do you work?" asked the detective.

Long rubbed his eyes as he mumbled, "Cap Collins' gas station in Kettering."

Detective Keen switched gears and asked the key question, "Mr. Long, have you sent any letters to Mr. Frank White at the Stolle plant?"

"No," Long said, as his eyes darted to the floor.

"Then you won't mind giving me a handwriting sample will you?" the detective asked.

Long looked up, first at Detective Keen, then at the uniformed officer. "Why?" he asked.

"Well, Mr. Long, if you didn't threaten Mr. White, there's nothing to worry about, right?" Detective Keen said as he handed Long a single sheet of white unlined paper. Long didn't respond as he took the paper and sat on the edge of his bed. Detective Keen handed him his clipboard and told Long to print his name and the same words that were written on the envelope addressed to Frank White. Detective Keen had typed them in all capital letters at the top of the paper. Long used a pencil on the top half of the page. On the lower half, Detective Keen told him to print it again using a ballpoint pen.

"FRANK WHITE (RED) STOLLE CORP (DAYTON)
1525 W RIVER. RD"

Long did not say a word as he labored and printed the group of words two times as instructed. He handed the paper and clipboard to Detective Keen. Keen was ready to leave when he turned and asked Long, "Do you mind if I take a picture of you, right here, right now?" Long wanted to say no, but he agreed reluctantly. He put on a blue work shirt over his white undershirt and stood against the wall. Detective Keen took the picture and waited a few seconds until it mechanically ejected from the front of a Polaroid camera. Keen carefully held the wet picture between his index finger and his thumb until it dried. He showed it to Long and then turned it over and jotted down his initials and the date on the back. The photo of the white man in his forties with black hair, black framed glasses and a light blue shirt came out clear.

Keen smiled and said, "I'm a pretty good picture taker." Long did not like Keen's quip. Keen dropped the photo and handwriting sample into a ten-by-fourteen-inch manila case file envelope, labeled "Complainant: White, Frank. Stolle Plant. Shooting to Kill, 12.31.71 Suspect: Neal Bradley Long. Type of Weapon: shotgun." "Menacing Complaint, 7.31.72."

Neal Bradley Long's Polaroid photograph was a close match to the physical description of The Midnight Slayer. The weapon used in the Frank White shooting on New Year's Eve was a shotgun, assumed to be sawed off due to the wide pattern. It was the same kind of weapon used in the July 31st drive-by shootings on the West Side. Unfortunately, those two facts did not register with Detective Keen.

Detective Keen gave Long his business card and thanked him for his cooperation and walked out with the uniformed officer. Long sat motionless on the corner of his bed. He wondered if the police suspected him in the West Side drive-by shotgun shootings, too. The shooting of Frank White on New Year's Eve and the threatening letter to White brought the police to his door. His delusional ego did not consider the possible consequences that loomed overhead. He took a swig of whiskey and headed down the hall.

Neal Bradley Long opened a window in the bathroom and sat on the toilet. He thumbed through one of his favorite paperback books about invisible creatures from outer space and the paranormal. The visit by police faded quickly as he took a few tokes of a marijuana cigarette.

A seldom-seen smirk eased across Long's sweaty face. He was the man hundreds of cops searched for. Long thought about how they had him in their hands but they couldn't see his "other self," The Midnight Slayer. The blue haze and pungent odor enveloped the marginal man who lived every minute on the edge.

Long was un-phased by the visit by Dayton Police. He was a vigilante, a lone wolf on a mission. Four days after the visit by Detective Keen, Long headed out for another nighttime ride through the West Side.

———◦———

Monday morning, August 21, 1972, 12:20 a.m., John Ferguson, a black man age forty-four, walked alone across the Sunrise Avenue Bridge on

West Riverview Avenue near West Third Street. Like many other people during the hot summer in poor neighborhoods, Ferguson waited until the cooler nighttime to run an errand. Ferguson walked about three blocks from his house on his way to a Sunoco Service Station to buy cigars. He noticed a car slowly move up behind him. Ferguson turned. He was struck and spun completely around by the blast from a 12-gauge 00 buck shotgun shell. Ferguson was hit in the left forearm and in the center of his stomach. The ammunition, designed to take down the largest of prey, did its job as Ferguson hit the sidewalk. The 00 buck ripped Ferguson's gut open and exposed his bloody intestinal organs that glistened under the streetlights.

Ferguson was near death as his blood pooled and seeped over the curbside. The first officers arrived on the scene and immediately summoned emergency assistance. Ferguson was barely conscious, but he managed to tell officers that a lone white man, with dark hair and glasses, shot him from the window of a tan car. Ferguson was unsure of the make or model of the vehicle but he indicated that the driver slowly drove away toward the West Side.

A bloody shotgun shell wad, later identified as a Remington Peters shotgun shell, was removed from his stomach during surgery. Ferguson was in critical condition.

———◦———

The Dayton Police dispatcher received two more urgent calls during that early morning that involved drive-by shotgun shootings by a white man in a car. Although the vehicle descriptions varied, the M.O. was the same as the Ferguson shooting, except the new shootings involved use of #2 shotgun shells.

At 12:40 a.m., "Reports of shots fired, possibly two men wounded at the corner of Germantown and Summit. Two black men were shot at as they stood on the sidewalk. They sustained minor wounds in a leg and arm. They got a glimpse of a shotgun that stuck out the car window and they ducked before it was fired."

At 12:50 a.m., another call was received. "Two men shot, on the street, 3210 McCall." Both men received shotgun wounds to the thighs and one in the hand. Shots were fired from about sixty feet away by a white man who drove away in a car.

As Neal Bradley Long made his way back to his room at 238 West Grand, he saw a black man, Eddie Frison, in a phone booth at West Riverview and North Williams Street. Long slowly drove alongside the phone booth and pointed his shotgun out the window of his car. The shotgun jammed or miss-fired and gave Frison a few seconds to fall to the ground near the passenger side of Long's car. Long manipulated his weapon and aimed at Frison again. The weapon jammed again and Long's potential victim escaped.

Frison watched from the bushes as Long drove away. He called police at 1:30 a.m. and described the shooter as a white man in a blue shirt who drove a GM car.

———◄○►———

The Lieutenant in charge of Field Operations ordered all available police crews into the West Side, save a few crews left for emergencies in other districts. Despite efforts to saturate the West Side with officers, the suspect car escaped the area. Long avoided crossing back through the heavily populated midsection of the West Side. Instead, he headed to the western city limits at Gettysburg Avenue and turned east on sparsely populated Nicholas Road. He knew the route well as it passed very near his old workplace, the Stolle plant. On his way back to his room at 238 West Grand Avenue, Long cut through downtown to avoid the West Side.

When Long got back to his room, he hid his shotgun beneath the sink. His routine was simple. He drank whiskey, smoked a joint, went to sleep, awoke the next morning and watched the news. Long enjoyed hearing the TV anchor call the shooter "Midnight Slayer." For the first time in his life, he was somebody. He was a man to be feared.

———◄○►———

"You gotta' be shittin' me," Major O'Connor said when the police dispatcher called his home and woke him from a snoring sleep. He cleared his head and laid back on his pillow in the dark. The phone pressed to his ear. O'Connor listened to details of the shooting spree. O'Connor was still foggy when he asked, "Is this Monday?" Before the dispatcher could answer O'Connor said, "Didn't the last sniper shootings happen on July 31st, a Monday, too?" The question was rhetorical and silence followed, as the wheels started to turn. "Never mind," he told the dispatcher. "We've got one hell of a problem. I'll be coming to the office."

—◦—

John Ferguson barely survived his wounds from the shotgun blast on the Sunrise Avenue Bridge. The news media conducted interviews with victims, black leaders, police officials and many others as DPD grappled with the fact that a racially motivated serial shooter was on the loose.

Extra patrols were ordered on overtime. Teams of detectives were assigned to work every night on the West Side from midnight to 6:00 a.m. Despite intense efforts, no leads developed. DPD established a 24/7 telephone tip line in Dick Section for citizens to call. Nothing panned out. After nearly one month and no new shootings or solid leads, the beefed up patrol and detective details were cut back and patrol operations returned to normal schedules by September 15, 1972.

—◦—

September 18, 1972, Roy Mantle, Document Analyst for the Crime Lab, dictated a new letter to Detective R. R. Keen.

> Subject: Laboratory Case #72-2909, Frank R. White, "Shooting to Kill," occurred at 1525 W. River Road.
>
> On August 31, 1972 the laboratory received as additional evidence for handwriting comparison, the following items:
>
> Item 1. One white sheet of paper identified as containing requested handwriting samples from the subject Neal Long.
>
> Item 2. Two white sheets of paper that had been previously provided submitted to the lab on August 2, 1972 and identified as containing the questioned hand printing.
>
> The hand printing in Item 1 was compared with that in Item 2. Although many comparative characteristics of seemingly individuality were observed, it was not possible to

233

determine beyond a reasonable doubt that the hand printing in Item 1 and Item 2 is exclusively unique to one individual.

Signed, Roy L. Mantle

———◦———

Detective Keen received the Crime Lab report Wednesday, September 20th. He was disappointed to see that the handwriting analysis did not provide sufficient evidence, on its own, to pursue Neal Bradley Long any further for the shotgun shooting of Frank White. In the absence of eyewitnesses or any other corroborating evidence, and no admission by Long, Detective Keen closed the case, with his supervisor's approval, as "Inactive - Not Cleared." The letter from the Crime Lab was placed in the case file, re-sealed and filed away.

Detective Keen's file was never examined or compared with the Midnight Slayer cases. Long's Polaroid photo was an undiscovered jewel that was never shown to victims and witnesses of the Midnight Slayer.

———◦———

Narcotics Detectives Baker and Spells continued to spend time assisting Homicide, but leads had gone cold. They stopped to see a reliable informant on a Friday night, around 11:30 p.m. They arrived at a bootleg joint called Frank's Bamboo Hut at Riverview and Dow, just a few blocks from some drive-by shotgun shooting scenes. Frank Williams, a dark-complected black man, balding and in his late fifties, was the operator of the joint. Inside was a homemade bar, covered with bamboo. A half-dozen tables were crowded together in the dimly lit establishment on the first floor of an old two-story house. The Bamboo Hut was situated across from the huge Dayton Tire and Rubber Plant. Frank was a small-time operator, and he often provided solid criminal intelligence information. Frank was an observant man, and he knew odd things about people. He snitched on the habits and associates of drug dealers who came into his place. In exchange, Baker and Spells never bothered Frank.

When Frank saw Baker and Spells enter, he motioned them over to a dimly lit corner of the bar. Frank boasted of a God-given gift of prophesy called Omancy, a legacy "gift" that dated back centuries ago in Africa.

Frank said he could see the future of a person's life based on their birth sign and the meaning of the letters of their name.

Frank leaned close, his eyes darted side to side and signaled urgency. It is either bullshit or something important, Baker thought. "Dan, Tony," Frank said in his low raspy voice. "I have some ideas about the man who has been shooting people on the streets on the West Side." Spells looked at Baker and did not say a word as both men sipped their beers. "Men, I believe it's a white man. Yes, white, killing black men. He can't stop himself." Frank closed his eyes and slipped into his Omancy mode the detectives saw many times before. Frank rocked back and forth, placed his palms to his forehead. He swayed and became light headed. Baker and Spells helped him to a chair and sat down.

Frank spoke in sound bites. "Too many things . . . we lost too many . . . shot dead . . . but there is a . . . a sign and I see it, I see important letters."

"Christ Almighty Frank! Lost who, what?" Baker, often the impatient one, said as he peeled off the label of his beer bottle. Spells looked at Baker with a "STFU" faux glare.

Frank's voice lowered to a whisper. "John F. Kennedy, JFK," he said, emphasizing the K. Then loudly, "Martin Luther King, Jr. MLK." Frank spoke louder, "Robert F. Kennedy, RFK!" Frank coughed and looked drained. He slowly muttered "K . . . K . . . K."

Baker and Spells looked at each other. They knew that Frank liked drama. They waited for the other shoe to drop.

"And?" Baker said in a low voice.

Frank said, "*K* is the eleventh letter in the alphabet! Damn it! Three K's times eleven is thirty-three!"

Spells took a drag of his fading cigarette. "Frank, what the hell you tryin' to tell us?"

Frank furrowed his brow and the drama peaked. He looked directly into Baker's eyes, then Spells' eyes. "It's the Ku Klux Klan, a KKK man doin' the killin', don't you see?" Quietly, Frank leaned forward to Baker and Spells as they huddled. "He'll shoot thirty-three before he's done. Three K's times eleven . . . is thirty-three! More will die," Frank said as he slapped his hand on his knee. "More will die!" Frank picked up his drink and swallowed the double shot in one gulp. "He won't stop until he shoots thirty-three! By the gods of Omancy, it's true!"

The detectives finished their drinks and thanked Frank. As Baker and Spells walked out, Frank shouted, "It's true!"

The detectives left Frank's Bamboo Hut and drove to the tiny White Tower corner restaurant for breakfast. Over coffee, they decided to talk to Homicide Squad on Monday morning and learn more about the Midnight Slayer cases and tell the Omancy story to the Dicks.

When Baker and Spells walked into Dick Section at about 10:00 Monday morning, it was swamped with activity from the weekend. About fifty assorted crime victims, witnesses and others there to see a detective lined crowded hallways outside as they waited to be called in. The Homicide Squad office was also busy. Baker and Spells caught the attention of Homicide Detectives Gary Prugh and Robert Stevenson. Both men were glad to get out of the busy office, and the four men stepped across the hall to a private room.

Detective Stevenson, the senior man on Homicide, was five feet, ten inches, thin and slightly round shouldered. He always wore his suit coat. His jet-black hair, matter-of-fact manner and his voice made him a dead ringer for Detective Sergeant Joe Friday, the emotionless L.A. detective on the TV show, *Dragnet*. Detective Prugh, in his early thirties, was tall, trim and a natty dresser. He wore retro-grade glasses and never had a blond hair out of place.

After the men exchanged pleasantries and good-natured insults about work and other cop talk, they got down to business. Baker and Spells told about the psychic prediction Frank made that more will die. Thirty-three will be shot by the Midnight Slayer. Baker and Spells thought they would be laughed out of Dick Section for the psychic story; instead, they were met with unsmiling expressions. Detective Stevenson said, "Look fellas, thanks a lot. We've already had so many kook fortune tellers and psychics come out of the woodwork until it ain't funny. We ignore most, but your guy has thrown out a number. Who the hell knows? Some of those people are probably not psychic, they just may know something and cover it with a screwy story. We take it down and keep it in mind. Otherwise, we just work on our normal leads. Thanks, and keep tabs on your crystal ball guy, okay?"

Detective Prugh joined the conversation, "But, you guys gotta know, we already have a dozen or more confirmed shootings. We believe our guy has shot at more people, probably missed some. The son-of-a-bitch will probably shoot a lot more, like your guy said. Who knows at this point!"

On the way back to their car, Baker and Spells realized that while they enjoyed freedom that comes with undercover work, the rest of DPD was consumed with the shotgun shootings.

————◄○►————

The string of drive-by shotgun shootings in July and August of 1972 triggered an aggressive response from the DPD. Street officers stopped white men they saw after midnight on the West Side. Field Interrogation Cards (FIC's) were used to document who police stopped or talked to. FIC cards were turned in on vehicles from all over the city that were close to the description of the shotgun-shooting suspect's vehicle.

Detectives from specialized units like the Organized Crime Control Unit were drafted to help with investigative leads that required surveillance of a possible suspect or vehicle. With so many Dicks involved from different units, natural competition took over. Some detectives were determined to solve the case, and they hoarded information to give them an edge and receive the glory for themselves.

Within weeks, some quick arrests were made and touted to the news media that the possible "Midnight Slayer" suspect was in custody. Those hasty arrests faded quickly. One such incident involved two "hot shot" detectives. Their informant named a white male suspect in his forties, who owned an auto parts junk yard on Dayton's East Side. The alleged suspect was described as an outspoken racist who kept several shotguns at his shop, one of which was sawed-off.

With a rather weak search warrant in-hand, a dozen detectives planned a raid of the junk yard. They listed a shotgun as evidence sought. Before they left DPD Headquarters to go to the junk yard, the two detectives told a television cameraman, nicknamed "Scoop" Phillips, of the raid and divulged the time and location to ensure coverage of the action. Word spread around peers in the media and Scoop was tailed by other reporters. Scoop followed carloads of detectives and Montgomery County Prosecutor, James Brogan. The circus-type atmosphere started when Major Grover O'Connor's cruiser led a caravan of cops and reporters into the gravel parking lot in front of the junkyard. They hurried into the lot and emerged from a large cloud of dust. Some carried shotguns. A half-dozen detectives rushed into the office, guns drawn, and ordered the owner, Larry Metcalf, to freeze. The action-packed raid was caught on video and made great TV and press photos.

About two hours later, police came outside with Metcalf and took him downtown. Detectives carried two shotguns concealed under a blanket.

For the next twenty-four hours, the media buzz was positive for police. The shotguns, neither of which was sawed off, were checked out by a ballistics expert. No similarities were found with the type of weapon or ammunition used in the street shootings. A polygraph test of the potential suspect did not work out well. What started out as questioning soon evolved into harsh interrogations. Detectives had no physical evidence whatsoever that implicated Metcalf. They colluded with the polygraph operator and tried to break the suspect for a confession. Egos of the two lead detectives and the conceited "I-can-break-anyone" polygraphist, were poised to accept a coerced confession. Metcalf continued his denial, and the polygraph charts did not establish deception. Finally, Metcalf demanded an attorney and he was released with no charges.

It was a low point for DPD. The black community had high hopes that the Midnight Slayer had been captured. It was not true. A blanket of fear descended over the West Side again. The two hot shot detectives who led the raid disappeared and licked their wounds.

Major Grover O'Connor displayed his disappointment when he told the media that DPD had, indeed, detained an innocent man. The entire junkyard investigation was a bust from the beginning, and it left nearly everyone involved with a realization that no one, including DPD, had the slightest idea who the real Midnight Slayer was.

Neal Bradley Long watched TV coverage about the arrest of the junkyard man and his release from custody. Long saw the swarm of police officers as they descended on the junk yard. Long leaned close to the screen when he saw the white working man in handcuffs and paraded past a crowd of reporters who yelled, "Are you the Midnight Slayer?" Long watched curiously as he saw the junkyard man's "perp walk" into the City Jail. One detective boasted before the cameras, "Yep, I think we got 'em!"

Long was amused by the TV story as DPD swarmed like bees on a hive and then quietly released the suspect. The incident told him one very important fact. He obviously was not a suspect in the West Side shootings. He also realized Grover O'Connor and his men had not abandoned their search to catch the Midnight Slayer.

Neal Bradley Long decided to stop shooting, for awhile. He also decided he would drive a different car.

THIRTY-NINE

12-Gauge Shotgun vs .357 Magnum

Mysteriously, drive-by shotgun shootings of black men by a white suspect stopped after August 1972. The DPD exhausted all leads and tips. They had no idea who was responsible.

In early 1973, Grover O'Connor realized a career-long dream when he became Chief of Police in Dayton. O'Connor was ready to serve, but he faced two significant issues that could bring the city and his career to its knees. First, the Midnight Slayer was able to shoot and kill blacks at will, and police looked inept. Second, the push to desegregate Dayton Public Schools rekindled the hateful division between blacks and whites in the city. Parents on both sides of the Great Miami River saw their children in the crosshairs of social change. Many of them reacted like bears whose cubs were threatened. The police were drawn into the school busing issue more and more every day as they responded to calls of protesters, fights and threats.

Chief O'Connor sat in his recliner at home after work and sipped a scotch and water. He was seldom besieged by self-doubt, but it washed over him. Privately, O'Connor was frustrated at the inability of police to get solid leads on the shotgun shootings. That concern was matched by worries about racial tension in neighborhoods and schools. The big Irish cop did not finish his drink. Finally, sleep eclipsed his worrisome thoughts and covered him like a blanket.

————◄○►————

The Dayton School Board remained embroiled in controversy as the public school desegregation case continued through the Federal Court system. Federal District Judge Carl B. Rubin decided that Dayton schools were indeed segregated. He ruled in favor of a School Board plan to allow black and white students to be bused voluntarily to attend newly proposed "science centers and other part-time programs." The NAACP appealed the decision to the Sixth Circuit Court of Appeals and argued it was a token gesture. The voluntary program did not begin to resolve discriminatory practices and failures of the segregated dual school system.

The school desegregation case stirred racial tension between blacks and whites and fed another crisis that devastated portions of the city. Hundreds of white families in neighborhoods adjacent to Dayton's West Side made a panic decision and abruptly sold their homes and moved to the suburbs or country to avoid forced school integration. Greedy and unscrupulous realtors took advantage of the racial tension and capitalized on panic sale of homes called, block busting. Some realtors went door to door and handed out flyers: "Sell Now! Prices are falling everyday! You wait, you lose!"

Houses listed for ridiculously low prices. Fear was rampant during what was called "The Panic." Once panic sales began, home prices fell like dominos. "White flight" to the suburbs accelerated as people escaped the city.

Once a struggling neighborhood experienced sudden changes in its racial makeup or saw an influx of blacks or low-income whites, lenders drew a "Red Line" on a map around that neighborhood and refused to provide home loans. That neighborhood was cited as a "high-risk" neighborhood. Even the Federal Housing Administration tacitly supported Red Lining. Realtors and speculators paid cash and purchased homes and apartment buildings for pennies on the dollar. Red Lining hastened the demise of once proud neighborhoods.

Some blacks saw a chance to move out of the West Side and into better houses in formerly white neighborhoods. Realtors quickly flipped houses for cash profit. The faster blacks moved into a neighborhood, the faster the panic spread. However, not all "panic" homes were sold or rented. Many sat vacant and fell into disrepair. Crime and vandalism swept through rapidly changed neighborhoods and killed off small business districts that previously served the residents. The West Side ghetto spilled beyond the natural boundary of the Wolf Creek and into Dayton View like ripples in water.

Neal Bradley Long was sick and tired of claims of discrimination voiced by black leaders and their demands to integrate schools, which required busing children across town. Long's school-age children attended neighborhood schools on Dayton's East Side. Their schools were targeted for mandatory cross-town busing under the proposed NAACP Plan. Long stewed in his own racist juices at the thought of "coloreds" mixing with his children. He was determined to stop the efforts to bus children, even if it meant he had to kill more black men and start another riot.

———<o>———

The early summer of 1973 was milder than usual, and it enticed people to spend more time outside, even on Dayton's West Side that had endured a series of drive-by shotgun shootings during the prior summer. Dayton Police had not solved any of those cases, and the unknown white male suspect was still at large.

———<o>———

The Midnight Slayer terrorized West Side streets again Monday, June 10, 1973, as he stalked two young black men who walked on the sidewalk in a residential neighborhood in the 3700 block of Delphos Avenue. Richard Walton, age twenty-one, and his friend, Roosevelt Jackson age twenty, were engaged in a conversation at 12:45 a.m. and hardly noticed a car as it approached. The driver was a white man with black hair and black rim glasses. The car, described as either a General Motors or Ford product, slowed in the middle of the street. It was headed in their direction. Jackson saw the barrel of a shotgun as it stuck out the driver's window, but it was too late to avoid the loud and fiery blast of #2 shot.

Walton was closest to the shooter and caught the brunt of the shot in his upper chest and neck. He spun around violently and collapsed on the sidewalk. He bled profusely and choked on his own blood. Jackson was only slightly wounded in the upper arm but he also fell to the ground. Long paused a second, looked at his handy work and assumed both men were dead; then he slowly drove away.

Jackson was in shock but managed to scream for help until someone looked outside and called police. Richard Walton died shortly after he arrived at St. E.

-----◄◊►-----

Tuesday, September 4, 1973 at 12:30 a.m., the body of Isaiah Black; black male, 26 years old was found on the sidewalk near 1673 Miami Chapel, about ten blocks from the Stolle plant. He died two days later at St. E. from a shotgun blast to his back. There were no witnesses.

-----◄◊►-----

The Midnight Slayer shooting cases of 1972 and 1973 soon turned cold. No leads, no suspects. The rare white-on-black shootings seemed to be beyond the experience and ability of DPD to solve. However, the M.O. of the Midnight Slayer established a pattern of shootings and habits of the unknown suspect. Black male victims were shot when they were on foot and vulnerable. Shootings were in the same geographical area of the West Side and the northern fringe along Wolf Creek. The incidents occurred during mild or warm weather months, on similar days of the week between midnight and 5:00 a.m. There was no connection between victims or incident locations. All shootings were totally random. The shotgun pellets and wadding used were similar, and physical descriptions of the white male shooter were generally the same.

The Homicide Squad did not make the connection that the M.O. of the Midnight Slayer was identical to the murder of Lester Mitchell in 1966. DPD's hasty and convenient conclusion in May 1967, based on the jailbird snitch's information that the killer of Mitchell was dead, ended any review of the Mitchell case and comparison to the Midnight Slayer who was still active.

The DPD reacted to the M.O. analysis of shootings in 1972 and 1973 and increased targeted patrols once again. Detectives tightened the screws on informants, prostitutes, drug dealers and bootleg joint operators, but little was gleaned. Black community leaders formed volunteer citizen patrols in various neighborhoods. Initially, DPD discouraged the patrols because they feared vigilantism. Ultimately, the groups were recognized by DPD, which loaned them forty single-channel radios and white baseball caps. They patrolled in two-man teams and drove their own vehicles. The citizen patrols were ordered not to carry weapons, and they acted as eyes and ears for the police department from midnight to 5:00 a.m. They were soon dubbed the "White Hat Patrol" under the guidance of a DPD sergeant.

Several small groups of black men rejected the citizen patrols and formed loose-knit vigilante groups that patrolled with bats and clubs in their cars. After a few confrontations with police and some mistaken identity assaults on white motorists that resulted in arrest of some members of the groups, the vigilante groups faded.

There was no sign of the Midnight Slayer. After ten days, fatigue took its toll on the White Hat Patrol as most citizens worked a full-time job, and the extra hours on patrol proved uneventful. Patrols were cut back. Nearly everyone believed the shootings had not ended.

The Midnight Slayer managed to elude capture, even though in some instances he moved about the West Side for more than an hour during his shooting sprees. The shooter was apparently never stopped by police. Police informants and the DPD Tip Line did not offer any solid tips in the identity of the shooter. Rumors began to circulate in the West Side that the killer must have inside information about the police that enabled him to evade capture.

———◦———

September 26, 1973, at about 1:30 a.m., a black man named Edward Tillman, age thirty-nine, walked alone and stopped to wait for the traffic to pass so he could cross the street at Germantown and Summit Streets. A young man, Michael Jackson, age seventeen, left Ben's Hamburger Stand on the corner when he saw a dark blue two-door Ford, possibly a 1968 model, as it drove past. The driver, a white man, came to a stop along the curb on Germantown Street. Jackson watched as the man slid across the front seat of the car and fired two shots at Edward Tillman from the right passenger side window. Jackson did not see the weapon, but he saw the blasts. Edward Tillman fell to the sidewalk, mortally wounded by eleven gaping 00 buck entrance wounds in his upper back.

James "Emmet" Watts, a fifty-year-old black man, drove through the intersection as the shots were fired. At first, he thought a car had backfired.

Then he realized he had seen shots fired from a blue Ford driven by a white man.

Watts, the owner of a private detective business, was licensed to carry his Model 586 Smith & Wesson, .357 Magnum revolver with a four-inch barrel. Watts noticed that the car was a 1968 Ford Fairlane. The Ford sped away and Watts gave chase as Long ran the red light at the next intersection at Summit Street. The Ford went into a Shell gas station lot, made a U-turn and quickly headed eastbound onto Germantown Street. Long pulled to the curb and waited as Watts sped westbound up the hill.

Neal Bradley Long opened fire from his driver's seat window as Watts sped by in his 1969 Oldsmobile. A few 00 buck pellets struck Watts' car. Watts ducked, hit the gas and made a U-turn and chased the Ford that turned south on Broadway. Watts, in hot pursuit, fired his handgun at the Ford as they weaved through the streets toward Nicholas Road at speeds over seventy miles per hour. Long's car surged ahead.

Watts lost sight of Long's Ford but surmised the shooter probably continued on South Broadway and crossed the bridge over the Great Miami River into Moraine City. Watts sped in that direction and crested the crown on the two lane bridge and continued for about a half mile.

Long waited ahead in a gravel parking lot along the road. He parked his Ford at an angle on the opposite side of the road and turned the headlights off. Long sat in the driver's seat and reloaded his shotgun with three rounds of 00 buck shells. There were no streetlights outside of Dayton, and as Watts headed south, he nearly passed Long's unseen car when Long opened fire. Watt's Oldsmobile was struck about a dozen times in the windshield, driver's door and the roof line. One round penetrated the car door and tore open Watts' left knee. Watts slammed on his brakes and managed to slap his car into reverse. He backed away as fast as he could.

Long fled and spewed gravel and dust as he headed south into the darkness. Watts drove north to a nearby gas station where he collapsed due to a large loss of blood. Watts survived his wounds and was able to offer a good description of the shooter.

———◦———

As Long drove through downtown headed back to his room on West

Grand Avenue, he felt satisfaction in his ability to open fire in a busy area, shoot at will and fight off an armed pursuer. Long was aggressive and cool under pressure. He knew too many people saw his dark blue, two door Ford Fairlane 500 so he decided that he would not venture into the West Side for a while. He parked his Ford outside the City of Dayton. He hid it in Cap Collins' parking lot behind the gas station in suburban Kettering and mixed his car in with other cars that awaited repair. Long used another old car parked at his ex-wife's house for a few months.

————◄○►————

The devastating wounds suffered by Edward Tillman on September 26th claimed his life on October 7, 1973 at St. E. Hospital. The next day, over 150 blacks led by ministers and civil rights leaders marched and carried signs in front of City Hall. They demanded more police action. Sumpter McIntosh believed the shootings were civil rights violations under federal law and he used a bullhorn and yelled demands for DPD to do more and for the FBI to get involved in the investigations.

A block away in the U.S. Post Office and Federal Courthouse Building, commonly called the Federal Building, a group of FBI agents watched the demonstration from their office windows. Despite the fact the shootings were the most unique crime wave in Dayton's history, the FBI had not offered DPD any meaningful assistance. The FBI viewed the racially motivated random shootings as "local crimes."

By the end of the year, the number of homicides in the City of Dayton reached 105. Dayton's murder rate was the highest per-capita rate in the U.S. A violent city made worse by the Midnight Slayer. Dayton's five-man homicide squad was in desperate need of help.

FORTY

Why Do Bad Things Happen
To Good People?

Dayton civil rights leader, Sumpter McIntosh, led many grassroots efforts to improve the lives of black people in Dayton. Despite his controversial reputation and his use of harsh rhetoric, he was viewed by the black community and Chief O'Connor as an honorable man. He was a family man dedicated to the non-violent approach for social change and the end of discrimination against black people.

The fifty-three-year-old Sumpter McIntosh was also a small business owner. He opened a store in the heart of downtown Dayton where he sold African art, clothing and gifts. Monday, March 4, 1974, at about 9:15 a.m., McIntosh was on the sidewalk in front of his new shop, The House of Knowledge, when he heard a robbery alarm. Two young black men robbed the Potasky Jewelry Store next door. The armed robbers escaped with about $25,000 in jewelry and cash. As the robbers ran down the sidewalk headed toward their getaway car, McIntosh stepped into the middle of the sidewalk and held up his outstretched arms as if to embrace them and stop the crime. He said, "Stop! Stop!"

The robbers could not stop, and they ran directly into McIntosh's open arms. One man, Calvin Farmer, pulled back, pointed his gun and fired directly at McIntosh. He was shot in the chest. McIntosh fell to the sidewalk as the two men fled. Scores of people on the sidewalk and on buses watched in horror. Within minutes, Dayton Police flooded the area and a witness provided the license number of the getaway car driven by an accomplice.

Sumpter McIntosh was dead on arrival at Miami Valley Hospital at 9:52 a.m.

Dayton Police Detective Sergeant William "Bill" Mortimer and Detective Ralph Beu-tell, both of whom knew McIntosh, responded to the robbery call and arrived moments later. The dispatcher provided the address of the getaway car's license registration, and Sergeant Mortimer and Detective Beu-tell sped to the apartment building in the 1100 block of Staley Avenue. Police surrounded the suspect's location.

The long two-story public housing building on Dayton's West Side faced another unit across an open area. Sergeant Mortimer and Detective Beu-tell watched the suspect's doorway from their vantage point a few doors away in the same building. The suspects ignored orders to surrender, and two of the suspects brandished their weapons out the door.

Suddenly, two small children ran out of a doorway very near Sergeant Mortimer, right into the direct line of fire. Sergeant Mortimer stepped out to pull the children to safety and he said, "Go inside!" Those were the last words he ever uttered as a bullet struck his head.

The children made it inside as two suspects fired more shots and ran from the apartment. Police fired and wounded one suspect and captured the three men. Detective Beu-tell was also injured by shrapnel, but the big man's anguish at the loss of his best friend and boss overshadowed his pain. Sergeant Mortimer was dead on arrival at St. E.

Detective Baker was off duty when he learned of Sergeant Mortimer's death. Baker lived a few blocks from the Mortimer family, and he rushed to their home. The house was soon filled with police officers, clergy, family and friends. The crowd spilled into the yard. Grief was heavy in the air. A few years earlier, the Mortimer family lost Bill Mortimer's brother, Paul, who was also a Dayton Police Detective Sergeant. Paul died in the line of duty from a hepatitis infection contracted at the scene of a bloody homicide.

On that fateful day, two icons in the community died as they tried to help others. Two men who knew one another and held mutual respect for each other were gone. Once again, Dayton suffered another unimaginable loss in one day, both men suddenly and violently gone from the face of the earth.

The funeral for Sergeant Mortimer was held at Aldersgate United Methodist Church on Old Troy Pike in Huber Heights, Ohio just five blocks from his home. Hundreds of police officers and a like number of citizens paid their respect. Among the citizens who attended Mortimer's funeral were a few dozen blacks, including ministers, who made the approximately fifteen mile trip from the West Side to the white suburban neighborhood. On that day, and at that time, there wasn't a hint of racial division.

Detective Baker was joined by Detective Spells, and they stood together in the long line of police officers that curled around the outside of the church. They finally made it inside and waited their turn to walk by the casket. As they were about thirty feet away from Sergeant Mortimer's casket, there was a commotion of sobs and anguished cries at the side door of the church. Baker turned and saw the McIntosh family as they were ushered in. Led by Sumpter McIntosh's son, a dozen family members met the Mortimer family and meshed together as one in their grief. Hugs, sobs and overwhelming sadness finally gave way to the heartfelt appreciation because the McIntosh family came to console, even in their own time of sorrow. Baker later learned that some of Mortimer's family had visited the wake for Sumpter McIntosh as well.

As Baker and Spells watched, tears streamed down their faces. Many hardened police veterans and others were deeply moved by the scene. The black and white families were brought together by tragedy, yet they shared love and compassion.

The two families stood together in whispered conversation before the McIntosh family left. The room was thick with emotion as the minister rose. He asked for a moment of silent prayer for the two families, the city and its people during, "these difficult and painful days."

At the end of the service, the procession left the church. Police cars stretched for over one-half mile. The procession passed people who lined the streets. Men, women and children stood along the way and sobbed. Some saluted and held American flags. The silent police cars with red lights flashing followed the hearse as it moved slowly to the graveyard for a final salute, the playing of *Taps* at the final resting place of Sergeant Mortimer.

Death of the two men from different backgrounds and cultures caused a break in the seemingly never ending stories about the Midnight Slayer and concerns about when he might strike again. Even in death, Sumpter McIntosh and Sergeant William Mortimer were celebrated for their legacy. They left footprints in the sands of time for others to follow.

———◄○►———

Neal Bradley Long saw the news coverage of Mortimer and McIntosh murders and funerals. For Long, it was just another example of the "coloreds" who were out of control as they continued to rob and kill. Long was more interested in the news stories and talk he overheard at work about the NAACP school busing court case that was stalled in Federal Court. He did not offer his opinion to anyone; he just listened, and it got under his skin.

Long seldom drove his dark blue Ford after late September 1973 and through the early spring of 1974. He knew there was a possibility police had a description of his car that was used in the murder of the black man on Germantown Street and the shoot out with that "crazy nigger" who chased him into Moraine City. He wanted to sell or trade the car, but he could not risk that it might be traced back to him. Long decided to keep the 1968 dark blue Ford Fairlane 500.

April 11, 1974, Long took his dark blue car to the Earl Schieb Auto Painting Company at 2416 Stanley Avenue in North Dayton. The company was famous for its no-frills cheap paint jobs in one day for $29.95. Long selected a light baby blue color, and he was satisfied he could drive it again on the West Side without raising suspicion.

———◄○►———

Religion was important in any culture, but particularly in black communities. Their belief in God sustained generations of black people who endured slavery and faced hard-core discrimination in the modern era.

Churches were located all over the West Side of Dayton, from the small storefront church on West Fifth Street where Lester Mitchell stood on the sidewalk the night he was murdered to the large Mt. Enon Baptist Church at 1501 West Third Street. Mt. Enon was exactly thirty blocks west of Emmanuel Baptist Church at 1501 East Third Street. The Churches were similar in size and equal in proximity to the West Third Street Bridge. One church was black; one was white.

Most of the storefront churches were found in the nooks and crannies of the ghetto. Their smallness did not diminish their fervor, beliefs or desire to make the West Side a better place. One such small church was Straightway Baptist Church on Dakota Street, just one block from the lot where H. Rap Brown incited a riot a few years earlier. The neighborhood bordered a railroad track at the West Third Street crossing. Many of the buildings nearby were boarded up or vacant since the riots in the late 1960s. Reverend William Wright Jr. was the pastor of the church. Reverend Wright, a black man, was fifty-six years old. He served as part-time minister to a flock of about twenty people each Sunday.

On the night of May 12, 1974, the last member left the church after the Sunday night service. Reverend Wright finished his prayers, gathered his car keys and with his bible under his arm, he headed for the door at 11:50 p.m.

As Reverend Wright stepped out front, he bent over slightly to lock the door. He did not see a car that drove down Dakota Street. It edged closely to the curb near where he stood. At about 11:55 p.m. on that fateful night, Reverend William Wright, Jr. was gunned-down as he departed the house of worship. Neal Bradley Long pulled the shotgun barrel back into the car and paused for a moment and looked at his victim as he died on the steps of the poor church. With a blank expression on his face, the Midnight Slayer drove away into the darkness of the ghetto.

An elderly woman who lived near the church heard a single loud blast at about midnight and called Dayton Police. She did not look out because she lived in constant fear. She quickly double checked the three locks on her front door, her only margin of safety.

Homicide Detective Gary Prugh responded to the scene and saw Reverend Wright's body as he lay on his back. The upward blast ripped his chest apart by 00 buck shot. A 100-watt light bulb cast an eerie dim light over a faded hand-painted sign above the church door, "Straightway Baptist Church, Reverend William Wright Jr. presiding." God's soldier died a sad and violent death on the battlefield in the ghetto. His goodness mattered not to his racist killer. Reverend Wright's blood-spattered bible laid next to his soulless body. When it fell to the ground, it opened to St. John, Chapter 14, verse 2: *"In my Father's house are many rooms; if it were not so,*

I would have told you. And if I go and prepare a place for you, I will come back and take you to be with me that you also may be where I am."

Detective Prugh took Polaroid photos of the body and noticed the open bible and the highlighted scripture. He stooped down and silently read the passage. The detective, who had seen many violent deaths, was deeply moved. His throat closed as he choked back unexpected emotions. Prugh gazed at an apparent simple good man who lay dead, shot down like an animal. He finished his gruesome work and wondered why bad things happen to good people. Why was this man murdered?

FORTY-ONE

The Devil's Luck

Neal Bradley Long sat on the corner of his squeaky bed and looked at the street map of the City of Dayton spread out before him. It was hard to see in the dim light from the single light bulb that hung from the ceiling. It was sweaty hot in the single room he called home. The small fan that sat on the floor barely moved the stiflingly hot air. Long studied the streets and twelve bridges that crossed the Great Miami River and Wolf Creek and connected to the West Side. Long took a few swigs of cheap whiskey. His resolve was bolstered by the slight burn of alcohol that eased down his throat.

It was 1:45 a.m. July 3, 1974, as Long carried his laundry bag that contained his shotgun and a mixture of shotgun shells to his car. He paused and looked at the new baby blue paint job on his Ford Fairlane 500. He was certain no one would suspect that at one time it was dark blue.

———◦———

The night air was hot and muggy. The city was in need of rain as the July 4th holiday period approached. Before Long drove away, he loaded his sawed-off shotgun and magazine with three shells and laid his weapon on the back seat. He covered it with a dark sheet. Long drove onto Riverview Avenue and headed to the West Side.

Within ten minutes, Neal Bradley Long turned onto Holt Street and saw three young black men as they walked together at North Williams Street. Long eased his baby blue car along the street and stopped near the corner. He reached over the seat, retrieved his shotgun and waited as his prey approached. Long pointed his sawed-off shotgun barrel out the driver's window and opened fire.

James McKinney, age seventeen, who lived a few blocks away, took the brunt of the first vicious blast. Two more shots followed in rapid succession. McKinney grabbed his throat that was torn open and gushed blood. McKinney could not breathe, and he spit blood as he collapsed on the sidewalk. His neck and upper chest were struck by over one hundred pellets. McKinney died within seconds. His body lay slumped in the gutter in a massive pool of blood and tissue. His two companions, Johnnie Mitchell, age nineteen and David Lee, age eighteen, also received shotgun pellet wounds. To the disbelief of the two survivors and a witness who drove by, Neal Bradley Long calmly drove away.

Twenty minutes later, the Dayton Police Dispatcher sent police crews to West Grand and Grafton, about ten blocks from the first shooting. Fletcher Richardson, a black man age twenty-one, walked along the sidewalk when he saw a light blue Ford that drove past him suddenly stop in the street. For the first time in the series of shootings, Neal Bradley Long got out of his car to attack his victim. He reached in the back seat and pulled out his sawed-off shotgun. Richardson turned and ran. Long opened fire; he shot Richardson in the back and knocked him to the sidewalk. Richardson remained conscious and survived the attack. He got a quick glimpse of the shooter on the dark street.

Richardson described the shooter as a medium build white man, age forties, dark medium-length hair, dark frame glasses. He wore a light blue short-sleeve shirt and dark trousers. The shooter drove a light blue two door Ford, possibly a Fairlane 500 model.

———◄◊►———

Chief O'Connor was notified of the murder of James McKinney and the other shootings. He immediately went to Headquarters to meet with the Captain of Detectives and the Homicide Squad Sergeant. A dozen detectives were already engaged on the latest two shooting cases, and they funneled into the office around 4:30 a.m. and started their paperwork. The frustration was palpable, and O'Connor's presence raised the intensity level as he formulated his strategy for the coming days.

Chief O'Connor pressed detectives to use their newly acquired commercial identification tool called the *Identi-Kit System.* Two detectives trained to use the kit met with witnesses from recent shootings and spent about two hours with each person. They built a composite facial description. The *Identi-Kit* divided the human face into different sections on transparent plastic layers with outlines of various mouths, chins, eyebrows, foreheads and noses. Facial components were selected by witnesses and layered onto a white screen until the closest match was made. Detectives then sampled other features until the witness was able to build an entire composite of the suspect's face.

Within a few hours, a composite of the suspect was completed and photographed. Fletcher Richardson, the most recent victim, gave it about a 60% confidence level. Nevertheless, police finally had something to show, albeit an ordinary looking white man in his forties with dark hair, ear long side-burns and black plastic frame glasses. Unfortunately, the composite generally fit thousands of average looking white men in the Dayton metro area. However, it was a start. Chief O'Connor finally had something to go on.

Detectives fanned out across the city and showed the photo composite to informants. The photo was clipped above the visor in every police car in the city and county.

The *Identi-Kit* composite photo was released to the news media as a potential suspect in the Midnight Slayer series of shootings. While dozens of tips were phoned in to the DPD Tip-Line, none panned out.

At the Dayton FBI office, clerks dutifully clipped all news stories related to major crimes or activities at DPD. The composite photo article was removed from the newspaper and reviewed by agents. It was routinely filed away in their DPD Clip File. The Midnight Slayer shootings were routinely tracked and reported to FBI Headquarters under "Urban Guerrilla Warfare," even though the FBI viewed the racist shootings as a "local matter."

As word of the description of the Midnight Slayer spread throughout the black community, a bizarre rumor circulated that the shooter was a white off-duty Dayton Police Officer. The description of the suspect, a white male, age thirty-five to forty, light blue shirt and dark trousers, was similar to the description of DPD uniforms. Chief O'Connor erupted into a full-blown rage when it was suggested by a rookie newspaper reporter. The young man was intimidated by the big Irish cop's response. The rank and file police officers appreciated O'Connor's outburst. Most worked hard and served honorably since the riots and throughout the drive-by shootings. Cops were primed and ready to respond appropriately if some poor bastard on the street mouthed the rumor that a cop might be the Midnight Slayer.

———◄○►———

Neal Bradley Long was indeed a lucky man as he eluded the clutches of the law. He never followed a detailed plan or scheme when he hunted his victims, and he shot them from his car. Long's physical appearance seldom changed. He always wore black plastic frame glasses and the uniform provided by Cap Collins' Service Station, a light blue shirt and dark blue pants. He was never stopped or chased by police after a shooting. It was something Long thought little about, but it drove DPD Homicide Detectives crazy.

———◄○►———

Rows of metal cabinets filled the Records Room adjacent to the Detective Section. Filed in the 'Inactive - Not Cleared' section along with hundreds of cases, was a manila folder titled White, Frank. 'Shooting to Kill and Menacing threats' 12.31.71. Suspect: Neal Bradley Long. Inactive - Not Cleared. The Polaroid photo taken of Long in the summer of 1972 by Detective Keen was never viewed again. Long's photo showed that he was a white man, in his 40's, dark hair, black framed glasses and a light blue shirt. His photo matched the description of the Midnight Slayer. The photo waited in vain to be discovered and shown to witnesses in the drive by shotgun shootings.

Five years earlier, Neal Bradley Long sat in the DPD Detective Section and confessed to an old violent crime that involved a black victim. He told Homicide Squad Sergeant Howard Krisher that he committed a "possible murder" on a bridge that crossed the Great Miami River. Long made the confession Halloween night, October 31, 1966, just sixty days after Lester Mitchell was gunned down by a white man who fired a sawed-off shotgun from his car. Long told detectives, "I have done my job. I have confessed, now you know where you can find me."

Neal Bradley Long was known to the Dayton Office of the FBI for his Communist affiliations from 1962 to 1966, and his troublesome letter to U.S. Attorney General Robert F. Kennedy. Long's personal information, residence, etc. was on file in the Confidential FBI Indices. The three largest Psychiatric organizations in Dayton, St E. Hospital, Good Samaritan Psychiatric and Dayton State Hospital, all knew of Neal Bradley Long's violent history and his diagnosis in 1966 and 1967 as a dangerous person. His photo was included in his file at the time of intake at all three locations. None of the organizations made a connection to the Midnight Slayer with Long's description and violent tendencies.

Neal Bradley Long had "the devil's luck," indeed, as he evaded identification as a possible person of interest in the Midnight Slayer investigation.

FORTY-TWO
"I'll Resign"

Chief of Police, Grover O'Connor agreed to meet with a coalition of black leaders at his office at 6:00 p.m. July 10, 1974. The group included one woman and five men. They had a list of demands to give O'Connor. At the top of their list was their frustration about the inability of DPD to stop the Midnight Slayer.

The meeting began when Chief O'Connor walked into the conference room. The group was polite and smiled as the Chief sat his dark stained coffee cup on the table. O'Connor was notorious for drinking black coffee, no matter the time of day.

O'Connor greeted each person by name. The tension was palpable, but it eased as old acquaintances warmed to the Chief's serious but sincere personality. Chief O'Connor gently took control of the meeting when he told them he wanted to speak first, even though the group was prepared to start with their demands.

Chief O'Connor looked tired and exasperated. "I know you want answers and action about the drive-by shootings. I know you have demands; by God, I would if I were you. Please remember, this is my town, too, and the violence is tearing my heart out ... but I know that it is far worse for you and the hardworking people you represent." The Chief broke eye contact and looked down at his empty coffee cup before he continued.

"I know some of you blame me. I understand if you do." O'Connor paused and scanned the group of familiar faces. A mixture of memories flashed through his mind like a fast-moving movie.

The Chief's voice grew stronger. "I'm prepared to resign if I no longer have your confidence. On the other hand, if you believe we can get through these times together, I damn well want to finish the job, but I won't stay here if I'm part of the problem. I'm going to walk out of this office and give you some time . . . aw hell," he said and stood up, "I need a refill anyhow," as he looked at his empty cup. His stab at levity helped break the tension.

The black ministers and leaders were taken aback by Chief O'Connor's unanticipated frank offer to resign. They caucused for twenty minutes.

C.J. McLin, Jr., Attorney James H. McGee and Ms. Miley Williamson spoke and said they saw the Chief's sincerity and realized he and his department were doing all they could. The group dropped their agenda. They reached a consensus that the wave of shootings and murders was better solved if they work together and not focus on blame. Attorney McGee called O'Connor back into the room and told him they would continue to support him as Chief of Police.

With the crisis in confidence over, the Chief explained some new initiatives. He detailed actions his officers had taken including aggressive stop-and-frisk tactics that he knew ruffled some feathers. O'Connor then invited Tyree Broomfield into the meeting and shared Broomfield's expanded role in the wake of more drive-by shootings. Broomfield, a black civilian employee, headed the Conflict Management Team. The team members consisted of men and women, blacks and whites, sworn police officers and non-sworn employees. They were as un-conventional as they were diverse. Their casual appearance resembled that of the hip television show, *The Mod Squad*.

Their charter was to be visible on the street and build a communication network in the community to help prevent and manage tension and rumors in the city, particularly among black youth.

The Conflict Management Team worked with the White Hat Patrol and the Uniformed Patrol Division and developed information through their own network of sources.

Chief O'Connor ordered the Organized Crime Control Unit (OCCU) to have its best detective teams involved in the investigation. He wanted every unit of DPD to press hard for information. He ordered OCCU to use their undercover capabilities to conduct surveillances on possible suspects as needed.

C.J. McLin, Jr. cringed at the thought of OCCU detectives getting involved. "OCCU detectives?" He asked in a questioning tone. "Who might that be, Chief?"

Chief O'Connor, often called the "Big O," thanks to his size and John-Wayne-type demeanor said, "Well, Baker and Spells on narcotics come to mind," he stated with a slight grin as he sipped coffee that had gone cold.

"Chief, with all due respect, those guys have terrorized the West Side with their raids and no-holds-barred tactics," McLin said. Then he added, "I've got a problem with that."

"Problem?" The Chief looked at McLin. "You've got a problem? I have a whole city full of problems," O'Connor said. "I can keep these guys on a leash, so to speak, but I need men like them who push the limits. I also need the smooth guys, too. I need them all working this thing. I'm sure you understand." The Chief continued, "The people these detectives 'terrorized' were god-damned heroin and cocaine dealers. The kind of work I expect them to do goes way beyond playing patty-cake." Others in the room did not say a word. McLin was on his own on that topic.

The Chief was on a roll, "Look C.J, let's lay it on the table, okay? This shooter case is unlike anything we've ever dealt with before. Two summers, two series of racial shootings with around twenty black men shot on the street." He paused and leaned his elbows on the conference table. O'Connor continued, "Trust me to manage this, I need your support." Some said yes, and others nodded their agreement.

Attorney McGee had one more question for the Chief. "Is the FBI working on these shootings, too?"

Grover O'Connor took a few seconds to formulate his answer. "The answer is basically, no. I've talked to the ASAC in Dayton and he said it's a local matter. Beyond the basic things we can get anytime from the FBI, such as fingerprint or ballistic comparisons of bullets, which we don't have in a drive-by shotgun case, they haven't offered squat. As far as their agents helping or being assigned to the cases in the event of possible federal civil rights violations, it's a big fat NO! They haven't offered any informant or intelligence information, either. I'm not happy about it, and I'm still working it."

The meeting ended with promises to reconvene as needed.

The sound of a shotgun blast echoed again on the city streets at 12:10 a.m. Monday, July 22nd. A young black man was wounded in the leg by shotgun pellets as he walked along the sidewalk at Central and Superior Avenues. A car driven by a white man sped away through the residential neighborhood. Within minutes, and only ten blocks away, the next victim was not so lucky. At about 12:20 a.m., Willie Buford, a black man age twenty-three, was shot as he walked alone and crossed the poorly lit street in front of 1233 Everett Avenue. The blast tore his chest and stomach wide open and spilled his guts onto the street. A car believed to be a two door Ford, driven by a lone white man, sped away in the darkness. Willie Buford died at the scene.

———◁○▷———

A short time after the second shooting, Dayton Police mobilized its new "Saturation Plan." Crews responded to pre-determined key intersections and thoroughfares. They parked and observed traffic. Other patrol cars moved through alleys, checked parking lots and stopped any white man driving a vehicle on or near the West Side that matched the suspect's description.

At about 12:45 a.m., shots rang out again about twenty blocks away from the last shooting, two blocks off the busy West Third Street at 146 Lorenz Avenue. Kevin DeLoney was outside with a friend. He was shot in the arm with shotgun pellets by a man in a passing car. DeLoney barely got a glimpse of the shooter but was certain it was a white man who used a shotgun. The car was described as possibly a sky blue car that sped away.

———◁○▷———

Neal Bradley Long made it back to his room on West Grand Avenue. He was certain he killed the man on Everett Drive, but he wasn't sure of the others. He fired at random at a few other people that night but he had not taken the time to stalk them. He believed he probably missed his targets.

Long knew his media nickname, the Midnight Slayer, would soon be heard on the news again. He felt powerful as he sipped bourbon and smoked a joint before he fell asleep. His room was hot, his undershirt wet with sweat. His dreams were cloudy and troubled.

When he awoke, he faced another bland and hopeless day. Long went to work later and repeated the same thing he did all other days; pump gas and change tires with no hope of anything better.

———◁◦▷———

Homicide Squad Sergeant Jess Kline, age fifty-one, was exhausted and out of ideas. On a Friday night after work, he made his usual stop at the Veterans of Foreign Wars Post on Nebraska Avenue in Huber Heights. As he relaxed with his drinking buddies, he couldn't help but rack his brain for an idea, anything that would break loose some leads in the Midnight Slayer case.

Perhaps the gin & tonic popped loose a few brain cells as a far-fetched idea hit him. Kline thought about new computers used to search and sort huge amounts of data. He spoke out loud to himself, "Holy shit! The car. The light blue 1967 or 1968 Ford. It's the only one we hear about lately."

All of a sudden, Sergeant Kline felt like a young detective again. His energy surged. He used the bartender's telephone and called Detective Prugh at home. "Gary, I want you to send a tele-type to the Ohio Bureau of Motor Vehicles, (BMV). See if they can give us some of those fancy new computer print-outs on every damned 1967 and 1968 Ford Fairlane two-door and Ford Fairlane 500 two-door model automobiles in Montgomery County and the four counties that surround us; Green, Darke, Warren and Miami."

Detective Prugh said, "Okay boss, will do. You think it will be a lot?"

Sergeant Kline responded, "They are supposed to have something new called a searchable computer database or whatever the hell they call it." He added, "I'll see you Monday. Keep this quiet."

Monday morning, Sergeant Kline was summoned to Chief O'Connor's office. As Kline sat down, the Chief walked up to him and loomed over him as he sipped coffee. "I got a call from the Director at Ohio BMV in Columbus about some request you made."

"Well, Chief, I was going to tell you . . . "

O'Connor cut him off. "Jess, it's a stretch, but I like your idea. God knows, we don't have much more going and it's a good time to do this. BMV said they would make this a priority on their mainframe computer and put extra people on it. They should have the printouts ready tomorrow morning."

Detective Prugh drove to the BMV office at 1970 West Broad Street in Columbus, Ohio. He went to the Records Room near their large mainframe computer system. Prugh signed for the printouts on 18-inch wide NCR continuous form-feed paper. The clerk used a cart and transported the bulky load to the detective's car. Detective Prugh raced back to DPD.

Sergeant Kline was stunned when he saw the amount of data on the printouts. He glanced at the summary sheet that listed registration information for 950 Ford Sedans, 1967 and 1968 models. More than 500 were Ford Fairlane 500's, two-door sedans. Each vehicle listed included the registered owner's name, address, vehicle identification number and plate number.

The computerized vehicle registration system was new for Ohio. Only a portion of the vehicle information had been entered into the database since only a few months had passed since the annual vehicle license renewal period began and Ohio started loading information into the computerized database. Absent a complete file of all registrations and real-time updates, much of the information on the printout was out-of-date due to sales, trades, junked vehicles or owners who moved out of the area.

By noon the next day, Dick Section was full of detectives. Each was assigned a list of vehicle registrations to track down. Their initial focus was on cars titled in Montgomery County and the City of Dayton. Eventually they fanned out to surrounding counties. Detectives Baker and Spells were given more than forty cars to check in their spare time. Dayton detectives wore out a lot of shoe leather and burned a lot of gasoline as they went to last known addresses of each registered owner of Ford Fairlane 500s. The process usually led to a daisy chain of dead end leads. Detectives often tracked down two or three owners per car before they learned enough about the car and its owners or drivers to take it off the list.

Baker and Spells also pursued a specific task. It was a long shot, but they believed a white trick that had been robbed by a pimp or a gang on the street may have sought revenge. They focused on past crime reports and photos of men arrested for solicitation of prostitutes on sting operations. They also looked at men identified on Field Interrogation Cards (FIC) who trolled for street prostitutes on the West Side. It was as good as any other approach to find a needle in a haystack.

Buried deep in the reams of BMV printout was Neal Bradley Long's name. In April 1971, he registered a 1968 Ford Fairlane north of Dayton in Miami County, where one of his children lived. At the time, Long lived in a rented room at 70 Fountain Avenue in Dayton.

————◄○►————

The bitter cold winter of 1974 was hard on Neal Bradley Long. He worked outside while he pumped gas, repaired and changed automobile tires at Cap Collins' Service Station. His boarding room at 238 West Grand was always cold and drafty. He stuffed rags around the only window in his room, but it was little help. The single steam heat radiator in his room offered irregular heat. Long used his hot plate to add a degree or two of warmth. Whiskey and marijuana helped put him to sleep.

————◄○►————

Neal Bradley Long claimed a dreadful niche in Dayton's violent crime rate. Since the summer of 1972, Long killed at least five men and wounded many others in nearly twenty separate nighttime drive by shootings. Overall, Dayton remained a very violent city. DPD Homicide Squad was swamped as they recorded 101 murders in 1974, once again, the highest per-capita rate in America.

————◄○►————

The school desegregation case continued to bounce back and forth from U.S. Federal District Court to the U.S. Sixth Circuit Court of Appeals. March 10, 1975, Judge Rubin approved a new plan offered by the white conservative Dayton School Board majority. The plan was designed to go further than the previous failed attempt to establish "Science Centers" but it fell far short of addressing the problem of inequality. The plan called for creation of a few "Magnet Schools" designed to attract a larger number of blacks to attend classes with whites.

The NAACP filed an urgent appeal with the Sixth Circuit Court on March 19th that charged the School Board had once again ignored the real issue of a discriminatory race-based dual education system.

The court battle was fodder for conversation all over Dayton. The racial divide grew wider. White flight to the suburbs continued as blockbusting of old beautiful neighborhoods spread. Many whites simply refused to send their children to school with "the coloreds," at any cost. Attendance at large white churches and synagogues in the area north of Wolf Creek fell, and many closed their doors and followed the white flight out of the city.

————◁◦▷————

Neal Bradley Long followed developments of NAACP's appeal, dubbed the "School Busing Case" by the media. He listened to chatter at work from customers while he pumped gas. He imagined a scene of his children forced onto a bus to go to school with the "coloreds." It was like a horror flick that played over and over on a loop. Neal Bradley Long believed race mixing was against God's law, and he would not let it happen to his kids.

Neal Bradley Long was driven to do his part. He studied maps of Dayton streets and decided to change his geographic pattern slightly and make a trip into the neighborhood where whites moved out and blacks swarmed in like bees. His first shooting of the new year was targeted for the north side of Wolf Creek, just a few blocks from the West Side.

March 23, 1975 was an unusually mild night. Neal Bradley Long cruised along West Grand Avenue. As he approached Kumler Avenue, he slowed to a near stop. At about 1:10 a.m., two black men, ages nineteen and twenty-one talked and sipped cheap wine from bottles in paper bags as they walked along the street. A blast of the shotgun was the first they became aware of the Midnight Slayer. Fortunately for both men, the shotgun blast was errant and they only sustained pellet wounds in their hands and legs. Painful enough, both men fell to the ground and screamed for help. They saw a light blue late model Ford Fairlane as it drove away.

————◁◦▷————

April 1, 1975, Neal Bradley Long moved away from 238 W. Grand and relocated on Dayton's East Side. He rented a room in a boarding house at 22 South June Street. His new address was just two blocks from where he used to live on South Torrence Street, which was also near Emanuel Baptist Church at 1501 East Third Street. Long's new address was close to his children and his ex-wife, Grace. His 3 p.m. to 11 p.m. shift allowed him to help his family. He stopped by regularly, had a meal, ran errands and took the kids to school. Long took Grace to her job as a cafeteria worker at the Delco plant downtown. He frequently took one of the extra old cars he had at her house and left his light blue '68 Ford Fairlane 500 parked in the gravel parking space at the rear of his boarding house on June Street. The Longs maintained a very basic relationship but never drew close again after their divorce in 1971.

Grace told her husband she was afraid their children would be bused to school with "coloreds," and she was visibly upset. She said she would call the School Board again and complain. Long felt like a weakling because his wife handled the School Board calls rather than asking him to call. He suppressed his feelings of worthlessness, for the moment. Grace noticed that Neal acted distant, and he was withdrawn much of the time. He told her he heard "voices" again. She detected alcohol on his breath most of the time.

Wednesday, April 23, Long returned from an errand and saw a Dayton Police car parked out front of his boarding house. Long's gut churned but he remained stoic on the surface. A uniformed police officer talked with the elderly landlady, Mrs. Kimmey. She saw Long and yelled and waved, "Neal, somebody broke into a few rooms today. Your room was one of them!"

Long hurried down the hall to his room and found the hasp and padlock pried loose and his room ransacked. He immediately knelt down and looked under his bed where he had hidden two shotguns, one sawed-off. He began to sweat when he found his green army duffle bag was gone. A coffee can was also stolen from a kitchen cabinet. It contained about $37.00 in cash he had squirreled away.

Long sat on the floor as Mrs. Kimmey and the officer came to his door. Long stood when the officer asked, "Sir, I'll be making several reports. Is anything missing?"

Neal Bradley Long feigned hesitation and looked around. Long was not sure if he should mention the shotguns. "Well, yes officer. I'm missing two 12-gauge shotguns. One is a Mossberg. I think, some money, ah . . . about $37.00. I kept the guns for hunting." That did not arouse the officer's suspicion. Many men who lived in boarding houses kept weapons.

A police report was filed and listed the complainant on the Aggravated Burglary No. 449919 as "Neal Bradley Long, White male, 47, 22 S. June Street Apt. 9."

As soon as the officer left, Long went outside to his light blue 1968 Ford Fairlane 500 that had gone unnoticed by the police officer. Long temporarily moved his blue Ford to the Emmanuel Baptist Church parking lot. Many neighborhood cars used the lot during the week. Long suspected Grace's brother as the probable thief. He was an addict and had stolen from Long before.

Long decided he had to move again. By the time a Burglary Detective attempted to follow up with Long, he was gone. Long left no forwarding address.

----◄○►----

Neil Bradley Long knew it was important to live close to the bridges that led into "nigger town." Quick in-and-out access to the West Side was vital. On May 1, 1975, he moved to a second floor apartment at a boarding house at 656 South Main Street. He was only two blocks from the Washington Street Bridge that crossed the Great Miami River into the lower West Side. Long thought it was perfect.

----◄○►----

One of the most vibrant business strips in Dayton was on North Main Street, about twenty blocks north of downtown. A mixture of restaurants and popular bars gave the streetscape an energetic feel. Joe Bissett's Rib King Restaurant and the Tropics Nite Club were anchors in the area. A forty-eight-year-old station house for the Dayton Fire Department's Company 14 was the most recognized landmark in the area. A few doors up the street, Dayton Sports Gun Headquarters store at 2336 North Main Street enjoyed a record year for gun sales. The riots in the late 1960s and continuation of drive-by shotgun shootings on the West Side boosted sales.

Neal Bradley Long walked into the store on May 22, 1975. The manager, Greg Meyers, greeted him. Long wore a blue work shirt and black framed glasses. He asked to see several shotguns. The manager noticed the customer was not a novice as he handled several weapons. He ran his fingers over the stock and barrel, and he never asked any questions about the weapons. The manager leaned on the counter, palms down, and watched Long make up his mind.

Long favored a Charles Daly Auto-Pointer shotgun capable of rapidly firing a total of six rounds. The manager told Long, "You'll have to sign the federal form before I can ring it up."

Long nodded "yes" and filled out the purchaser's portion of the Bureau of Alcohol Tobacco and Firearms (ATF) Division form, No. F 16869.

Long used his ex-wife's address, 622 Cosler Street, Dayton. He listed his personal information and his Ohio driver's license number. However, he lied on his response to a Certification question: "E. Have you ever been adjudicated mentally defective or have you ever been committed to a mental institution?" Long lied and wrote "no" because he was committed to Dayton State Hospital in late 1967. An honest answer would have disqualified his purchase.

Long paid cash for the shotgun and a cleaning kit for a total of $156.85 and headed to his room on South Main Street. There was little chance Long's purchase triggered any sort of notice or lead for homicide detectives who worked the Midnight Slayer case. There were no systematic investigative inquiries underway at gun stores or second-hand shops, and ATF had not put out any alerts.

Once again, Neal Bradley Long was armed and dangerous, but with a better weapon capable of rapidly firing more rounds. Long sawed off the barrel of the shotgun to about twenty inches in length. He was itching to take his new weapon to the "killing field."

———◦———

Neal Bradley Long was anxious to finish his shift at Cap Collins' Service Station. When he left work at 11:00 p.m. May 22, 1975, he drove straight to his new place on South Main Street. He drank some bourbon and smoked a joint while he loaded his new shotgun with 00 buck shotgun shells. Fourteen hours after he purchased the new shotgun, Long carried it to his car wrapped in a sheet. He headed toward the Washington Street Bridge. It was about 12:25 a.m.

———◦———

Long crested the hump in the four lane bridge and turned north onto side streets and looked for "colored" people on the street. He passed the area where Lester Mitchell was gunned down September 1, 1966. He felt satisfaction as he passed the spot. As Long drove through the intersection of Norwood and Louie Streets, one block from the river, he saw a group of blacks as they milled around. He heard music and saw cars parked in front of 302 Norwood where a loud birthday party was underway. About thirty to forty black men and women were on the porch and in the front yard dancing and playing loud music.

Long circled back, drove along the other side of the wide street, and stopped his car. Hardly anyone in the party noticed the white man in the light blue car. Long crawled into the back seat and braced himself. He pointed the new Charles Daly shotgun toward the gathering of blacks about sixty feet away.

BOOM!..BOOM!.. BOOM!.. BOOM! Four blasts rang out. The shots were fired in rapid succession from the semi-automatic shotgun. George Ingram, a forty-year-old black man, and two others fell to the ground. A dozen 00 buck rounds hit the front of the house and the cars parked out front. The sound of the shotgun and cries for help shattered the night. Witnesses saw a white man fire from the back seat of the car then he climbed over and drove away. Confusion reigned, as some witnesses said the shooter was white and others said he was a "light colored" man. Witnesses all agreed on one thing: the shooter drove a newly painted baby blue two-door car.

George Ingram and his two friends were lucky they survived their wounds.

Neal Bradley Long was very satisfied with his new shotgun as he drove across the West Third Street Bridge into downtown.

FORTY-THREE

Homicide Squad

As the mild spring weather of 1975 yielded to warmer temperatures, it did not signal the joy and more relaxed lifestyle people normally welcomed. The West Side slogged through efforts to recover from several devastating riots and a wave of drive-by shootings of black men during the past three summers.

The shotgun shootings resumed earlier in the year in 1975 than in the past three years. Despite efforts of the DPD and grassroot initiatives by black community leaders, such as the White Hat Patrol, feelings of dread lurked in the air.

Neal Bradley Long was consumed by his obsession with hatred of race mixing and the battle that was underway in the federal courts. On June 1, 1975, the three-judge panel of the U.S. Sixth Circuit Court of Appeals upheld NAACP's appeal and rejected the Dayton School Board's Magnet School Plan and labeled it insufficient. The Court Of Appeals ordered the District Court Judge to draw up a new plan to ensure desegregation of Dayton Public Schools and to correct racial inequality in education. Mandatory cross-town school busing was required. Black children had to attend formerly all-white schools and white children had to attend previously all-black schools.

Neal Bradley Long feared most for his young son Mark who attended an elementary school in East Dayton. Long would not stand for forced integration.

————◄◦►————

Chief O'Connor reacted to the resumption of drive-by shootings after the Norwood Avenue incident in May. Street patrols were beefed up and intelligence-gathering activities increased. The Chief added new men, full and part-time, to the Detective Section, particularly the Homicide Squad. Lieutenant Riley recommended to the Chief that Detective Baker transfer from the Organized Crime Control Unit, Narcotics Squad, to the Homicide Squad.

Detectives Baker and Spells knew it had been just a matter of time until they were reassigned and moved on to new jobs. Spells was not ready to give up the streets and night work. He wanted a little more time in the OCCU. On the last night they worked together, Detectives Spells and Baker went to dinner at Dominic's Italian Restaurant. Over hot plates of lasagna and spaghetti with meatballs, they drifted into a discussion about the NAACP desegregation battle with Dayton Public Schools. Spells talked about his strong beliefs that desegregation of Dayton Public Schools was sorely needed. He touched an emotional nerve as he told stories about his family's experiences with discrimination in school and employment. Spells was disappointed and discouraged about the way whites fought so hard against equality. He was also bitter about how the race issue was constantly brought up in police hiring and promotions.

Baker listened to his partner and friend, a man who grew up on the West Side. Spells was a complex man with a sweet family caught in the jaws of a vice. He lived in a segregated city and worked in a police department that only mouthed equality for black cops.

The heavy conversation raised unanswerable questions and laid bare Spells' feelings, seldom seen. He took a drag of his Marlboro cigarette and suddenly smiled through his pain. "Well, Mr. Homicide Detective, you get your ass in gear and catch the S.O.B. Midnight Slayer, Spells said. "Partner, it's been good. We'll do it again, okay, Bake?"

The two men stood in the middle of the busy and noisy restaurant at 1:30 a.m. and shook hands. For the first time in all the years the two men knew each other, they gave each other a quick guy hug followed with a slap on the back, as men often do to cover their real affection and respect for each other. They shared so much happiness, pain and hard work as partners on the streets. The men walked to their cars and drove away in different directions, to different worlds, one black and one white.

Since Baker became a cop, he was hooked on the energy and danger that came with working nights on the West Side. There was something about the night air, city lights, different people who came out on the street, the illegal gambling and bootleg joints, bars, snitches, music and women. Life after dark seemed raw and rich to him. He could not stop drinking it in. Baker spent more time at work than with his family. Although Baker knew he had to adjust to doing more paperwork and endure more scrutiny from his bosses, he knew he would enjoy special independence and freedom as a Homicide Dick.

———◦———

Detective Baker reported for duty and met with Homicide Squad Sergeant Jess Kline. Kline was glad to get another full-time man, especially one with previous experience. When Baker walked in on Monday morning, he no longer looked like a street Narc. He was dressed in a dark blue sport coat, grey slacks, white shirt and tie. His long scraggly goatee and Elvis sideburns were gone, but a Fu Manchu moustache teased his upper lip. Baker's hair was long by Dick Section standards, but not pony-tail long, as it had been. Jess Kline acted as if he didn't recognize a somewhat clean-cut Detective Baker at first. After a few "who are you?" questions, Kline said, "Welcome aboard."

Baker was briefed on the squad's workload, including his own caseload of routine homicides, shootings, stabbings and felony assault cases. Baker was assigned to work with Detective Prugh on the Midnight Slayer cases.

Dozens of Dayton Police officers and detectives worked long hours. Rumors of cancelled vacations added more pressure and stress. Sergeant Kline vented his frustrations and told his men, "Hell, the so called Midnight Slayer has stopped! We got all these cops ready to catch this guy and he ain't nowhere to be seen!"

Detectives ran out of leads. Nothing was shaking. After three summers of drive-by shotgun violence, many cops believed it was only a matter of time before the Midnight Slayer struck again. But when? Where?

FORTY-FOUR

People Are More Than Pins On A Map

After the U.S. Sixth Circuit Court of Appeals rejected the City of Dayton Public Schools Desegregation Plan on June 1, 1975, and remanded the case back to the District Court in Dayton, Judge Carl B. Rubin sought an expert to help the Court devise a plan. He settled on a man with vast experience in school desegregation.

On June 24, 1975, Carl B. Rubin, United States District Judge, Southern District, Ohio West Division, Cincinnati, issued an order:

> Pursuant to the remand of Federal Civil Case 72-137, NAACP, et al, Plaintiffs v. Dayton Public School Board, et al, Defendants, this Court proposes to appoint as an expert witness Dr. Charles Glatt, of Ohio State University, Columbus, Ohio, for the purpose of investigating, determining and reporting to this court a plan of desegregation for the Dayton School system.

The judge set a show-cause hearing for Monday, July 7, 1975 for the parties to agree or object to the appointment of Dr. Glatt. July 7th, Judge Rubin ruled the appointment would proceed and Dr. Glatt headed for Dayton, Ohio.

When Neal Bradley Long heard the news about Dr. Charles Glatt and his new role on behalf of the Federal District Court, he was convinced he had to do more to stop race mixing. Long believed he had to act before it was too late. His two school-age children attended Dayton Public Schools, and rumors were rampant around East Dayton that blacks and whites would be forced into buses and the same classrooms. School was scheduled to begin the day after Labor Day. Not much time, Long thought, as he cradled his new shotgun on his lap.

————◄○►————

Dr. Charles Glatt of The Ohio State University was one of the nation's leading experts in cases that involved desegregation plans for public schools. Glatt had successfully helped courts and communities design, implement and monitor regional and single-school district desegregation plans. His most recent consulting contracts involved Chapel Hill, North Carolina and Indianapolis, Indiana.

Dr. Glatt was an imposing forty-six-year-old white man. He stood six feet tall and had long reddish hair. He often wore leisure suits with a necktie, white shoes and a wide white belt. A bright and dedicated man, Glatt was on his fourth marriage. He and his wife, Johnena, shared a total of five children. Dr. Glatt enjoyed his hobby of gardening at their suburban Columbus, Ohio, home. He planned to spend his work week in Dayton and weekends at home in Columbus.

Dr. Glatt was born in Frost, Louisiana, and educated at Louisiana State University, the University of New Mexico and employed at Ohio State University. As a youth, he lived in rural southern towns. Glatt was taught that whites and blacks were not to mix, but that philosophy did not sit well with him.

By age twenty, he became Reverend Charles Glatt, a ministerial school graduate and pastor of an all-white Baptist Church in Pineville, Louisiana; however, he resigned after pastoring one year.

He was attracted to work with civil rights issues related to segregation in public schools. Glatt frequently told people he was guided by two documents in his work: the U.S. Constitution and the Holy Bible.

Dr. Glatt was well aware of racial attitudes and emotions generated as a result of efforts to desegregate public schools. He was also aware that violence was possibly directed at him or anyone who worked to implement racial equality in education. Glatt received direct and anonymous threats when he worked on past consulting contracts that dealt with school desegregation. One particular threatening experience stood out.

While in Indianapolis, he visited a barber for a long overdue haircut.

The barber continually stared at Dr. Glatt. Finally, the barber recognized Glatt from television news stories about school desegregation. The barber paused during the haircut and said to Glatt, "You know, if I still had kids in school, I'd kill you. What do you say to that?"

Dr Glatt, in a vulnerable position in the barber's chair quipped, "Well, I can tell you one thing. I'm mighty glad you don't have any kids in school."

Telephone threats, anonymous threatening letters and suspicious packages often showed up in Dr. Glatt's office in cities where he worked on school desegregation plans.

———◇———

Dr. Glatt reported to his first day of work in Dayton on Monday July 14, 1975. He took measures to protect himself. His wife was concerned threats would be made against her husband. She asked, "Are you afraid someone might try to hurt you?" Charles Glatt didn't hesitate. "I don't see any threat connected to the shooting of blacks on the West Side." He then laughed and added, "No . . . I'm white." However, Glatt did take precautions based on his past experiences. He often switched rental cars to reduce chances of being followed. Although his contract provided for a hotel room in Dayton, he usually stayed with friends in their homes and kept supplies and extra clothing at the hotel. He varied his routes to and from work and appointments. Glatt also used four different parking lots near his office and he seldom entered his office building through the same entrance. Dr. Glatt secretly carried a loaded .32 caliber revolver in his briefcase and had done so for years.

His office was located in the forty-year-old three story United States Post Office and Federal Courts Building, commonly called the Federal Building. It stood prominently in the heart of downtown Dayton at 118-120 West Third Street. The three-story, half-block-long limestone building was an imposing structure with sixteen columns that graced its front. The first floor was occupied by the U.S. Post Office with fifteen walk-up service windows surrounded by elegant polished brass facades and light fixtures. The rear portion of the first floor housed Judge Rubin's chambers, his courtroom, general office space and conference rooms. Dr. Glatt's office was located near Judge Rubin's area. Both offices were sealed off from the main post office corridor and the general public by lockable solid wood double doors.

The second floor of the Federal Building accommodated two other courtrooms and support staff. The third floor provided office space for the U.S. Marshal, ATF, IRS and overflow space for the FBI that had other space downtown.

During the previous months, dozens of anonymous bomb and death threats were received at the federal telephone switchboard and district court offices directed against the federal court about the NAACP busing case. The U.S Marshal and FBI documented the anonymous threats but did not share information about the threats with the DPD. Federal security was ramped up when ten armed uniformed Federal Protective Officers (FPO) were permanently assigned to building security during business hours. Security was complicated since hundreds of people went directly to the post office each day. FPO was instructed to allow visitors to pass freely to Dr. Glatt's area without scrutiny. Officers focused on security for Judge Rubin's Chambers and checked ID and hand carried packages to that area.

Dr. Glatt took little time to set up his office in room No. 100. He was highly sought after so he made himself immediately available to the media in his office and at public meetings. He believed in being accessible, and soon he had many visitors to his office from local officials.

———◁▷———

While Dr. Glatt's arrival in Dayton was big news, Neal Bradley Long decided to recapture attention of the media and the city.

———◁▷———

"Two dead so far, two wounded. Three separate drive-by shootings. The suspect is a white male driving a blue car. He has not been apprehended," said the Dayton Police Dispatch Sergeant, William "Bill" Folkereth.

Chief O'Connor rubbed his weary eyes and awakened in his favorite chair where he had fallen asleep. "What the hell, Bill. What time is it?"

"Chief, it's 2:05 a.m. Good morning, sir."

It was early Friday morning, July 15, 1975, and it had been almost two months since the last shooting by the Midnight Slayer when he fired at the street party on Norwood Avenue.

"Good morning my ass! Give me some details," the Chief chopped back.

As the Chief penned some notes, Sergeant Folkereth began, "Well, on the first one we got a call at 1:00 a.m. at 608 Cincinnati Street. A twenty-one-year-old black man named Robert Hoard. He's dead at the scene, on the sidewalk. He was shot while he set a garbage can on the curb for pick up. Shot in the back and side with a blast, probably #2 shot, judging from the huge number of wounds. No one saw the shooter."

"The second shooting went down at around 1:20 a.m. at North Western Avenue and West First Street. Two people shot, not critically. Leonard Goff, black Male, twenty-one, and Glenda Gay, black female, twenty. They were standing on the sidewalk. You may be familiar with their names from some old arrests. It appears to be the same suspect. He fired a shotgun from his car window at Goff and also wounded Gay who was standing on the curb about fifty feet away. She was hit by the spray of pellets. The white male suspect was driving a blue Ford. The third one," Folkereth continued, "is at 331 Edgewood, near West Riverview Avenue. We received a call on a man down, possibly intoxicated, in the street. When the officer arrived, he found Larry Romaine, black male, twenty-seven. He was dead at the scene, probably for up to an hour or more. He had been shot in his side. Almost cut him in half. So far, no witnesses."

Chief O'Connor hesitated and swallowed his frustration rather than waste time venting. "Who's on it?"

Sergeant Folkereth told him the entire Homicide Squad was covering the three shootings, "but so far, no new leads."

The Chief immediately dressed for work and headed to his office. He racked his brain, "What else can I possibly do?"

———◦———

The day after the shootings, July 16th, the Dayton Office of the FBI updated their confidential Indices Files at the Cincinnati Field Office and FBI HQ in Washington D.C. Despite the fact the FBI quietly followed the drive-by shotgun shootings for three years, they did not offer any investigative or specialized assistance to DPD. The FBI did not see any connection to the racial shootings on the West Side even though they were privy to the racially-motivated threats to the federal court about the federal desegregation case. The FBI was the only law enforcement agency in the region that had a complete picture of events, threats and intelligence. It was not in the FBI's DNA to share. Entry into the FBI Indices read as follows:

JULY 16, 1975. TELETYPE. UNSUB; SHOTGUN SHOOTINGS OF LARRY KEITH ROMAINE (DECEASED)—VICTIM; ROBERT EUGENE HOARD (DECEASED)—VICTIM; GLENDA GAY—VICTIM; DAYTON OHIO, JULY 15, 1975, EM, POSSIBLE URBAN GUERRILLA WARFARE, CINCINNATI FILE 157 -6340.

For years, the FBI secretly categorized the Midnight Slayer shootings on Dayton's West Side as "URBAN GUERRILLA WARFARE," defined as: "The actions of a person or a group who uses force, fear and terror to interfere with or destroy operation of the government or implementation of its constitutional protections, laws and policies."

———◄○►———

Citizens in the West Side and the growing mixed-race neighborhood in Lower Dayton View, just north of the Wolf Creek, reached a new level of alarm and vigilante activity. Many black parents did not allow their children out after dark. Young black men followed cars driven by whites. Confrontations and assaults were reported. Police stepped up arrests of people who carried guns and other weapons in their cars. They also seized baseball bats, chains and other vigilante tools. Nerves were raw.

Chief O'Connor provided more walkie talkie radios to the citizens' White Hat Patrol. Two new leaders headed up the group, AbDul Zafr from Project Cure, a drug treatment program, and General Mwesi Chui, a leader in the local Black Nationalism Movement. Newspaper stories encouraged more volunteers for the White Hat Patrol and neighborhood crime watch groups.

A ten thousand dollar reward was set up with donations from major companies for information leading to capture and conviction of the Midnight Slayer. The Chief of Police revealed in a July 18th news conference that he contracted with Dr. Charles Scheidler, a Dayton Psychologist, to develop a profile of the Midnight Slayer to assist in his identification and capture. Dr. Scheidler worked at the University of Dayton and was proficient in testing police applicants. However, he admitted that he had not been involved in such a profile program before, but he "could do it, perhaps with the help of a psychiatrist." Dr. Scheidler said it would take a few weeks, at the least, for completion of a profile that might offer clues to the Midnight Slayer's background, habits, personality, traits, likes and dislikes and his mental state. The FBI watched from afar and did not offer their expertise to develop a profile.

———◦———

Dr. Charles Glatt walked into Chief O'Connor's office at 1:45 p.m., July 18th for a scheduled meeting. Dr. Glatt knew the important peacekeeping role of police in school desegregation plans and he was eager to meet the man affectionately known as "The Big O" he had heard so much about.

Their smiles were genuine, and they quickly dispensed with pleasantries as both men wanted to talk about Glatt's role. As he sipped from his stained coffee mug, the Chief offered Glatt a cup, which he politely declined. Glatt was distracted by a large map of the City of Dayton displayed on the Chief's wall. Glatt studied the curl of the Great Miami River through the heart of the city and a concentration of red color stickpins clustered on the West Side and a few on streets in Lower Dayton View along Wolf Creek. A studious man, Dr. Glatt silently counted the bridges that separated the West Side from the rest of the city. Dr. Glatt said aloud, "Twelve." He stood with his left hand on his hip and stroked his chin with his right hand.

"Those pins show where our so-called Midnight Slayer has hit," said the Chief. "This has been going on for..."

Dr. Glatt politely interrupted, "Chief, that's the second reason I'm here to see you. I know it's been going on now for four summers."

The two men moved to a small conference table and could not help but size each other up, even though they just met. Chief O'Connor asked, "Are you wondering if some man is angry enough about school desegregation to be our killer?" If Glatt knew of the dozens of threats received by the court, he did not share them with the Chief.

Dr. Glatt glanced toward the pin map with about thirty red pins. Each represented at least one shooting victim. "Chief, I don't know, I'm just speculating, but I've seen a lot of white people with a bloodthirsty look in their eyes on every desegregation project I've ever worked on. This is gut level stuff here, you know, busing someone's kid across town to be with a race of people their parents hate." Glatt gave a wry grin and softened his comments a bit. "Well that leaves you about twenty thousand angry white men as suspects, right Chief?" Chief O'Connor appreciated the morbid humor and nodded faux agreement.

The two men sat in silence and pondered the subjects of racial hatred, desegregation and murder. "I'm just saying, Chief, I don't know much about Dayton yet, and I don't mean to offend you and the hard work of your officers."

"No offense taken, Dr. Glatt. I'll be damned if I know the answer. It has been four hellish years." The Chief added, "I'll get busy on those twenty thousand suspects right away if you get busy on taking care of the kids that need a good education. Deal?" Their new relationship was off to a good start, but it was about to suddenly take a detour.

Dr. Glatt left the Chief's office to attend a scheduled meeting down the hall at DPD with Dr. Ed King, head of the Dayton Human Relations Council, and several commanding officers of the DPD and their key staff members. Their agenda was to establish security plans for the opening day of school in September. Protests were expected at various locations involved in desegregation all over the city. Bus stops, routes and school building security needed well-thought-out and coordinated plans.

At the end of the meeting, Dr. Glatt emphasized the planning session and all subsequent meetings should be held in strict confidence to protect integrity of plans and avoid undue alarm to the public before the plan rollout in late August.

Dr. Glatt left DPD and walked two blocks to his office in the Federal Building. When he arrived, he was surprised to see two newspaper reporters waiting to talk to him about the meeting he just attended regarding security planning for the first day of school. Glatt was a man who didn't mince words; he demanded to know who informed the press of the meeting. The reporters barely knew Glatt and weren't intimidated by his outburst. They pressed him with more questions. Glatt said "I'm not discussing this any further," and shut his office door.

Dr. Glatt telephoned Ed King and Chief O'Connor separately and demanded they find out who leaked the information. Chief O'Connor resented the accusation and told Glatt that it was probably not preventable. "A lot of people in town, including some cops, hate the school busing plan and believe it is tearing the city apart." The goodwill between Glatt and O'Connor suffered a major setback. Dr. Glatt saw the divided city firsthand.

———◦———

White flight of residents from the City of Dayton continued at a rapid pace. Dr. Glatt wanted to see it with his own eyes. He took a driving tour of areas adjacent to the West Side, particularly the area north of Wolf Creek, known as Dayton View, which had been hit hardest. He was stunned at the number of houses with "For Sale" signs in the yard. He learned about speculators and unscrupulous realtors who spread rumors in order to list properties and sell for low figures to absentee landlords. Many houses were empty with tall grass and old newspapers piled up at the door. Some were vandalized, and damage was visible from the street. He saw black families moving in and white families moving out. Moving trucks, pickup trucks and rented trailers moved about. Some small businesses were boarded up, and police activity was evident. It was depressing as Dr. Glatt realized the city was in a steep decline. He rode through downtown and saw signs of businesses closing. The heart of the West Side had barren lots and boarded up buildings where businesses once thrived.

When Glatt returned to his office, he was so irritated at the visible sign of white flight that he dictated a letter to the Human Relations Council demanding that they take action to find a way to disallow 'For Sale' signs in Dayton View. In part, his letter stated, "The Council should endeavor to disallow 'For Sale' signs until schools have been desegregated and a cooling-off period has been experienced so the process of guaranteeing constitutional rights for children can have a fair test in the Dayton School System."

The Council studied Glatt's letter but saw no way to limit the freedoms of individuals, realtors or lenders regarding their properties and contracts. It was another bitter pill for Dr. Glatt.

———◦———

Chief O'Connor was frustrated and repeated his request for assistance from the FBI through ASAC Robert Carmichael. The FBI and Justice Department had not provided any of their specialized services, such as profiling, information from their Indices files or FBI agents to work in the field with DPD detectives. In his plea for help, O'Connor told Agent Carmichael, "My department has exhausted all available avenues of investigation, and we need help to catch this murderer who has shot at and killed blacks over the past three years." The story finally leaked to the newspaper.

The headline in the August 1, 1975 *Dayton Daily News* proclaimed:

"FBI DOESN'T HAVE O'CONNOR BID FOR SNIPER KILLING AID."

The story described an unhelpful bureaucratic response that said:

> ...Requests from Dayton Police must be funneled through the Justice Department's Civil Rights Division in Washington D.C., not through the FBI. Once filed, the request would be evaluated and a determination made whether the request should be forwarded to the FBI for their consideration. The Justice Department spokesman said, "The Criminal Division knows nothing of a request. Normally, local law enforcement should be able to handle crime in their area. In states like Ohio, with a strong civil rights law, they should also ask for help from state officials." The Justice spokesman said, "If there is ever any evidence offered of a civil rights violation, we'd be more than happy to respond and give assistance called for under the law."

When O'Connor read the headlines, he flung the newspaper across his office and pages flew all over the place. As he stood at his office window, angry thoughts spun in his head. He looked up the street two blocks to the east; he saw the columns at the front of the Federal Building where some FBI offices were located. The Chief muttered to himself, "Justice says we should ask for help from Ohio State Officials. Hell! The Ohio Civil Rights Commission doesn't have criminal investigators, profilers and access to Indices files. What am I supposed to do, call the Ohio State Highway Patrol to help with directing traffic around crime scenes? Horseshit!"

The FBI and U.S. Justice Department played a bureaucratic game with Chief O'Connor. Unfortunately, black people who lived in the West Side were the losers in the game.

FORTY-FIVE

The Yellow School Bus Ain't What It Used To Be

Dayton Public Schools started classes Monday, September 8, 1975, and the familiar yellow school buses took on another meaning to many people in the city. They were no longer mere transportation. The yellow school buses became weapons in the war against separate and unequal education for thousands of black children in the City of Dayton. What used to be an atmosphere of renewal and anticipation at the beginning of a new school year was an atmosphere of apprehension for children and parents.

While Dr. Glatt prepared documents to present to Federal District Court Judge Rubin, a few thousand black and white children were shuttled to unfamiliar neighborhoods and schools. Children reflected thoughts and fears voiced by their parents. Tension was high. Children were used like lab rats for social change. Many parents, black and white, felt a loss of control since their children no longer walked to neighborhood schools within blocks of their home. Instead, they boarded buses and crossed the Great Miami River.

When children arrived home at the end of the school day, they were often grilled with questions by nervous and fearful parents. Meaningful learning and parental support suffered.

Dr. Glatt's detailed plan recommended dramatic restructure of the racial makeup of Dayton schools and expanded busing. His recommendations also assumed the planned changes resulted in higher academic potential for all students. Glatt, a pragmatic man, believed the short term trauma of busing would give way to healthy change.

Neal Bradley Long made his own assessment of the benefit of school desegregation. He hated it. He saw school buses on the streets, some filled with blacks and some with whites, as they carted children across town like cattle on the way to slaughter. He worried most about his twelve-year-old son, who attended Orville Wright Middle School in East Dayton.

Long often drove by his son's school and watched buses full of black children as they entered his neighborhood. He also drove past Eastmont School where Mark was bused to attend mixed-race classes with blacks a few times a week. Long parked his car at each school, went inside and looked around the lobby. As he watched the ebb and flow of black and white children in the halls, it sickened him. He kept his right hand in his pocket. The feel of cool metal on his loaded .22 caliber pistol gave him a feeling of power in the midst of powerlessness. Long thought about killing people in the office, but the urge passed in favor of a more important target.

———◦———

On his way to work at Cap Collins' Service Station, Long cut through downtown and past the main offices of the Dayton School Board at 348 West First Street. He eyed the parking lot and alley alongside the building. He noticed the easy access in and out of the area. In fact, he saw that he could easily drive up a ramp onto I-75 South and be on his way to Kentucky in mere minutes if he was in a hurry to leave town. The thought of killing one or more black School Board Members was tempting.

———◦———

Detectives Baker and Prugh were having a late snack at Dominic's restaurant, when Detective Tony Spells walked in. "Hey fellas, if you're going to stop for a drink, don't you think you ought to hide your detective car, instead of parking it out front in a no-parking zone?"

"Oh officer, I'm so sorry!" Baker said, dripping with sarcasm, "Here's ten dollars. Will this cover the fine?" They all burst out laughing.

The three men caught up on goings-on in their lives and work over beer and deep fried mozzarella sticks and marinara sauce. Spells carried a stack of auto registration printouts. In his spare time, he checked 1967 or 1968 Ford Fairlane 500s. "This is so much bullshit! I bet I've visited twenty places." He paused a minute and asked, "What you guys think about the shootings out West. Any leads?" Baker and Prugh only shrugged their shoulders and shook their heads no.

Spells said, "I'm about out of my mind worrying about my kids with all this confusion going on about busing. It wouldn't surprise me if the son-of-a-bitch doing the shootings is a KKK bastard like Frank the bootlegger said, right Bake?" he asked as he looked at Baker. "Look guys, my kids go to Dayton Schools. Yours don't." It was obvious Spells was dead serious and all the BS stopped. He continued, "If my kids have to ride a bus across the river to the East Side to go to a good school with good books, good science labs and good teachers, then I have to say I'm all for it." Spells was on a roll. "Just the same, I know that there are a lot of white men out there who hate blacks enough to kill over their precious white babies having to go to school with us blacks. Of course that don't keep those same bastards from coming on my side of town to buy some poon-tang . . . does it?"

Spells was frustrated as a cop and as a parent. "Well, I'll keep checking a hundred car registrations and hope something breaks."

Baker looked at Prugh. "Maybe we need to talk to the schools, the School Board and the Federal Court and find out who's been pissed off enough to make a threat or come to their attention. You know, these sick-os often telegraph their intentions well before they do something stupid."

Prugh agreed. "We'll make a list right away and get on it, but those guys at the Federal Building and the School Board haven't said shit."

———◦———

Neal Bradley Long awoke Thursday morning, the 18th of September, 1975. He immediately thought of bus loads of "colored" kids headed to his son's school. He propped himself up in bed and took a few swigs of bourbon. He decided to leave for work early to pick up his ex-wife, Grace, and drop her off at work at the Delco plant on East First Street in downtown. When Long arrived at her house on Cosler Street, Grace was at the door with a tearful look on her face. Long feared bad news. Grace told her ex-husband that his maternal grandfather died early that morning in Lexington, Kentucky. The funeral arrangements were set for the coming Sunday. Long was distressed at the news, but his outward emotions remained flat. "How much more can go wrong?" he mumbled as his broken mind raced through his thin existence. Long was frustrated, as he knew his son was on a school bus across town just so the coloreds" could get their way.

After he dropped Grace at work, Long returned to his room at 656 South Main Street and jotted down directions to the funeral home in Lexington, Ky. He also laid out a map of the City of Dayton streets and studied routes in and out of the central downtown area and routes to Interstate 75 South. Long made special note of the location of the Dayton School Board building and the DPD.

Neal Bradley Long was delusional and he made a change in his avenging homicidal thinking and tactics. He believed that if he cut off the head of the snake, the snake would die. Long was sick of Dayton, Ohio, the "coloreds," the law and white people who wanted to mix up the races. He knew that God did not want that for white people, and God told him that he should act soon.

Before Long left for his 3:00 p.m. to 11:00 p.m. shift at Cap Collins' Sohio Service Station, he went to his landlady's apartment and told her he had to leave town for a while. He surprised her and paid three months' rent in advance, in cash. She offered to write a receipt, but Long walked away without a response. She folded the money and dropped it in her apron pocket. *Another hard luck story,* she thought.

FORTY-SIX

Judgment Day

"One man willing to throw away his life is enough to
terrorize a thousand."

—Wu Ch'i, circa 400 B.C

Friday, September 19, 1975, was one of those days all busy people suffer through from time to time when they realize their schedule has gotten out of control. Dr. Glatt double booked two important appointments, one in Columbus and one in Dayton. It was even more complicated since he had driven home from Dayton Thursday evening. Glatt planned to be in Columbus all weekend with his family and spend time working in his garden.

Dr. Glatt was scheduled to be on the campus of The Ohio State University, (OSU) at 2:00 p.m., but over breakfast, he remembered a schedule conflict. He also committed to an equally important luncheon and speaking engagement at noon in Dayton with community leaders and clergy. He re-scheduled the OSU meeting and apologized to his wife as he readied to leave home. Dr. Glatt hurried through his shower so he could leave by 10:00 a.m. for the ninety-minute drive to downtown Dayton. He left with his briefcase in hand and promised his wife he would be back that evening.

Dr. Glatt decided since he was going to be in Dayton after lunch, he would take advantage of his unplanned presence and stop by his office in the Federal Building. Ms. Tommie Jones, a Conciliation Specialist with the Justice Department out of the Chicago Office would be there as well. He could arrive around 2:00 p.m., work for a few hours and still get home in Columbus before late evening.

Neal Bradley Long woke Friday morning from a troubled sleep. He looked at the wind-up alarm clock near his bed. He rubbed his eyes. He could barely make out the time, 9:19 a.m. His alcohol-soaked brain began to dry out. His head pounded relentlessly from the headache left in the wake of too much alcohol. His television had been on all night. As he rolled over, he felt his .22 caliber revolver in the bed and he began to remember last night.

When he came home from work late Thursday night, he drank bourbon while he watched local news on television. A story reported the number of buses and extra costs for additional bus drivers used to transport children as part of the Dayton Public Schools' desegregation plan. Long wanted to end the busing. He pointed his gun at the television and fired imaginary bullets at faces on the screen.

Neal Bradley Long stumbled out of bed, he still wore his work clothes that he slept in all night. He was a mentally fractured man. Homicidal thoughts flooded every corner of his brain.

Long made his way to the small sink in the room. He placed his face in the sink and splashed cold water in his eyes, then fished for a rag. Long raised up as he wiped his face. He looked in the mirror above the sink. It was cracked in many places and distorted his reflective image. Long's face looked like a puzzle with ill-fitting pieces. He stared at the broken man framed in his view and said, "Is that me? Am I that broken?" and he ran his fingers across the uneven surfaces. Long's hopeless existence washed over him and he heard his father's voice again say, "Once you're born in a shack, you'll die in a shack."

———◁○▷———

Long was going to do what needed to be done today to stop the "niggers" from taking over. He stuffed a few clothes and a pair of shoes in a laundry bag along with some personal items, a razor and toothbrush. He knew he would not return to his apartment for a while; perhaps a long while, if he decided to stay in Kentucky after the funeral on Sunday. Long did not own much besides his personal items. He left his TV, Charles Daly sawed-off shotgun and another handgun in his room, closed the door and locked the padlock.

Neal Bradley Long carried one other item with him when he left South Main Street, his .22 caliber revolver. It was fully loaded with six rounds, and he had spare ammunition in his pocket. He did not look back. Long, the vigilante, set out to make things right.

He drove his 1968 light blue Ford Fairlane 500 to his ex-wife's house on Cosler Drive and arrived at noon. His son, Stanley, age nineteen, was home with Grace. Long used Grace's telephone and called his father in Miamisburg, south of Dayton. He told his father that he would stop by in the afternoon. Long's father and stepmother planned to ride along with him to attend the funeral in Kentucky Saturday afternoon.

At about 1:00 p.m., Long and Grace left Cosler Drive. She was due at work at 1:30 p.m. at the Delco plant downtown. Grace Long was visibly upset about their son, Mark, being bused and forced to attend school with blacks. She told Long she personally telephoned Dr. Glatt's office a few days earlier to tell him to stop the busing. She spoke with Dr. Glatt's secretary who promised Dr. Glatt would return her call. "Neal, he hasn't called me! I don't know what to do!" Grace exclaimed and broke into a sobbing meltdown. Long deeply resented that Grace was ignored. He hated Dr. Glatt even more.

Long barely contained his roiling anger. He froze and gripped the steering wheel. Seldom had Grace ever exploded. Years of bad marriage and being an absent father scrolled through his mind. A failure. Neal Bradley Long would make "them" pay for his pain.

After Grace got out of the car, Long made a U-turn and headed east to Orville Wright School to pick up his son, Mark, at 2:00 p.m. Long knew his son was bused to a different school that day and then returned to his home school. Long arrived at the school a few minutes early and went inside. He paced in the lobby near the main office while he waited for his son. When Mark walked toward him, Long saw that his son was upset. He waited until they got in the car to talk.

Mark told his father he did not like being bused to another school. He said there were only two other white kids in the class of about thirty; all the rest of the children were black. Long seethed. When Neal Bradley Long pulled up in front of Grace's house on Cosler, Mark's older brother Stanley was in the front yard and walked over to Long's car as Mark got out. Stanley spoke to his dad, but Long just sat there and stared straight ahead. Stanley later recalled, "It seemed like a long time, two or three minutes. It was like he was in a trance. I called out his name and he didn't seem to hear me."

Long told Mark, "You won't be bused anymore." He swerved the car out of the driveway and sped away. He headed directly for downtown Dayton. He stopped along the way to have a few swigs of bourbon. He touched his front trouser pocket. He felt the shape of the .22 caliber revolver, and it gave him strength. His thoughts were focused on ending race mixing in schools. Voices told him that God wanted it to stop, too. Long was on his way to carry out God's will.

———◦———

At about 2:15 p.m., Homicide Detectives Baker, Prugh and Sergeant Jess Kline met at the Embassy Bar on South Ludlow Street. The bar was located in the same city block as the Federal Building. All three men missed lunch, delayed by a meeting with the County Prosecutor on an old homicide case that was about to come to trial. Sergeant Kline agreed to meet with the detectives to hear about their idea to pursue another set of possible leads in the Midnight Slayer case. He was all ears because there were simply no new leads worth a damn.

The three men ordered lunch specials to save time. Baker laid his portable police radio on the table. Over din of noise in the restaurant and chatter on the police frequency, the three men got down to business.

Prugh and Baker suggested to Sergeant Kline the Midnight Slayer might be linked to anger about the Dayton Public Schools desegregation plan and busing. The sergeant agreed. Over coffee, the trio of cops penciled out agencies to formally contact: all levels of law enforcement, Dayton Schools, the Court and the U.S. Marshal's office. They planned to ask about a broad spectrum of suspicious encounters or names of disgruntled parents.

———◦———

At 2:30 p.m., Neal Bradley Long slowed as he drove past Dayton School Board offices on West First Street. He circled the block, pulled into a parking lot and stopped. Long sat for a few moments and heard God's command for him to act.

Neal Bradley Long perspired heavily as he entered the double doors of the Dayton School Board office building. The handgun was concealed in his pocket, and his hand rested on his gun. Long noticed no one was in the lobby. He looked at the building directory and ran his index finger down the list of names until he came to "John B. Maxwell, Board President, 2nd floor." Long assumed other Board Members were on the same floor and he could find more than one member.

He was sweaty, and there was a slight odor of alcohol on his breath. Long wore his light blue short-sleeve gasoline station work shirt. He got on the elevator and rode to the second floor. He walked the office halls and looked at nameplates on doors until he encountered Assistant Superintendent Norm Feuer and Secretary Mary White. Long stiffened. He gripped the gun with his hand in his pocket. "May we help you?" Mrs. White asked.

Long hesitated. While it was not uncommon to encounter citizens in the building, the two employees felt a bit uneasy about the deadpan look on the man's face.

"Where is Dr. Glatt's office?" Long asked in his typical low-affect voice as he adjusted his large frame black glasses that slid partially down his nose.

Mr. Feuer and Mrs. White felt a sense of relief when they learned they could re-direct the man who seemed strangely preoccupied. They told him how to find the Federal Building, three blocks away. Long did not respond. He turned and walked away, his right hand still in his pocket.

Mr. Feuer and Mrs. White looked at each other and shrugged their shoulders, glad that the strange-acting man left their building.

————◦————

Long pulled into the pay parking lot at West Third and South Wilkinson Streets. He could see the west entrance to the Federal Building just across the street. The lot was full, but Long told the attendant he would only be a few minutes. The attendant said, "Okay", and he let Long park alongside the attendant's shack. The attendant noticed Long was preoccupied when he paid his fee. Long quickly walked across Wilkinson Street and paused at the bottom of a dozen steps that led up to double doors at the northwest corner of the building.

Neal Bradley Long was glad he decided to carry his hand gun since it was next to impossible to smuggle a shotgun into the Federal Building.

Long climbed the steps and entered the building. He looked to his left down the corridor full of service windows at the post office. An armed uniformed Federal Protection Officer sat behind a long folding table. A sign was posted that stated identification checks and package searches were required. The officer stood up as Long approached. Long was not challenged since he did not have packages or a briefcase. The officer thought Long was headed to the post office but when he realized Long was not, he paused.

Neal Bradley Long asked, "Is Dr. Glatt in?" The officer said he had no idea as he motioned toward a set of double doors. Long nodded and walked toward the doors that led to an office area behind the Post Office corridor.

Dr. Glatt usually kept the doors to his area locked unless he made advance arrangements with a visitor for a specific time. The FPO never knew when Dr. Glatt expected visitors, so they let people pass if they asked for Glatt.

With so many unexpected changes to Dr. Glatt's schedule that particular Friday, doors to the main hallway to his office were closed but not locked. Neal Bradley Long simply walked through the unlocked doors and looked at office nameplates.

On a Friday afternoon, some workers left early and there were only a few people around. Long approached room 100C. He paused outside the door as he heard a man's voice. The man spoke rather loudly, as if he was reading something. Long glanced around and saw the nameplate on the door, "Dr. Charles Glatt."

Dr. Glatt sat in a chair across from the open office door. He dictated a letter into his recorder while Mrs. Tommie C. Jones, a black female, sat near the door and worked on her papers.

At 2:40 p.m., Neal Bradley Long appeared in the doorway. "Are you Dr. Glatt?"

"Yes, I'm Dr. Charles Glatt."

Neal Bradley Long drew his weapon, pointed it at Dr. Glatt, and announced, "I promised God I would do this. God told me to kill you!" Long fired his weapon.

"My God! Please don't shoot me!" Dr. Glatt screamed.

Dr. Glatt was struck three times in his chest. As his body turned, he was shot twice in the upper back and then once in the lower right jaw.

"God told me to kill you", Long said again.

Dr. Glatt was mortally wounded by bullets that tore through both lungs, his liver, intestines and one lodged in his jaw at the base of his brain. None of the bullets exited his body. Dr. Glatt slid out of his chair and onto the floor near his unopened briefcase with his own handgun inside.

Mrs. Jones was in shock and unable to speak. She did not move. Neal Bradley Long looked at her and said, "Lady, I'm sorry I had to do this, but I promised God that I would."

———◄O►———

Five security officers on duty heard gunshots and converged on the area. One officer immediately radioed his office to call Dayton Police and report shots fired on the first floor, near Federal District Court Judge Rubin's chambers. Within seconds, one security officer radioed his fellow officers, "Dr. Glatt's been shot! Stop a white man in a blue shirt!"

The Dayton Police emergency tone screeched loudly over every police radio in the city. The police dispatcher's voice sounded urgent. *"Attention all cars downtown, reports of shots fired, shots fired. First floor of the Federal Building, 120 West Third Street. Use caution. Respond as if a signal 99, officers need assistance. Be advised uniformed federal officers and plain clothes agents are armed and searching the building."*

Neal Bradley Long walked calmly back toward the front of the building. He mixed in with post office customers in the large hall as he headed to the west exit. He approached the door and intended to exit and cross Wilkerson Street to get his car that was parked at the mouth of the entrance to the parking lot. Long imagined he would head south on I-75 and disappear into the city traffic. He planned to drive six miles south to Miamisburg, Ohio, pick up his father and stepmother then flee to the safety of Kentucky, down home, as he had done many times before.

Neal Bradley Long was about twenty feet from the exit when three Federal Protection Officers, with guns drawn, ordered him to stop. Long complied. He raised his hands and when asked where his gun was, Long said softly, "In my back pocket."

Security officer David Galloway removed the gun and laid it on the folding table near the security checkpoint. Officer Galloway asked Long, "Why did you ever do it, what was on your mind?" Neal Bradley Long answered in an emotionless tone, "I promised God I'd kill Dr. Glatt. I had to kill Dr. Glatt because of the busing of kids."

Detectives Baker, Prugh and Sergeant Kline heard the dispatcher's urgent radio broadcast. They immediately ran to Baker's unmarked car parked in the "No Parking Zone" in front of the bar. Baker got on the radio, "Car 715 to dispatch, I'll be responding with two other plain clothes detectives, we'll come up from the west on Wilkinson."

The Police Dispatcher announced, "All cars, suspect in custody. FBI and U.S. Marshals on the scene. 2:54 p.m."

The Dispatcher called Baker, "Car 715, go to 'B' Channel."

Baker switched to the private non-recorded radio channel, "Car 715, go ahead."

The dispatcher said, "715, be advised, the shooting victim is Dr. Glatt, the school busing desegregation guy, you clear?"

Baker and Prugh recognized Glatt's name and looked at each other. Their thoughts were the same, "This may be our Midnight Slayer!"

Baker responded to the dispatcher, "We are clear on that, also be advised I have 710, Sergeant Kline and 714, Detective Prugh with me. We are pulling up at the scene now."

The Police Dispatch broadcasted, "All cars going to 120 West Third, the Federal Building. Be advised, our Homicide Squad is now on the scene, cars 710, 714 and 715. They will lead coordination with the federal authorities."

Baker, Prugh and Kline walked in the west entrance of the Federal Building and went directly to Dr. Glatt's office just as the Dayton Fire Department ambulance crew wheeled him out on a gurney. Glatt was bloody, unconscious and in grave condition. The veteran homicide detectives knew the look of violent death. It was over for Dr. Glatt.

Detective Baker asked a U.S. Marshal where the suspect was. He said the suspect was upstairs in their temporary holding and booking area with another Marshal and the FBI. The detectives ran upstairs to the US Marshals booking area but could not proceed past an outer office. The feds were the lead agency and the interaction would be touchy. The FPO was posted at the entrance to the Marshal's office and the detectives were told no one was allowed inside, pending clearance from the Marshal. Detectives Baker and Prugh waited and grew edgy knowing valuable time was being lost. They knew they had a small window of time to talk to the suspect to determine if he was connected to the Midnight Slayer shootings. They were damn sure he would 'lawyer up' quickly.

Sergeant Klein added to the urgency when he called Baker on the portable radio non-recorded channel, "Guess what, that son-of-a-bitch has a baby blue 1968 Ford Fairlane 500 parked across the street! I'll be upstairs ASAP!"

After about 15 minutes, U.S. Marshal Pelfrey opened the door to his office and saw Baker and Prugh waiting. He motioned for them to enter, "I knew you guys would be here soon, glad to see you."

The detectives walked in the old drab green facility with a rusty mesh screen holding cell and a few small interview rooms. A fingerprinting table, sink and camera stand were crowded into the area.

As Dayton detectives entered the room, they saw the shooting suspect. He was bent over a sink as he washed fingerprint ink off his hands. Baker and Prugh watched the man from behind. They noted his size, thick black hair and light blue shirt. The detectives stood quietly as he finally raised up. The suspect dried his hands and U.S. Marshal Pelfrey said, "There's two Dayton Police Detectives to see you." The man looked into the mirror over the sink and his upper body was perfectly framed in the mirror when he looked at Baker and Prugh.

Neal Bradley Long's face in the mirror was breathtaking as Baker and Prugh saw the perfect match to the composite *Identi-Kit* pictures shown around the city. Black hair, black frame glasses, long sideburns, expressionless face, blue shirt and his height and weight.

Long finished drying his hands and Marshal Pelfrey placed him in an interview room with a table and four chairs. The Marshal walked over to Baker and whispered, "Hey Dan, the FBI doesn't want anybody else talking to him. They already took a quick statement from him about Glatt. They are trying to find a lawyer for him and arraign him before a magistrate right away."

The Marshal told Detectives Baker and Prugh that Dr. Glatt died at Miami Valley Hospital, and his wife had been notified in Columbus, Ohio.

Baker and Prugh waited again as time ticked away. Baker finally saw Dayton FBI ASAC Robert Carmichael at about 4:00 p.m. Detective Baker told Carmichael that he and Prugh needed to talk to Long, ASAP. Agent Carmichael stalled and told the detectives the FBI already had a statement, and they would share it with DPD later. Baker insisted DPD needed to talk to Long about the series of shotgun shootings on the West Side. Agent Carmichael continued to stall, "I have to run it by the U.S. Attorney first since Long is in federal custody," and he walked away.

Baker and Prugh agreed if Neal Bradley Long gave a statement to the FBI, he must have waived his Miranda rights, "So he ought to be primed to talk," Baker said. "Let's get in there!"

When Sergeant Kline made it upstairs, he was collared by his detectives. Baker told Kline, "Sarge, we're going in right now and talk to the suspect. The FBI took a one page statement and they are rushing to get this guy in court as fast as they can. They haven't even made the connection to our shootings yet and won't give us permission to talk to him! We got to get to him, boss. It's now or never!"

Detective Prugh jumped in, "Right! He's the guy, Sarge. You ought to see the bastard. He's it, the light blue car, the busing, the whole nine yards, this is our guy!"

Sergeant Kline immediately backed his men. "If they don't like it, too damn bad," he said. "Go ahead. Get in there now and get him talking. I'll be right in with you in a minute. I gotta' let the Chief know we may have our guy."

The Marshal overheard DPD Dicks as they made their plan. He handed Baker a folded up blank Miranda Rights Waiver form on the sly. He also had the suspect's name written on a scrap of paper he handed to

Baker. Baker looked at it and said softly to Detective Prugh, "He is Neal Bradley Long."

Baker gave the Marshal a grateful smile, one cop taking a chance to help another, Baker thought. The Marshal grinned with approval and looked the other way while detectives opened the door to Long's room and Baker said, "Mr. Long?"

———◄○►———

The detectives tried not to show the urgency that screamed inside both of them. They approached Long in a matter-of-fact manner. They matched their demeanor to his emotional level, which was less likely to make him defensive. Baker and Prugh knew it was critical to talk to Neal Bradley Long before FBI agents rushed him into the courtroom.

"Mr. Long, I'm Detective Baker, Dayton Police." Baker placed his hand on Prugh's shoulder, "and this is Detective Prugh. We'd like to talk to you. You were probably expecting us," Baker said as he and Prugh sat down.

Neal Bradley Long moved his hands from the table to his lap and said, "Yes."

Detective Baker said softly, "Neal, it's over. We'd like to listen to you and let you get it off your chest, Okay?" Long nodded and stared straight ahead.

Long immediately made an incriminating statement, "Yes", he hesitated then added, "it's about those colored people gettin' shot on the West Side. I know I'm in trouble. I knew when I came in here and shot him. You guys would be talking to me about it."

"We'll need to show you a form first, Mr. Long," Detective Prugh said. It's about your rights."

"I know, I've seen it on TV, I know my rights," Long said.

"Neal," Baker said, "we want to make sure, so we'll give you this 'Rights Form' to look over." Baker slid it across the table with a pen. "And then we'll read it to you and if you're okay, we need your signature before we can talk a few minutes, Okay?"

When asked if he used any other name, Long said, "Carma. I also go by the name Carma."

Detective Prugh moved to a chair next to Long and went over the form. Prugh pointed to the words and read line by line until he finished.

Neal Bradley Long suddenly blurted out, "Busing kids to school is wrong. They teased my son, made him talk in class."

Neal Bradley Long took the pen and with a steady hand, he signed the form. It was witnessed by Detectives Baker and Prugh at 4:20 p.m.

Sergeant Kline knocked on the door. He entered and was introduced to Long. Baker scribbled a note to Prugh, "I'll try to find a tape recorder. Stall!"

Baker signaled to Sergeant Kline to step out of the room as Baker asked Long, "You need a coffee or water?"

Long replied, "Yes."

As soon as Baker and Kline were outside the room, Baker told Kline, "It's him, we need to get him on tape, quick!" At that moment Baker eyed a cassette tape recorder on a desk nearby and asked the clerk, "I need to borrow this, does it have a tape?" The clerk looked at the Marshal who nodded approval. The clerk put a fresh cassette tape in, unplugged the recorder and handed it to Baker. Baker and Kline re-entered the interview room with a water and coffee and placed the cups in the middle of the table.

Detective Prugh did not miss a beat as Baker quickly connected and tested the recorder while Long looked on. Long did not register any emotion.

Detective Prugh spoke as the cassette tape turned, "We're in the U.S. Marshal's Office, Federal Building, in an interview room. Present in the room are Sergeant Kline, Detective Baker and myself, from the DPD, and your name is?"

Calmly the Midnight Slayer identified himself. "Neal Bradley Long."

The man who hated colored people, the Midnight Slayer, the man who killed and maimed people at random, was ready to confess. His personal war to stop actions of local and federal governments to end segregation in Dayton Public Schools was over. It ended in a bloody shooting inside a Federal Building.

As Neal Bradley Long's recorded confession began, only three cops knew what was soon blasted on the airwaves and in newspapers across America, *The racist reign of terror in Dayton against black men was over. The Urban Guerrilla was in his cage.*

—◦—

Baker, Prugh and Kline were under extreme time pressures. They needed to think on their feet. They had to get sufficient details from Long to capture the scope of his killing spree such that it connected Long to the Midnight Slayer. The detectives were also careful that the evidence would clear legal hurdles and be admissible in court. The detectives decided to bracket their discussion. They focused first on the most recent shooting and then the earliest shooting, just in case they were interrupted by the FBI before they got enough.

Long confessed to the most recent murder, that of Mr. Hoard, on Cincinnati Street July 15, 1975. Then he confessed to the first shooting spree when he wounded Mr. Malcomb July 31, 1972. Long also confessed to other shootings within the four year bracket of time.

Neal Bradley Long said he picked his black victims at random, in warm weather when people were on the street. He only shot men, except for when he "accidentally" wounded Glenda Gay when he shot at her male friend July 15, 1975. Long also vividly recalled the murder of Mr. Tillman on Germantown Street, September 26, 1973 and the high-speed chase by Emmet Watts.

Neal Bradley Long said he always acted alone and always drank alcohol and smoked marijuana before he left his room and drove to the West Side to hunt down his victims.

Long said he preferred to live near bridges that led into the West Side because the bridge provided an escape route back to the white side of town. He did not regret his string of shootings and he did not show any remorse. He was matter-of-fact when he said he shot about "thirty coloreds."

———◄◦►———

The detectives expected an interruption at any time when the FBI returned to the Marshal's area, so they hurried Long's confession.

Suddenly, there was a commotion outside the interview room. Voices grew louder. "Where is he?" a male voice demanded.

The U.S. Marshal opened the door to the interview room and two other men were right behind him. They wedged into the room and peered over the Marshal's shoulder. The Marshal said, "His attorney is here."

Detective Prugh ended the interview and said, "It's 5:00 p.m." Prugh turned the tape recorder off.

His court appointed attorney pushed past the U.S. Marshal. FBI ASAC Carmichael was upset that DPD Homicide Detectives interviewed and recorded a federal prisoner without his permission. The attorney said loudly, "You can't talk to my client!" Sergeant Kline was not ruffled by such powerful men. He simply got up from his chair and said, "We're done. He's all yours."

The attorney demanded the Dayton detectives give the confession tape to the FBI. No one answered the lawyer. Detective Baker had already removed the cassette tape and slipped it into his suit coat pocket. He handed the recorder to the FBI ASAC and Dayton Homicide Detectives left the room. Sergeant Kline, along with Detectives Baker and Prugh, quickly trotted down the stairs with Neal Bradley Long's recorded confession. They exited the Federal Building and left the feds with their crime scene.

The smug attorney looked gratified that he had ordered the police around. When Agent Carmichael opened the recorder cover, the tape was gone. Agent Carmichael stood there with an empty tape recorder in his hands. The attorney gasped. Carmichael cursed, "That son-of-a-bitch, Baker!"

The Midnight Slayer's confession was in the possession of DPD, and it was on the way to Dick Section.

———<o>———

The U.S. Marshal, followed by a phalanx of FBI agents and uniformed Federal Protective Service Officers, escorted Neal Bradley Long into a second floor courtroom at 5:40 p.m. in the Federal Building. The court-appointed attorney accompanied Long. Neal Bradley Long wore his light blue service station shirt and dark trousers. He stood motionless and displayed a dead-pan facial expression. Long knew that moment would come some day. He stood stiffly as criminal charges were read by the U.S. Magistrate.

> Neal Bradley Long was formally charged with Murder, pursuant to Title 18, Sec. 1111, (a),(b) and Title 18, Sec. 245, Interference with Federally Protected Activities of the United States Code and held without bond. Both crimes were eligible for the Death Penalty.

Black people all over West Dayton were swept up in a range of mixed emotions after they heard local and national news bulletins about Dr. Glatt's murder. They were shocked and saddened by Glatt's death. They knew he was a target for assassination because he was a symbol of change to improve education of black children.

News broke at about 5:50 p.m., Dayton Police believe the man who shot Dr. Glatt was the Midnight Slayer. The message spread like wildfire. The fact Dayton Homicide Detectives had a taped statement by Long soon leaked and helped bolster confidence the right man had been arrested, at last.

Tragically, federal law enforcement officials failed to heed two years of anonymous threats directed toward Judge Rubin and the federal court over the busing case. Despite threats, a gaping weakness was allowed to exist in the Federal Protection Officers' Security Plan. After the shooting, one emotionally distraught federal officer told the *Dayton Daily News,* "We simply neglected to check visitors to Dr. Glatt's office," claiming a lack of resources. "It would have taken additional manpower to secure his office with so many people coming into the post office."

FORTY-SEVEN

The Midnight Slayer's Nest

Within minutes of the shooting in the Federal Building, the DPD and Dayton Office of the FBI launched parallel investigations. Up to the day Dr. Glatt was murdered, the FBI had not provided investigative support to the DPD. During four summers of shootings by the Midnight Slayer, the FBI and Department of Justice insisted the slayings and racially motivated drive-by shootings were local matters for police to handle. On September 19, 1975, the arrest of Neal Bradley Long suddenly became the nexus that forced some degree of cooperation between the two law enforcement agencies.

One of the first things the FBI did was an immediate search of their Indices files for the name Neal Bradley Long. They rediscovered their Indices entries about him, including Communism and the Kennedy letter.

After the murder of Dr. Charles Glatt, FBI ASAC Robert Carmichael and his superiors chose not to tell DPD they had known of Neal Bradley Long and his presence in Dayton for years. Meanwhile, Dayton Police Homicide Squad feverishly sought additional evidence that linked Long to the Midnight Slayer shootings. Long's 1968 light blue Ford Fairlane 500 was already in police custody, and a handgun was found in the trunk. Most significantly, large amounts of gun powder residue was found on the headliner and interior door panels caused when Long's sawed-off shotguns were fired from inside the car.

Baker and Prugh returned to DPD Detective Section with Sergeant Kline. Baker played the taped confession for Chief O'Connor. O'Connor smiled broadly and said, "We'll keep this, it's just a local matter. If the FBI wants it or a transcript, tell 'em to come see me!"

DPD detectives interviewed witnesses from the School Board offices, the parking lot attendant and citizens who saw Neal Bradley Long earlier the day of Glatt's murder. Long's arrest record was pulled up and it included three arrests for public intoxication in the late 1940s and 50s, about ten traffic tickets and the "Safe Keeping" arrest and commitment to Dayton State Hospital after Long threatened to kill his family on March 27, 1967.

A half-dozen uniformed police officers and detectives sped to Neal Bradley Long's rented room on South Main Street. They sealed the area around his room until a search warrant was obtained. Meanwhile, police combed through trash at the rear of the building and questioned other renters, occupants of nearby businesses and residents of houses for a block in each direction. Other detectives went to Cap Collins' Sohio Services Station in Kettering, Ohio and interviewed Mr. Collins and Long's co-workers. The FBI sent several agents to interview doctors at Dayton State Hospital.

Amid the flurry of activity, Baker and Prugh had Long's audio taped confession transcribed. Baker isolated himself in a corner of the homicide office and prepared the search warrant for Long's room. Baker knew the written narrative had to convince a judge that the need for the search was urgent, reasonable and necessary to recover evidence lawfully. He described the alleged crime, the location to be searched and he provided sufficient probable cause. The judge, prosecutor, Police Chief, dozens of detectives and uniformed officers and commanders all waited for Baker to complete the search warrant.

When the documents were done, Baker presented the package to the judge. The judge studied Baker's work and without any questions, he formally accepted Baker's sworn statement. Baker signed as the affiant and the judge approved the search warrant at 6:50 p.m. It was time to roll.

Sergeant Kline and Lieutenant Riley assembled a team of detectives who conducted the search of 656 S. Main Street, Room #2. Kline, Riley, Baker and Prugh all rode together to the house. They were followed by a caravan of television and other media vehicles.

Since Neal Bradley Long was not present at his room, Detective Prugh used Long's keys, retrieved from his personal effects at the county jail. Baker and Prugh entered Long's room first. They stood just inside the door, paused and gathered their bearings before the team initiated their search of the room.

Neal Bradley Long's dimly lit room looked like a hopeless place to live; a place where good and decent thoughts did not reside. A place of bad karma. Long's room offered a glimpse into the mind of a serial killer, the last person in the room. Experienced Homicide Detectives often tried to put themselves in the place of a victim or a suspect to see and experience what they last saw.

Baker scanned the room. It was as if he could see Neal Bradley Long inside as he fretted over busing and his hatred of the "coloreds." He imagined Long in the dingy, filthy room that served as his incubator of hate and intolerance, the place where Long repeatedly dulled his mind with alcohol and marijuana then loaded his shotgun and headed for the bridges.

Long's dirty clothing was piled on the bed and in a corner. The few small kitchen appliances had little food or signs of cooking. Spoiled bread and meat was in the tiny dirty refrigerator. Empty beer and bourbon bottles were piled in a garbage can that overflowed. The only sign of life was a half-dozen roaches that scurried from beneath the sink. An old portable black and white RCA TV, with a tin foil-covered rabbit ear antenna sat on a rickety cart in the corner of the room as if it presided over Neal Bradley Long's meager possessions.

The search of Long's rented room and preparation of sketches took several hours. Police finally left with numerous pieces of key evidence. The sawed-off Charles Daly shotgun purchased by Neal Bradley Long in May 1975 and used in the most recent drive-by shootings was found in a corner of a closet. A Ruger .22 caliber pistol and over eighty live shotgun shells were recovered along with dozens of .22 caliber bullets. A street map of the City of Dayton was spread out on a table. Three paperback books, *Brotherhood of Strange, California Gold* and *The Life of Geronimo* were found along with a few baggies of marijuana and drug paraphernalia.

The Charles Daly shotgun was turned over to a DPD Firearms Examiner. He rushed it to the crime lab. He fired the weapon for comparison purposes and confirmed test rounds matched the weapon used to kill two victims, Romaine and Hoard. Both were murdered less than an hour apart on July 15, 1975.

———◦———

The Dayton Police Dick Section was crowded to the max with detectives, uniformed police officers, FBI agents, prosecutors and defense attorneys. Two extra coffee pots were constantly refilled by secretaries as people milled about and waited for the start of one of the most notorious police lineups in Dayton's history. It was 10:00 a.m. Tuesday, September 23, 1975, and DPD conducted the identification line-up for the FBI. There were ten federal witnesses to the events that surrounded Glatt's murder. Witnesses included the parking lot attendant, employees from the School Board and the Federal Building.

Two Public Defenders were in attendance along with an Assistant U.S. Attorney from Cincinnati. Witnesses were brought in as a group and briefed on what to expect during the line-up. As lead detectives for DPD Homicide, Baker and Prugh watched the proceedings.

At precisely 10:20 a.m., the lights were dimmed and six white men, all dressed alike in grey work coveralls, black shoes, black hair, in their 40s with black frame glasses stepped onto a lighted stage. They all carried placards with a number they held in front, waist high with both hands. They stood with their backs to the wall and waited for instructions from Detective Beu-tell who sat at a desk at one end of the stage with a microphone and provided instructions. The witnesses were tense as the police lineup began.

Witnesses saw the men through a fine mesh screen. The men on stage could not see the witnesses in the darkened room. Each man was instructed to say the following phrases:

"Are you Dr. Glatt?"

"I promised God I would do this."

"Lady, I'm sorry I had to do this, but I promised God I would."

Each man stepped forward, walked the length of the stage and then returned to his place in line as instructed.

The five men who stood on the stage with Neal Bradley Long were police officers. Long held card number three. All federal witnesses identified Neal Bradley Long as the shooter.

Detective Beu-tell handled a second lineup a half hour later for eight additional witnesses to the series of Midnight Slayer shootings. Half of the witnesses identified Neal Bradley Long; the others simply were not sure. None of the witnesses from the Lester Mitchell case in 1966 were invited to identify that suspect. Not one of the veteran Homicide Detectives or supervisors who worked the Lester Mitchell case suggested that there could be a connection to the Midnight Slayer shootings. They accepted that Mitchell's killer had been killed as the jailbird snitch had said in 1967. Despite the M.O. being a solid match to the Mitchell case, the subject was never raised.

Since Neal Bradley Long was in federal custody and held without bail, Dayton Police and the Montgomery County Prosecutor did not immediately file charges against him. However, it was clear the prosecutor would eventually seek aggravated murder charges with a death penalty specification.

FORTY-EIGHT

Standing Before the Bar of Justice

Initially, Neal Bradley Long was held in the Montgomery County jail. However, he was secretly transferred by U.S. Marshals September 25, 1975, to the Medical Center for Federal Prisoners in Springfield, Missouri. Long was placed in isolation to prevent reprisal from black inmates. The change in Long's location served two important purposes for the feds. It permitted the FBI to take their time as they questioned him, and they isolated him from Dayton Police Detectives. Long's lawyers began an eighteen-month-long process when they filed a flurry of motions in U.S Federal Court and in Montgomery County, Ohio, courts.

Lead prosecutor, James Brogan, of the Montgomery County Prosecutor's Office prepared charges for the Midnight Slayer shootings and presented his case to the Montgomery County Grand Jury. Three of the strongest murder cases were selected, and indictments were returned that charged Neal Bradley Long with aggravated murder, with "specifications for the death penalty." Neal Bradley Long was indicted for killing Larry Romaine and Robert Hoard July 15, 1975, and for the murder of Edward Tillman September 26, 1973. Long was also charged with additional felony counts, aggravated assault, shooting to kill and felonious assault, for wounding five other victims who survived.

Neal Bradley Long faced five death penalty charges, two federal and three state. Long did not react openly or appear phased by the gravity of his situation.

Defense attorneys for Long requested and received numerous continuances for additional time needed as they prepared their defense case. Long entered a plea of "Not Guilty by Reason of Insanity" in federal and state courts. His plea triggered filings by Long's attorneys and by the Montgomery County lead prosecutor as each side requested psychiatric evaluations to determine Long's sanity at the time he committed his crimes and his ability to understand the charges and his rights. The tit-for-tat battle was underway. Each side sought multiple examinations from their preferred list of psychiatrists and clinical psychologists.

Media coverage that surrounded Neal Bradley Long's arrest and hearings in Federal Court about his mental state was extensive. Many newspaper articles were written about his history, family, employment and difficulties in his life, such as his stormy relationship and divorce from his wife. Long's history of mental health issues, time in hospital psychiatric wards and his admittance to Dayton State Hospital were also covered in great detail with quotes from various psychiatrists and doctors. Information was leaked from many sources. In addition, filings for discovery of the prosecutor's evidence and court testimony revealed a significant amount of information about Long.

September 20th, the day after Dr. Glatt's death, the *Dayton Daily News* front page headlined, "Long Ex-Mental Patient; Just didn't Go Along With Busing" and described his hospitalization in 1967 when Dr. Moronell, clinical director of Dayton State Hospital, described Long as "seriously mentally ill" at that time.

Another dramatic newspaper headline appeared two days later on September 22nd, "Long and Reality Split in 1968, Doctor Says." Dr. Robert Moronell, clinical director of professional services at Dayton State Hospital, said, "Long was a patient in 1967 and early 1968 and was correctly diagnosed as mentally ill with a psychotic condition since he believed he was hearing the voice of God." Dr. Moronell said, "Such a person [Long] isn't afraid of the consequences. He's not responsible for his actions." The doctor added, "Suppose you actually believe God is talking to you and God tells you to shoot someone. You get a gun, shoot and then you tell yourself you obeyed. Long's reaction portrays so clearly that he's not responsible for what he's done." Dr. Moronell was also quoted as saying, "Long's cultural environment is against mixing the races; he is a native of an Eastern Kentucky town which has a cultural environment that could have led Long to be racially prejudiced."

October 10, 1975, Dr. Jack Eardley, Chief of Psychiatry at the Medical

Center for Federal Prisoners in Springfield, Missouri, offered a different opinion when he notified Federal Judge Carl Weinman that "Neal Bradley Long is mentally competent and responsible. I am of the opinion that this man has been without mental illness for the past several months."

January 16, 1976, another psychiatrist, Dr. Sontag, completed his psychiatric evaluation of Neal Bradley Long. He reviewed Long's diagnosis in 1966 when he was admitted to Good Samaritan Hospital Psychiatric Ward with a diagnosis as "schizophrenic-paranoid type, very dangerous." However, in his analysis ten years later, Dr. Sontag concluded Long was "not legally insane. He [Long] is capable of conferring with his attorneys and of standing trial for the alleged crime." Dr. Sontag rendered the diagnosis and clinical sources: "Diagnosis [Currently] Explosive Personality, 301.4. (APA, DSM II, Second Edition)."

Doctor Sontag's interview with Neal Bradley Long revealed much about Long's motives. Long told the Doctor, "In 1972 a white man and his family were passing through West Dayton when the man was killed by a shotgun blast, fired by a black." Long said a news story quoted, "One of the black leaders stated he would not be responsible for the safety of any white man in West Dayton." The Doctor added, "Mr. Long sees his black shooting spree very much in the light of a vigilante or Ku Klux Klanner of forty years ago." More revealingly, Dr. Sontag said, "He [Long] feels the City of Dayton owes him a debt for him being a major factor in resolving violence in West Dayton."

April 4, 1976, Dr. Victor Thaler, a clinical psychologist also concluded Neal Bradley Long was mentally competent to stand trial. His interview of Long yielded a new and disturbing confession. According to Dr. Thayer, "Neal Bradley Long says he shot his shotgun at blacks approximately one hundred times and estimates he hit people about thirty-five times. In his [Long's] opinion, he may have killed as many as twenty people. He [Long] described all this with very little remorse." The admission by Neal Bradley Long was more than three times the number of cases identified by Dayton Police.

In an article in the *Dayton Daily News* dated May 6, 1976, titled "Long Acutely Psychotic," Dr. Jerome A. Logan, a psychiatrist in private practice, described Neal Bradley Long as suffering from a "residual-type schizophrenia. The ten years of hallucination commands from God are continuing evidence of acute evidence of psychosis."

June 22, 1976, the *Dayton Journal Herald* quoted Dr. Wayne A. Oliver, a clinical psychologist, in a report to Federal Judge Carl Weinman, that described Neal Bradley Long as a man, "... capable of extreme acts of depersonalized violence under the cloaking auspices of racial indignation. He envies and resents what appears to him to be the effortless and undeserved good fortune of minority groups." Dr. Oliver further stated, "Long has a primitive value system [which] determined his history of homicidal behavior... based largely on his own presumptive interpretation of the Old Testament."

Defense attorneys believed the news stories and court testimony prejudiced potential jury pools and public disclosures about his mental health created good arguments in the "court of public opinion" for a plea of "Not Guilty by Reason of Insanity." However, after numerous hearings and motions, the Federal Court ruled that Neal Bradley Long was mentally competent to stand trial for the murder of Dr. Glatt, and jury selection was ordered to begin.

———◦———

November 8, 1976, jury selection began for the federal trial of Neal Bradley Long for the murder of Dr. Charles Glatt. Ninety prospective jurors were selected, and the FBI immediately checked every person through their Indices to see if his or her name was ever entered into their confidential system. Eventually, the federal jury was impaneled.

On the second day of the trial, Neal Bradley Long abruptly changed his plea to "Guilty" in exchange for two death penalty charges dropped by the U.S. Attorney in federal court. Neal Bradley Long pled guilty and was sentenced to two consecutive life-terms in federal prison. Long was turned over to Montgomery County Sheriff and remained in custody until pending prosecution on three murders and five other shootings in Dayton were adjudicated.

Montgomery County Prosecutor James Brogan faced a major decision. How reasonable was it to pursue the death penalty in Ohio, if Long would be at least eighty years old when he returned from federal prison? Long was required to serve his complete federal sentence before beginning to serve any sentence under the state's prosecution for his Midnight Slayer crimes.

Through his attorneys, Neal Bradley Long offered a plea bargain and waived going to trial. Long would plead guilty to "Life" terms on the murder charges. County Prosecutor Brogan agreed to the offer and elimination of Ohio death penalty specifications. Neal Bradley Long had to plead guilty to Case 75CR1345: three counts of aggravated murder with consecutive life sentences plus five other non-fatal felony shooting charges.

Prosecutor Brogan knew the plea offer was solid because of his strong case. According to a quote in the *Dayton Journal Herald*, Brogan said, "The most damaging evidence against Long would be his own tape recorded statement in which he reportedly admitted gunning down more than thirty blacks. Sources who have heard the tape say Long was unbelievably composed without the slightest quiver and described in detail how he rode through West Dayton."

————◄○►————

June 22, 1977. "All rise. All rise," the Bailiff said in a strong voice. "Hear ye, hear ye. Montgomery County Court is now in session with the Honorable Judge Stanley S. Phillips presiding."

Judge Phillips entered through the door directly behind his ornate wooden bench. Judge Phillips, a former FBI agent, was a tall dark-haired man who projected authority and order. He paused, looked at the overflow gallery and extra uniformed Sheriff's Deputies in the room and said, "Good morning ladies and gentlemen, please be seated."

Neal Bradley Long wore dark trousers, an open-collar white dress shirt and an ill-fitting black jacket. He sat with his defense team and was rigid and passive. Prosecutor James Brogan sat with his team and Detectives Baker and Prugh, the State's Witnesses.

The stage was set. The characters were in place. Everyone knew a guilty plea was going to be offered and accepted. It was time to end years of fear and hateful violence.

Several of Neal Bradley Long's surviving victims were present in the courtroom, along with family members of some deceased victims. The news media was out in full force with reporters in the courtroom, cameras set up in the corridor outside and on the steps of the courthouse.

Judge Phillips started with case number 75CR1345 and patiently went through required reading of charges against Neal Bradley Long. He then read Long his rights and clarification of the change in Long's plea from "Not Guilty by Reason of Insanity" to "Guilty." At that point, the judge read each charge and asked Long to reply with his plea. Each count was read, three murder and five other violent felony counts for a total of eight. After each count was read, Long was asked "and how do you plead?"

Neal Bradley Long answered softly, "Guilty."

Detective Baker reflected back to the moment when he looked at Dr. Glatt on the gurney as he was dying. He recalled how calm Neal Bradley Long was moments after he shot Dr. Glatt. The scene of shotgun shootings and violent death seemed a million miles away from the church-like decorum of the courtroom. Baker kept his eyes fixed on Neal Bradley Long; vivid murder scenes flashed through Baker's memory like a movie. Despite being the center of attention, Long appeared more detached than anyone else in the room. His flat, quiet demeanor was deceptive. Baker knew Long was a very dangerous man.

———◦———

As everyone filed out of the courtroom, Detective Baker stopped and talked with Sergeant Kline and Detective Prugh. "Hey Sarge," Baker said as he tried to ease the tension. "How about a late breakfast at the Embassy? The three cops headed to the Embassy Bar and walked by the Federal Building. Neither of them looked at the building or said anything about the horror that occurred there September 19, 1975. It was over. Their personal thoughts and feelings about the Midnight Slayer shootings and many other brutal crimes they investigated would not be allowed to stir their emotions, that day. Some other day they would pay the personal toll of being Homicide Detectives and repeatedly dealing with sad and brutal crimes.

"Breakfast" consisted of beer and whiskey.

FORTY-NINE

Bridge Over Troubled Waters

For decades, the West Third Street Bridge was the symbol of segregation in the City of Dayton. It separated black from white as it crossed the Great Miami River from downtown into the heart of the West Side. It was often called "The Bridge of Hate," and in 1966, it was guarded by Ohio National Guard troops with fixed bayonets.

A few months after Neal Bradley Long's guilty plea in June 1977, some Daytonians participated in a solemn march and special ceremony. One half of the marchers began at 11:00 a.m. on West Third Street at the same parking lot where riotous mobs formed in past years. Hundreds of black and white people, including children and clergy, gathered with banners and signs that urged peace, equality and justice. They began their quiet and prayerful march and headed east toward the West Third Street Bridge. The marchers sang "We Shall Overcome" as they walked by police officers who held back traffic. Some citizens and police officers exchanged smiles and respectful nods on the same street where rocks and molotov cocktails were thrown during three terrible riots.

Simultaneously, city officials and over 150 citizens of both races gathered in front of Dayton Police Headquarters. They marched west, headed for the center of the West Third Street Bridge.

At 11:45 a.m., the groups joined together in hugs and handshakes. Two groups became one in the center of the "Bridge of Hate." The gray morning skies gave way to a bright sunny day as a brief dedication ceremony began. A short prayer and announcement followed as the crowd gathered around a shrouded object in the center of the bridge.

Two young children, one black and one white, randomly selected from the crowd, stood next to the covered object. On a signal, the children pulled the strings and unveiled two large blue signs that read, "The Peace Bridge." Applause erupted, accompanied by tearful emotions. It was a poignant moment. An annual tradition of coming together on The Peace Bridge was born. The signs were later mounted at each end of the West Third Street Bridge.

———◄○►———

Dan Baker, recently promoted to Sergeant, and Homicide Detective Spells agreed to meet to watch the ceremony on the bridge. They sat in Spells' detective car. Baker, dressed in full uniform, parked his marked cruiser next to Spells' vehicle. The two cops, one black and one white, watched the ceremony on The Peace Bridge from about one hundred yards away.

Detective Spells had recently been transferred to Homicide Squad, and Baker was getting used to leading his shift of twenty-five patrol officers.

Baker and Spells talked about race relations in the city. They wondered aloud if Dayton would ever overcome the riots, the effects of the Midnight Slayer shootings and the school desegregation case that was on its way back to the U.S. Supreme Court. The two cops did not pretend to have solutions to problems caused by racism and hate. They both had young children and worried about the future as much as any other parent.

Policing had changed. More black officers had been hired, and the use of technology in law enforcement advanced at a rapid pace. New officers were better trained and equipped. The two men were considered veterans on the job and their faces bore evidence of trying times.

They watched the unveiling of the sign on The Peace Bridge and heard applause from the crowd just as the police dispatcher called on Sergeant Baker's radio, "Car 330?"

Sergeant Baker answered, "330, go ahead. I'm with Detective Spells, car 716."

The emergency tone screeched loudly, BLEEEEP! "Car 330, car 716 and all West Side cars, report of an armed robbery in progress. Two men shot at the Beer Drive Thru Carryout at Hoover and Gettysburg. Use caution. The suspect is a black male, tall, wearing a red shirt, and he is still on the scene. He's barricaded in the back, holding a female clerk at gunpoint."

Baker and Spells glanced at each other. Baker hurried to his marked cruiser and switched on the overhead lights and siren. Detective Spells slapped a red light on the roof of his unmarked car. Both police cars headed out as the sirens screamed and lights flashed. They sped west on West Third Street, unsure what dangers awaited. The former partners and good friends took one more radio call together.

As hundreds of people stood on The Peace Bridge, sirens from Baker and Spells' cars disrupted the tranquility of the ceremony. As other police cars joined in the response, red and blue lights flashed, and cars raced by abandoned storefronts and vacant lots where prosperous businesses once stood before the riots.

The stream of police cars soon disappeared, screaming sirens faded and quiet returned. The sights and sounds were sobering reminders to those on The Peace Bridge that much more had to be done to heal the wounded city. The crowd joined hands, bowed their heads and sang, "We shall overcome, We shall overcome, We shall overcome someday . . . "

"Freedom is never voluntarily given by the oppressor;
it must be demanded by the oppressed."
—*Reverend Martin Luther King, Jr*

Epilogue

Blood in the Streets tells a story over four decades old, yet it has striking similarities to some horrible homicidal events of today. The mass murders in a movie theatre in Aurora, Colorado on July 16, 2012, the slaughter of young children at Sandy Hook Elementary School in Newtown, Connecticut and the mass killing at the Washington D.C. Navy Yard on September 16, 2013, all have common threads. Like Neal Bradley Long, the shooters were mentally deranged loners with a grudge. They were below the radar of mental health professionals and police. They acquired weapons without difficulty and planned their shootings for maximum impact.

The ugly story of racism, riots and murders from 1965 through 1975 and its effect on our people, our cities and our nation reveal lessons we must never forget.

"Those who fail to learn from history are doomed to repeat it."
—*George Santayana & Sir Winston Churchill*

NEAL BRADLEY LONG
D.O.B. September 11, 1927

PRISON

After Long entered a guilty plea, he was sentenced to two Federal and three State of Ohio life-term sentences for murder. He was also sentenced on five other felony shooting charges. Long was incarcerated at five Federal Bureau of Prisons Institutions: Springfield, Missouri; Tucson, Arizona; Phoenix, Arizona; San Diego, California; and Rochester, Minnesota.

"I'M SORRY"

On June 28, 1995, Neal Bradley Long responded to a request for an interview from *Dayton Daily News* Investigative Reporter, Wes Hills. Long declined the meeting but replied in writing:

> *"Hello Mr. Hills. I got your letter, was pleased to hear from you! You wanted to come and see me, but I don't think it would be a good idea. No, don't come, I'm a little bashful about meeting people. If you want to publish about me being sorry about the people I hurt ... that will be good. But nothing else."*
>
> *Neal B. Long (signed) "Thank you."*

DEATH OF NEAL BRADLEY LONG

Neal Bradley Long died of natural causes at age seventy on June 23, 1998, while incarcerated at the Federal Medical Center near Rochester, Minnesota.

BURIAL

Neal Bradley Long was buried at Forest Hills Memorial Gardens in Tipp City, Ohio, ten miles north of the City of Dayton. His final resting place is in the "HOPE" section of the modest graveyard along U.S. Route 25 North.

NEAL BRADLEY LONG'S RACIAL IDENTITY

Neal Bradley Long was motivated to shoot black men by his sympathy with the white supremacy goals of the Ku Klux Klan (KKK) in an attempt to stop "race mixing" in schools. He terrorized Dayton's black population and killed Dr. Charles Glatt. When Long died in prison, his race was listed on State File Number 1998-MN-016388 as "Unknown" - "Hispanic Origin-Yes." One wonders if his race was a family secret and if so, could it have contributed to a deep-seated backlash about integration of the races. Ironically, Neal Bradley Long, the "Midnight Slayer," was thought to be a white male, yet his prison records officially identified him as Hispanic origin. Whatever the secret or connection, Neal Bradley Long took the answers to his grave.

UNITED STATES SUPREME COURT

DAYTON BOARD OF EDUCATION v. BRINKMAN 433 U.S. 406 (1977)

433 U.S. 406

DAYTON BOARD OF EDUCATION ET AL, v. BRINKMAN ET AL

CERTIORARI TO THE UNITED STATES SUPREME COURT OF APPEALS FOR THE
SIXTH CIRCUIT

No. 76-539
Argued April 26, 1977
Decided June 27, 1977

The above captioned case, commonly referred to as the "Busing Case," was first filed April 17, 1972, in U.S. District Court in Columbus, Ohio. On June 27, 1977, the U.S. Supreme Court ruled it was, "... undisputed that the existing deseg- regation plan in effect in Dayton was working without serious problems." The Court said a current "Dayton School District Plan" should remain in effect for a year, subject to the order of the District Court. The Supreme Court vacated a judgment of the Court of Appeals, and the "... case was remanded for further proceedings." Rather than a year, the school desegregation plan remained under the supervision of the District Court in Dayton for twenty-five years, until 2002.

On April 15, 2002, thirty years after the busing case was originally filed, Federal Judge Walter H. Rice, U.S. District Chief Judge of the Federal District Court in Dayton, presided over a major settlement that ended years of litigation. Leaders of the NAACP, Ohio State Board of Education, Brinkman Plaintiffs and Dayton Public School Board members made the announcement. After two years of negotiations, a plan was accepted to allow parents to have their child attend a neighborhood school *or* select a first, second or third choice of a school.

The Dayton Daily News reported, "Gail C. Littlejohn, President of the Dayton School Board said, 'No longer is race a criterion for assigning students to schools in Dayton.'" Dayton Mayor Rhine McLin added, "It will mean everything for our city to have our children go to neighborhood schools. It is a turning point for our city."

In the calm of a courtroom, far away from the violence, hatred and turmoil, the busing case was settled on paper. The deep wounds and scars were still visible in the city, particularly on the West Side.

The strategic decision in 1972 to seek a Dayton School district-wide desegre- gation plan rather than a regional plan set up a perfect storm. The goal for equal education for black children in Dayton Public Schools came at a high price. The school system was nearly destroyed in the process. Many whites, including Neal Bradley Long, refused to accept the desegregation plan that drastically changed where and how their children went to school.

Although well meaning, attempts to legislate racial integration in Dayton Public Schools fed the disintegration of Dayton's economy, industry and population. Thousands of white families fled the city or utilized private schools. Like many poor whites and blacks, Neal Bradley Long was too poor to flee, and he felt trapped. Unintended consequences of the desegregation plan and busing were far-reaching. Violence by the "Midnight Slayer," three riots, skyrocketing crime and all-time high murder rates added to the misery. As residents fled the city, polarization of the races set in with blacks concentrated in the city and whites in the suburban ring. Enrollment numbers at Dayton Public Schools provided evidence.

In 1965, Dayton Public Schools had an enrollment of 60,633 students. By 1975, across-town school busing for desegregation hit its peak and student enrollment dropped to 44,165. By 1980, Dayton Public School enrollment dropped to 32,721 students.

The racial makeup of Dayton Public School students is most telling over time. In 1971, white students numbered 31,337 and declined to 17,699 by 1977. On the other hand, black student enrollment was 22,599 in 1971 and barely declined through 1977 to 20,538. Thus, more black students than white were enrolled in Dayton Public School.

In 1960, population of the City of Dayton was 262,332. In 1970, it dropped to 243,601 and by 1980 to 193,586 residents. The decline continued for the next twenty years as it fell to 166,179 in 2000. Dayton's economy suffered as major plants closed or moved, and there was little ability to attract new businesses or residents. Absentee landlords ruled poor neighborhoods.

The authors do not imply that busing children as part of school desegregation was the sole cause of erosion of Dayton's social and economic stature. A multitude of tragic circumstances negatively impacted the city. Yet, some still argue, regardless of financial and other costs, efforts to desegregate Dayton Public Schools were necessary. It was certain that racial equality in education would not occur voluntarily. Without the bold steps taken to foster integration, black students would have continued to experience a "second class" education.

THE RELUCTANT
FEDERAL BUREAU OF INVESTIGATION (FBI)

The FBI compiled information on Neal Bradley Long, AKA Carma Long, since 1962. Information held by the U. S. Government included material that prompted the Government to label Long a "Communist, 4 yrs." The author filed three separate requests for release of documents and information archived on Neal Bradley Long. The requests were made via the Freedom of Information Act (FOIA) with the United States Department of Justice (DOJ) and the Federal Bureau of Investigation (FBI). Some limited and highly redacted information was received. An attempt was made to obtain the letter Long wrote to Attorney General Robert Kennedy, but the request was denied and the information was withheld. Two separate appeals were filed, and both were denied. The Chief of the Administrative Appeal Staff wrote in his final rejection that the FBI/DOJ would "... not confirm the existence or non-existence" of the letter Long wrote to Attorney General Robert Kennedy about FBI Director, J. Edgar Hoover. An interesting statement in light of the fact its existence was referenced in the FBI's Indices previously provided to the authors.

One wonders what information the FBI has about Neal Bradley Long that is too sensitive for public release forty years later. Did he threaten J. Edgar Hoover? Was he linked to serious Communist or KKK activities? Was he an FBI Informant? We are denied the answers.

The U.S. DOJ and the FBI remained on the sidelines during the terrorizing attacks of the "Midnight Slayer." The series of racist shootings was unprecedented in that era, yet neither the FBI nor the Civil Rights Division of the DOJ ever offered their vast resources to the Dayton Police Department. Chief Grover O'Connor asked directly for help from the FBI but the U.S. DOJ Civil Rights Division told the Chief to work through State of Ohio's resources since the shootings were a "local matter."

While the FBI withheld support from a community and police agency in dire need of their wide-ranging expertise, the FBI tracked and reported the series of racial drive-by shootings to FBI Headquarters. The FBI tracked the "Midnight Slayer" under their highest domestic violence-reporting category as late as 1975, *"Urban Guerilla Warfare."*

In 2013, the FBI describes similar purpose-driven targeted acts of violence (i.e., formerly Guerilla Warfare) as *"Domestic Terrorism."* While the Dayton Police Department labored to solve the "Midnight Slayer" shooting spree, the FBI never disclosed their knowledge of Neal Bradley Long. The FBI only became involved when Dr. Charles Glatt was murdered in the Federal Building.

Since 9.11.01, much has changed in law enforcement. One can only hope that the Joint Terrorism Task Forces (JTTF) that exist in every state and many metropolitan areas have overcome the lack of cooperation and communication between local, state and federal agencies. The 2013 bombing at the finish line of the Boston Marathon is a stark reminder that more interagency sharing of information must be done to protect America; failure to do so leaves the door open for more "Neal Bradley Longs" and "Boston Bombers."

PUBLIC RECORDS

City of Dayton, Ohio. Office of Public Affairs.

City of Dayton, Ohio. Department of Planning and Community Development

Dayton History Foundation. daytonhistorybooks.com.

Dayton Police History Foundation. daytonpolicehistory.org

Dayton Public Library. Dayton, Ohio.

Madison County Library. Berea, Kentucky.

Miami Conservancy District. Dayton, Ohio.

Minnesota Department of Health. Olmstead County Bureau.

Montgomery County, Ohio Coroner's Office.

Montgomery County, Ohio Prosecutors Office.

U.S. Department of Justice (DOJ). Freedom Of Information Act (FOIA). www.justice.gov.

U.S. Federal Bureau of Prisons. www.fbop.gov.

U.S. Supreme Court. Dayton Board of Education v. Brinkman, 433 U.S. 406 (1977) No. 76-539.

University of Kentucky Libraries. nkaa.uky.edu

Wolfe County Public Library. Campton, Kentucky.

NEWSPAPER/MAGAZINE/BOOKS/JOURNAL/ INTERNET ARTICLES

"A timeline: Black History in the Miami Valley." www.daytondailynews.com/ content/project/blackhistory/time.

"Annual Report of the Adjutant General." Ohio Army National Guard, 1966.

Dayton Daily News and Dayton Journal Herald. Dayton, Ohio. See separate detailed list for Wright State University, Special Collections and Archives, Dayton Daily News Collection.

Diagnostic and Statistical Manual of Mental Disorders (Second Edition). DSM-II. American Psychiatric Association, 1968.

King, Jr., Dr. Martin Luther, visit to Dayton, Ohio. November 1964. University of Dayton "Campus Report", January 1999 and www.jumpbackhoney.com.

Heck, John and Sarah Heck, Our Shining Badges, Dayton, Ohio. September 2012.

"In Clay County, Ky. It takes some doing to escape a Sizemore." *Wall Street Journal,* October 28, 1986.

Jet Magazine. October 9, 1975.

Keel, John, *Our Haunted Planet,* Fawcett Publications, New York NY, 1971.

Kessler, Ronald, *The Secrets of the FBI,* Crown Publishers-Random House, Inc. New York, 2011.

Macklin, John, *Brotherhood of the Strange,* Ace Books, Charter Communications, New York, 1972.

"Media Coverage of Collective Violence: An Analysis of Description Bias in the 1967-1972 Race Riots." Research by Anthon D. Perez. College of Liberal Arts and Letters, University of Notre Dame. Fall 2000.

National Underground Railroad Freedom Center. www.freedomcenter.org.

National Law Enforcement Officers Memorial. Washington, D.C. nleomf.org.

Ohio Historical Society. Columbus, Ohio. Ohiohistory.org.

"The Civil Rights Movement, 1964-1968." Southern Methodist University. http://faculty.smu.edu/dismon/change-CivRts2b.html.

"The *Daily Worker*"-Spartacus Educational. www.spartacus.schoolnet.co.uk. USAworkerD.htm.

"The *Daily Workers*" (Archives of the former "*Daily Worker*") www.marxist.org.

The *"McCarran Internal Security Act of 1950."* Westlawinsider.com.

"United States Senate Select Committee. Supplementary Detailed Staff Reports of Intelligence Activities and the Rights of Americans." Book III. Final Report. "Warrantless Surreptitious entries: FBI *"Black Bag"* Break-Ins and Microphone Installations." April 23, 1976.

The Murder of Emmett Till", www.pbs.org

U.S. Bureau of Statistics, Washington D.C.

U.S. Census Bureau. www.census.gov.

"Who was Lee Harvey Oswald?" *Wall Street Journal,* Nov. 1983 wsj.com.

MISCELLANEOUS

Putnam, Lucy. Public History Program, Wright State University. February 26, 2003. Transcribed interview of Mr. Percy Vera, Dayton, Ohio.

Potyondy, Patrick, Graduate Associate, The Ohio State University, Department of History. Associate Editor, Origins: Current Events in Historical Perspective. Editor, UHA Newspaper.

ATTRIBUTION FOR IMAGES
Authors' Personal Collection.

City of Dayton, Ohio. Department of Planning and Community Development. Image of City map.

Dayton Daily News Archive, Special Collections and Archives. University
Libraries, Wright State University, Dayton, Ohio.
Gem City Saver Magazine, Spring 1967. Dayton, Ohio.
Miami Conservancy District, Dayton Ohio. Aerial image.
Montgomery County Prosecutors Office, Dayton, Ohio.

SITE VISITS
Berea, Campton, Climax and Richmond, Kentucky.
Dayton Aviation Heritage National Park. Dayton, Ohio. www.nps.gov.daav.
Dayton, Ohio: Visited each residential and employment address for Neal
Bradley Long from 1966 through 1975. Retraced the probable routes driven
by Neal Bradley Long. Visited the scene of all homicides and other locations
of riots, shootings and major events.
Visited locations of twelve bridges that spanned Wolf Creek and the Great
Miami River during the decade of the story. The bridges separated the
West Side from other parts of the City of Dayton. Bridges crossed at North
Gettysburg Avenue,, North Western Avenue and Bridge Street, Rosedale
Drive, North Summit Street, North Broadway Street, North Williams Street,
Riverview Avenue & Sunrise Street, West Third Street, West Fifth Street,
Washington Street, Stewart Street and South Broadway Street.
The "Dayton Peace Bridge." The West Third Street Bridge that spans the Great
Miami River.
Forest Hills Memorial Gardens Cemetery. Tipp City, Ohio.
United States Post Office and Federal Courthouse. Dayton, Ohio. (Now Federal
Bankruptcy Court Building).

NEWSPAPER ARTICLES
**Newspaper articles from the *Dayton Daily News* (DDN) Archive, Special
Collections and Archives, University Libraries, Wright State University,
Dayton, Ohio.**

The DDN Collection includes articles from the *Dayton Daily News* and the *Dayton Journal Herald.* Both newspapers were owned by Cox Enterprises and co-located at the same facility on South Ludlow Street in downtown Dayton, Ohio.
The *Journal Herald* was the morning paper and the *Dayton Daily News* was the
evening paper. They were the only daily newspapers in Dayton during the 1960's
and 1970's and eventually merged into one newspaper, the *Dayton Daily News.*

"7 Rike's Demonstrators Guilty Of Trespassing", April 6, 1964.
"Barber Figures He Fixed Negro", April 12, 1964.

"Riot Racked West Side in 1955", May 8, 1966.

"West Side '66'" (a six-part series) began on May 8, 1966.

"These Are The Leaders", May 10, 1966.

"West Side Parents Claim Schools Aren't Adequate", May 12, 1966.

"Cleveland Riot Warns Other Cities", August 17, 1966.

"Negro Man Gunned Down by White Man", September 1, 1966.

"Witness Saw Victim Shot Down in Street", September 1, 1966.

"It Started Along West Fifth . . . And Spread", September 1, 1966.

"Negro's Shooting Ignites Violence", September 1, 1966.

"Mayor Hall, McIntosh Yell Accusations Amidst W. Third's Broken Glass",
    September 1, 1966

"Riot Or Peace; Matter of Minutes", September 1, 1966.

"Troubled Radios", September 2, 1966.

"Angry Police Criticize "Amateur" Interference", September 2, 1966.

"Negro Ministers In Front Line", September 2, 1966.

"Riot Continues" (3 Civil Rights Men Arrested)", September 2, 1966.

"Witnesses Picked Up In Negro Shooting", September 3, 1966.

"Quiet Prevails At Mitchell Funeral", September 7, 1966.

"Was Lester Mitchell Shot By Pedestrian?", September 13, 1966.

"Influence of (Stokely) Carmichael A Factor in Area Future?", September 20, 1966

"Shots Fired From Across The Street Police Say", September 20, 1966.

"Man Confesses To "Stabbing" Back in 1944", November 1, 1966.

"W. Side Ban Lifted For Walley, Riley" (AKA Batman and Robin), January 26, 1967.

"Busing Law Farfetched?", February 20, 1967.

"Call for School Board 'Balance' Facing Fight?", February 20, 1967.

"Riot-Starting Murder Solved, Police Believe", May 25, 1967.

"Cincinnati Riot Continues; Negroes Shoot White Boy", June 15, 1967.

"Last Night's Sad Story", June 15, 1967.

"Police Draw 12-Hour Shifts", June 15, 1967.

"Trouble Trigger", June 15, 1967.

"Rap Brown's Speech Started It - (Major) Martz", June 16, 1967.

"Second Night: Fires, Vandalism Flare Anew", June 16, 1967.

"Youthful Groups Roam Dayton's West Third", June 16, 1967.

"Cities Study Charges Against Rap Brown", June 17, 1967.

"3 City Patrolmen Say They Were Fired Upon", July 28, 1967.

"Officer Panicked, Tried To Plant Gun, Watt Says", September 19, 1967.

"Mobs Loot Stores; 100 Taken to Jail", September 20, 1967.

"West Dayton Hit By Violence", September 20, 1967.

"West Side Cooling Off After Rally, Disturbance", September 21, 1967.

"Violence Control Tactics Hit", September 21, 1967.

"Police Investigate Riot Brutality Charge", September 21, 1967.

"Negroes March Quietly In Collier Ruling Protest", January 28, 1968.

"Collier Quits Force; Police Cancel Hearing", January 31, 1968.

"Rioting Grows Across Nation", April 9, 1968. (Following murder of Dr. Martin Luther King Jr.)

"Task Force Plans Petition", July 15, 1968

"4 Policemen, 6 Cruisers Disabled During Ruckus At Close Of Fair", September 4, 1968.

"One Year Later -- Not Much Change For Area Negroes", February 27, 1969.

"Discrimination Cited As Spark", April 11, 1969.

"Racial Disturbances At. Col. White H.S .", October 1, 1969.

"Rookie Shot Three Times", January 25, 1970.

"Slain Officer Had Date With Alter", January 26, 1970.

"We are all Racists, Carle Tells Board", April 3, 1970.

"Chief's Report Of Plot Rapped", August 29, 1970.

"Panthers Deny Shoot-Out Plan", August 30, 1970.

"Igleburger(Chief): No Plans On Blacks", August 31, 1970.

"BUSING!... This Word Stops At All Integration Approaches", November 15, 1971.

"Adopt Integration Plan, Buy Buses...", February 1, 1972.

"Blacks, Whites Clash, Stivers Closed Down", March 23, 1972.

"Stivers Closed By Fights", March 24, 1972.

"To Ride A Bus Or Not: Issue Not That Simple", August 14, 1972.

"2 Wounded By Shots From Cars", August 21, 1972.

"Two More Shootings Probed", August 22, 1972.

"Two Shot At, One Victim Hospitalized", September 26, 1973.

"W. S. McIntosh Slain, Officer Killed in Chase", March 4, 1974.

"Veteran Officer Aide To Chief", March 4, 1974.

"Death Of A Hero" (Sergeant Mortimer), March 5, 1974.

"House Passes Bill Banning Cheap Handguns", March 6, 1974.

"Psalm, Gospel of John Spoken for Mortimer", March 8, 1974.

"Sniper Shots Kill One, Wound Two", July 4, 1974.

"Sniper May Have Hit Before", July 16, 1975.

"Shootings May Be Tied to Past", July 16, 1975.

"Gunman's Profile Sought", July 18, 1975.

"Reward $10,000 For Slayer of 2", July 18, 1975.

"Tacit OK Given Street Patrol", July 27, 1975.

"FBI Doesn't Have O'Connor Bid For Sniper Killings Aid", August 1, 1975.

"Closings Expected From Busing Order", August 3, 1975.

"Hit-Run Case Witnesses Saw White Man, Blue Car", September 21, 1975.

"Luncheon He Almost Forgot Put Glatt In Dayton On Friday", September 20, 1975.

"Glatt Killing, Hit-Run Blasts Linked", circa September 20, 1975.

"Court Security Missed 1 Office", September 20, 1975.

"Glatt's Accused Killer Faces Charges", September 20, 1975.

"Long, You Won't Be Bused Again", September 22, 1975.

"Shot Blacks, Long Told Police", September 22, 1975.

"Long Gives Detailed Story", September 22, 1975.

"Suspects Past Unstable", September 22, 1975.

"Suspect Described As 'Nice, Quiet Guy'", September 23, 1975.

"Glatt Thought Sniper Slayings Related", circa September 1975.

"Long, Ex-Mental Patient, Just Didn't Go Along With Busing", September 23, 1975.

"Glatt Sensed Trouble Ahead", circa September 23, 1975.

"Long Once Spoke of Killing Family", September 23, 1975.

"Glatt Quit Ministry, Became Crusader For Rights", September 23, 1975.

"Suspects (Long) Past Unstable", September 23, 1975.

"Metropolitan Option Best Of Desegregation Plans", December 3, 1975.

"Glatt's Widow To File Plan In Court", December 7, 1975.

"Long And Reality Split in 1968 Doctor Says", circa October 1975.

"More Charges Against Long Await Finding Of Stolen Gun", circa October, 1975

"Long Plea Bargain Possible", June 14, 1977.

"Long to Plead Guilty Today", June 22, 1977.

"Long Acutely Psychotic Psychiatrist Says", June 22, 1977.

"Kin Of Two Murdered Ponder Long's Plea, Life Sentences", June 23, 1977.

"Long Sentenced", June 23, 1977.

"Key Dates In City's Five-year Desegregation Battle", June 27, 1977.

"Long Said He Shot When He Felt Like It", July 2, 1977.

"Long Starts 2 Life Terms In Missouri Security Jail", July 11, 1977.

"Busing Plan Inappropriate, City Schools Say", April 21, 1979.

"Police's 'John Wayne' Recalls Days On Force", October 3, 1993. (Twenty-five years after the fact, Chief O'Connor admits approval of illegal wiretaps on Black Panthers in late 1960's and reflects on "old style " police tactics).

"Neal Bradley Long's Rampage Recalled", July 19, 1999.

THE W. S. McINTOSH AWARD

April 28, 1976, the Dayton Black Police Association (BPA), presented Dayton Police Detectives Dan Baker and Gary Prugh the *W. S. McIntosh Award* for their work on the Midnight Slayer case. BPA President Leon Frazier, also a Dayton Police officer, noted that, "... the white officers pointed out Neal Bradley Long, the suspected murderer of Dr. Glatt... in the U.S. Post Office Building." He added, "What made this case so interesting is that Baker and Prugh didn't have to direct their concern toward Neal Bradley Long. In fact, since the murder took place in the Federal Building, the investigation was totally in the hands of the federal marshals. Prugh and Baker showed their concern for the black community by getting involved anyway." *Jet Stone News* —Dayton, Ohio 1976.

ACKNOWLEDGEMENTS

We began the process of writing but soon learned that talking and dreaming about writing a novel requires tremendous discipline and dedication to accomplish the goal. The ability to finish was achieved in large part due to encouragement and support from many people.

Mr. Wes Hills, a former hard-nosed investigative news reporter for the *Dayton Daily News*, was blunt in his belief and encouragement that the story of racism, riots and murders in Dayton begged to be told. We were also fortunate to become friends with author Pamela Bauer Mueller and her husband Michael at Jekyll Island, Georgia. In the peaceful grandeur along the Atlantic Ocean, Pamela and Michael provided encouragement, coaching and follow-up through the entire process. A former colleague and distinguished author, Dr. William "Bill" Bass, Professor Emeritus, University of Tennessee (founder of the "Body Farm") offered sage advice. Montgomery County Prosecutor Mathias Heck Jr. and Public Information Officer Greg Flannigan were supportive and accommodating. Trustee Steve Grismer of The Dayton Police History Foundation was always helpful.

Mr. Gino Pasi, Archivist at Wright State University Libraries (Special Collections and Archives) in Dayton, Ohio provided terrific support during several visits. Dr. Thomas Rueth, a Clinical Psychologist and Professor Emeriti, University of Dayton shared his valuable knowledge about Dayton State Hospital and the 1968 Diagnostic and Statistical Manual of Mental Disorders (DSM II). Dr. Patrick Donnelly, University of Dayton (a research co-author with Dan Baker) offered important ideas about presentation of sociology and crime data. Cold Case Detective Donna Pack, (Ret.), Dayton, Ohio Police Department shared her background knowledge. Three other friends in different fields reviewed and edited the manuscript, thanks to Dennis Sizemore, Timothy 'Bets' Wegner and Nathan Lefebvre.

Editor and author Pam Pollack, NY, NY provided valuable guidance that improved the structure of the story. Our copy editor, Dr. Christa Preston Agrio of Dayton, Ohio polished the manuscript. Patty Osborne of Vancouver, Canada deserves much credit for the terrific job of design and format of the book and its cover. Finally, thank you to Charles Baker for assistance with photos, computing issues and up-to-date technology.

Daniel L. Baker
Gwen Nalls

THE AUTHORS

Daniel L. Baker. Dayton, Ohio Police Department, 25 years. Lieutenant, Violent Crime Bureau, Organized Crime Control Unit and Hostage Negotiation Team. Director of Nuclear Safeguards and Security at three U.S. Department of Energy/ National Nuclear Security Administration sites. Executive Director, University of Tennessee Law Enforcement Innovation Center and National Forensic Academy (NFA), Knoxville, TN. Received 2007 International Association of Chiefs of Police *August Vollmer Award for Forensic Excellence* at the NFA. Consultant/Executive Director, City of Cincinnati, Ohio following riots in 2001. Led new Citizen Complaint Authority to independently investigate allegations against city police regarding excessive force, shots fired and death-in-custody. Co-Author, "Criminal Localism Varies", *Journal of Sociology and Social Research, University of Southern California*, 1986. A.A.S. Sinclair College, B.S. and M.S. Degrees, University of Dayton. Licensed Professional Counselor (LPC). Certified Chemical Dependency Counselor, Ohio.

Gwen Nalls. Licensed Attorney, State of Ohio. Twenty-five years as senior executive for several major corporations on multi-billion dollar government contracts at five U.S. Department of Energy locations and assignments in the UK. Gwen grew up on Dayton's West Side and received her education in the segregated Dayton Public School system. A.A.S. Sinclair College, B.S. University of Dayton, M.S. Central Michigan University, J.D. Salmon P. Chase College of Law - Northern Kentucky University. Dan and Gwen have been married for more than twenty years.